Royston

Letchworth

🐌 Buntingford

Stevenage

Bishops Stortford

Hertford   Ware

ⲩn
.C.

Hatfield

Cheshunt

Barnet

The Birds of Hertfordshire

The Birds

of

Hertfordshire

by

The Reverend TOM W. GLADWIN
and
BRYAN L. SAGE

Bird Illustrations by
PETER WALTON

WARE
CASTLEMEAD PUBLICATIONS

First Published in 1986

CASTLEMEAD PUBLICATIONS
Swains Mill, 4A Crane Mead,
Ware, Herts., SG12 9PY
Publishing division of
WARD'S PUBLISHING SERVICES

ISBN 0 948555 01 7

British Library Catologuing in Publication Data

Gladwin, Tom W.
   The birds of Hertfordshire
   1. Birds — England — Hertfordshire
   I. Title II. Sage, Bryan III. Walton, Peter
   598.29425′8   QL690.G7

   ISBN 0-948555-01-7

Printed in Great Britain
in 10pt Century Type
by Anchor Brendon Limited, Tiptree, Essex

Foreword

I welcome *The Birds of Hertfordshire* by The Revd Tom W. Gladwin and Bryan L. Sage. This is an updated version of *A History of the Birds of Hertfordshire* by Bryan L. Sage (1959), covering the years 1958–82. The authors write feelingly of the much greater difficulties facing the compilers of a modern county list not only because of the tremendous increase in the number of records but because of the teasing problems with the present centralised systems for Rare Birds and Rare Breeding Birds.

To many people Hertfordshire is a county which is largely an extension of London's suburbia and it is true that part of it falls within the recording area of the London Natural History Society. Never the less, it is an attractive county with quite a large breeding population. One hundred and thirty species are known to breed or have bred there. Although the county has suffered greatly from developments, including many agricultural changes which owe more to economics than to conservational insights, it has had gains in recent years in its avifauna, including Greylag Goose, Canada Geese, Hobby, Common Tern and Cetti's Warbler, with increases in other species such as Collared Dove. Against this, Corncrake, Whinchat and Stonechat have been lost, while others, notably Woodcock and Barn Owl have decreased.

These changes, with a wealth of other information, are detailed in the very full accounts for each species, prepared with great care, which form the major part of the book. The authors are to be congratulated on a notable addition to the county avifaunas, compiled with painstaking care and skill.

STANLEY CRAMP

Prologue

The preparation of this book has been accompanied by many problems, most of which can be said to have been of a logistical nature common to any such project. Today, however, anyone setting out to write a county bird book is faced with problems of a kind with which earlier writers of such works did not have to contend. Ornithology has now become a scientific discipline, which is all to the good. Regrettably, however, it has also become over-burdened with bureaucracy, local politics, petty jealousies, obsessive secrecy and, in addition, has become more centralised.

We now have the British Birds Rarities Committee (whose annual reports are published in the journal *British Birds*) which, since 1958, has been assessing records of those species regarded as national rarities. Sometimes records are rejected which, in the opinion of local report editors and committees who are often more familiar with circumstances and the observers concerned, are perhaps acceptable. This inevitably results in the occasional 'loss' of valid records. Perhaps there needs to be a greater interchange of information between national and local rare bird committees.

High scientific standards are never the less essential when it comes to assessing records of the more unusual species, and this applies locally as well as nationally. The standards must be applied consistently to all records without fear or favour. Unfortunately, within Hertfordshire (as no doubt elsewhere), this has led to a few instances where individual observers have refused to submit records unless they are all accepted without question. This attitude is thoroughly unscientific and most regrettable. It would be helpful if such observers could accept that rejection of a record is not a statement of disbelief or an expression of doubt about their personal integrity, it is simply a matter of ensuring that the basis of the historical record is the subject of sound and consistent definition and satisfies established scientific requirements.

We also have the Rare Breeding Birds Panel which has collated records of the rarer breeding species since 1973, and also publishes its reports in *British Birds*. Reports are sent to this panel or committee by individual observers as well as the editors of local bird reports. The problem facing the would-be authors of county bird books is that individual observers can (and often do) send reports direct to the panel with a request that the details should not be divulged to the relevant county report editor or recorder. In the published reports of the panel, details are normally given for each species under county headings without actual localities or sites being mentioned in many cases. In some instances even the county is not revealed, but is simply referred to by a letter code. Since the panel will not reveal any of the details of individual records unless the observer concerned agrees, authors of county bird books may find themselves confronted by an impasse and be unable to build up a complete historical picture.

As a result of this secretive policy we cannot be certain that all the species accounts in the present book are complete; we have been unable to obtain the relevant details for those species (hopefully few) where observers have decreed that they should not be made available to the county report editor.

We have reason to believe for example, that the account of the Goshawk is not complete. Similar problems have arisen in compiling the histories of the Hobby and Sparrowhawk; much earlier secrecy regarding breeding sites of Little Ringed Plover has led to the difficulties discussed under that species. A further problem occurs when two or more observers submitting records of the same birds seen at a single location on varying dates, use different site names. Not surprisingly this can lead to the records being treated separately as though they refer to different birds. One example of such confusion concerns records of Cetti's Warbler published in *British Birds* by the Rare Breeding Birds Panel and hopefully corrected in the present book. Once again, better liaison and interchange of information would reduce such inaccuracies.

Perhaps the biggest disadvantage of secrecy about rare breeding birds is concerned with their conservation. Some sites which may not be considered to be of great significance in the national context may be very important locally. It is vitally important that organisations, including local planning authorities genuinely concerned with conservation, are aware of the presence and location of rare species. The future for such species can be greatly improved by the wise dissemination of information. For Hertfordshire it is our suggestion that the Rare Breeding Birds Panel deposits copies of the relevant data in the custody of the County Biological Records Centres maintained by the North Hertfordshire District Museums Services and at the St. Albans City Museum. In the meantime there is the risk of sites being lost because important information is not available when critical decisions are being made.

The preparation of this book has entailed the searching out and examination of a large volume of published material as well as the county record cards. Newsletters, bulletins and periodic reports are regularly produced by a wide variety of organisations such as ringing groups (particularly those at Maple Cross and Rye Meads), local natural history societies, local members' groups of national organisations such as the Royal Society for the Protection of Birds (RSPB) and the British Naturalists' Association (BNA). It would be helpful if all such organisations deposited copies of all publications in the Biological Records Centres referred to in the previous paragraph.

During our examination of the material at our disposal we have been concerned on a number of occasions to find that qualifications stated by original observers have been overlooked in published reports. Statements like 'may have bred' have sometimes been translated into 'bred'. Further, the presence of juvenile birds in late summer does not necessarily constitute evidence of breeding in Hertfordshire.

Finally, there is one other aspect that should be mentioned, and this concerns the peripatetic hordes of birdwatchers popularly known as 'twitchers'. These individuals tend to concentrate at favoured sites in search of rarities, and contribute little or nothing to ornithological science since the majority do not bother to send in records and are only concerned with seeing these birds. At best this can be regarded as a relatively harmless expression of the Victorian collecting mania. Sadly however, there have been several incidents where an over-abundance of enthusiasm and selfish behaviour has resulted in excessive disturbance and damage to fragile habitats. Some 'twitchers' seem to be unaware or unconcerned that frequent disturbance of tired and hungry birds, particularly in winter, may seriously disadvantage the very object of their pursuit even, on occasions, causing death.

Despite the many problems referred to we have been fortunate and privileged to have received a great deal of encouragement, support and co-operation in producing this book.

TOM GLADWIN and BRYAN SAGE

August 1985

Acknowledgements

The preparation of this county avifauna has been greatly assisted by many people in very many different ways. Indeed, such a work is fundamentally dependent on whatever information is made available. We are therefore greatly indebted to all those observers who have provided records for publication in local and national reports or have responded to our many enquiries during the preparation of this work.

We are especially grateful to Trevor James who unselfishly undertook the huge task of reading and meticulously checking the typescript. His patient attention to scientific accuracy and consistency, his considerable knowledge of Hertfordshire's natural history, and his many helpful suggestions have resulted in widespread improvements to the original manuscript. We are further indebted to him, and also to Brian Sawford, both of the North Hertfordshire Museums Service, for their initiative in supplying unpublished and important records and manuscripts of which we had no previous knowledge.

Alan Harris, Michael Harris, Toby Small and other members of the Rye Meads Ringing Group, and Peter Walton (the current recorder for birds) advised us on many of the species essays. Peter Delaloye and the Maple Cross Ringing Group kindly gave us access to their records and valuable information about parts of the Colne valley.

Peter Moles kindly supplied counts from Tring Reservoirs and Figure 6.8. Graham White assisted with the interpretation of data from the Lea valley. Chris Mead and Ken Smith generously granted us unlimited access to the field data used in the production of the *Hertfordshire Breeding Bird Atlas* (Mead and Smith 1982), and permission to reproduce the maps from that work. By special arrangement, Chris Mead and the British Trust for Ornithology provided complete files of ringing recoveries of Blackbird, Song Thrush, Reed Warbler and Sedge Warbler. Miss Elspeth Marshall typed a large part of the original manuscript and Andrew Sharp assisted with word processing facilities. We are deeply grateful to them all and to Alan Ward, our publisher, for his encouragement throughout.

Finally, our special thanks to Peter Walton our illustrator who has chosen familiar Hertfordshire sites as the background for many of his excellent drawings. We feel privileged that our work should have been so beautifully enhanced.

Contents

List of Illustrations

List of Colour plates

List of Tables

The Birds of Hertfordshire

1
Introduction

The present book is not intended as a replacement for *A History of the Birds of Hertfordshire* by Bryan Sage which was published in 1959 (with some additions and corrections in Sage 1962), but as a continuation and update covering the 25-year period from 1958–82. One difference however is that the area covered by this book is the County of Hertfordshire as modified by boundary changes made on 1 April 1965. These changes are detailed in Chapter 2. Records of particular interest for 1983 and 1984 are given in Appendix O. The nomenclature and sequence of species follows Voous (1977).

The species accounts basically follow the same pattern throughout in that current status is summarised (as at the end of 1982), followed by a brief statement of the specie's status as given by Sage (1959). An exception is made in the case of those species for which there were 10 or less records in Sage (1959) and these are listed in full in the present book. The main part of the text deals with the history of each species for the period 1958–82; where a species has occurred on 25 or fewer occasions within this period the records are given in full. The status of the less common non-breeding species is generally assessed as follows:

Very rare	1 – 10 records
Rare	11 – 25 records
Scarce	26 – 50 records
Occasional	51 – 100 records

The category in which each species occurs in the county is also stated and the following definitions are used:

Vagrant
Passage migrant (spring, autumn or both)
Winter visitor
Summer visitor (breeds)
Resident (breeds)

The species essays for birds which are of common or frequent occurrence, and rarer, particularly aquatic forms which tend to occur at relatively few sites, have been produced as a continuous text. It is hoped this will enhance the book's readability. In some other cases, however, the records and histories have been semi-tabulated where it was felt such presentation would facilitate comprehension of a species status as well as assist future historians.

The *Hertfordshire Breeding Bird Atlas* (Mead and Smith 1982) contains maps showing the distribution of breeding birds between 1967 and 1973. These maps based on tetrads, i.e. 2km × 2km Ordnance Survey squares, have been reproduced in Chapter 7. Where relevant, the number of the appropriate map appears in the page margin against the species described.

1

Throughout the book the time periods used in analyses are either calendar months, e.g. in the case of wildfowl counts, or European Standard Five Day Periods, *Auspicium* 5 Suppl. (1973).

Whilst a period of 25 years may not seem a very long time the task of preparing this book has been enormous, primarily because of the vast amount of data that had to be collated and analysed. The years since 1957 have seen a phenomenal increase in the popularity of birdwatching as a hobby, with more observers sending in records for the county bird report. At the same time, concern over the changing face of Hertfordshire's environment has also increased, with the result that much serious research has been undertaken to assess the effects of these changes on the birdlife of the county. These research activities are discussed in more detail below.

The threats to the Hertfordshire countryside and its birdlife are many and varied. Urbanisation and industrialisation continue to increase, as does the construction of new roads. Population pressure on the countryside has also grown steadily with more and more recreational demands being made on habitats such as woodlands and gravel pits. The greatest changes of all however, have been those wrought by the farming community and private landowners, changes which are not peculiar to Hertfordshire. Profit-seeking farmers, encouraged by tax incentives and the largesse of bountiful subsidies of taxpayers' money, have converted hundreds of hectares of pasture to cereal farming. They have drained water-meadows and other wetland habitats, ripped out countless kilometres of hedgerows in order to create a prairie-type landscape suitable for the deployment of massive combine harvesters and other heavy machinery, and felled copses. Other landowners have felled many hectares of deciduous woodland to make way for fast-growing conifers which provide a quick cash return — activities again subsidised by the taxpayer through the medium of grants from the Forestry Commission. It must, in fairness, be said that not all farmers and estate owners are of this type; many have made welcome contributions to nature conservation in the county. Never the less, the detrimental changes made by what may well be a minority are painfully obvious.

Ornithological research in the county has taken several forms. Most notable have been the various co-operative projects organised by the British Trust for Ornithology. For example, the 1968-72 National Atlas which mapped the distribution of breeding birds in the British Isles on a 10 kilometre square basis provided the foundation for the eventual publication of Mead and Smith (1982). In this book the distribution of breeding birds in Hertfordshire was mapped on a tetrad (2 x 2 kilometre square) basis, thereby providing for the first time detailed data which hitherto had been conspicuously lacking, particularly for the common and widespread species.

Data from the *Common Birds Census* (CBC) project, initiated in 1961, which has covered up to 40 census plots in Hertfordshire and adjacent counties, has provided invaluable information on population fluctuations of the breeding species of farmland and other habitats. Periodic long-term population censuses of certain other species (for example, Great Crested Grebe, Grey Heron and Little Ringed Plover) have provided further valuable information. The National Survey of Rookeries in 1975 revealed marked changes in the numbers and distribution of this common species within the county.

Wintering waterfowl in Hertfordshire have been well studied under the National Wildfowl Counts scheme started by the Wildfowl Trust in 1947, and continued ever since. The counts are made monthly from September to March inclusive, and the information obtained over the years has been most useful in the preparation of this book.

An essential foundation for any book on local birds are the county bird reports. Hertfordshire has been well served in this respect and annual reports have been published by the Hertfordshire Natural History Society since 1878. Part of the county falls within the area covered by the London Natural History Society and many Hertfordshire records also appear in their annual bird reports, the first of which was published in 1936. In 1959 this society published *The Birds of the London Area* which contains a great deal of information relating to Hertfordshire. Other records have appeared in more localised publications: for example, those of the Ruislip and District Natural History Society (notably records from the Colne valley south of Rickmansworth), the Bishops Stortford Natural History Society and the Lea Valley Project Group.

Bird ringing has provided a mass of important data about populations, migration and other aspects of behaviour in the county. The first ringing station to be established was in 1962 by the Rye Meads Ringing Group at Rye Meads Sewage Purification Works adjoining the confluence of the Rivers Lea and Stort. Periodic reports since 1959 when ringing at Rye Meads first began, include not only ringing data but much other valuable information. The Maple Cross Ringing Group, operating at Maple Lodge Nature Reserve, has also made a significant contribution to ornithology in the county since it was established in 1971.

2

The Hertfordshire Environment

2.1 Geography

Hertfordshire is an inland county of 163 415 hectares (403 803 acres). The
present county boundaries were established at 1 April 1965 when Barnet
and East Barnet Urban Districts became part of the London Borough of
Barnet, and Potters Bar Urban District, formerly in Middlesex, became
part of Hertfordshire. Additionally some small rural parcels of Hemel
Hempstead Rural District were transferred to Bedfordshire, and a small
rural area of Bedfordshire to Letchworth Urban District. There were no
further changes as a consequence of local government re-organisation at 1
April 1974.

Approximately 64 km (40 miles) from east to west, and 53 km (33 miles)
from south to north, the county has its centroid near Lemsford Village at
latitude 51°48′ N and longtitude 0°14′ W.

A relief map of the county is provided as Figure 2.1. As can be seen most of
the county is between 46 metres (150 feet) and 151 m (500 ft) above sea

Figure 2.1   *County of Hertfordshire –*
Relief Map

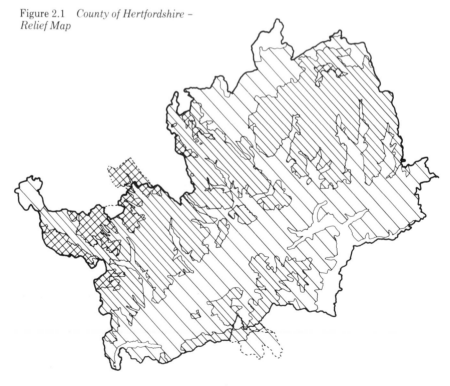

4

Figure 2.2 *Chalk Stream – River Chess. One of Hertfordshire's least polluted chalk streams and a typical habitat of the Kingfisher.*
Photo: © Trevor James

level. The chalk of the Chiltern Hills stretching along the northern boundary from Tring to Royston provides the highest ground. It reaches its highest point of 245 m asl (804 ft asl) near Hastoe, Tring. Distinctive, very steep scarp slopes in the west become progressively gentler, and the height of the hills decreases towards the east. In general the height of the land decreases south-eastwards away from the dip slopes of the Chilterns. Two important plateaus of relatively high ground rising to above 125 m asl stretch from Bushey to Cuffley along the southern boundary, and from Hatfield to Redbourn. The latter, known as the Hatfield Divide, determines which chalk streams run into the rivers Colne and Lea.

Since 1951 the human population of the county has increased by about two-thirds. The population figures (those for 1951 and 1961 having been adjusted for the 1965 boundary changes) were:

Year	Population (000's)
1951	566
1961	788
1971	925
1981	955

Hertfordshire lies immediately north of London and most of its population, as evidenced by Figure 2.3, is resident in the southern half of the county. During the 25-year period 1958 to 1982 greater leisure time and mobility, mostly due to reductions in employed working hours and increases in car ownership, have resulted in larger numbers of people gaining access to the Hertfordshire countryside thus increasing pressure, by public disturbance, on bird populations.

Hertfordshire County Council's Analysis of Land Use Allocations shows that in 1982 the land area of the county was used or allocated as follows:

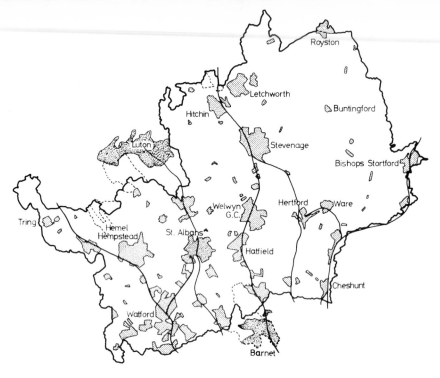

Figure 2.3   *County of Hertford – Population distribution and railways*

Land use allocation category*	Area ('000s ha)
1 Industry and warehouses	1.6
2 Shops	0.1
3 Residential (includes whole of villages)	22.4
4 Offices and public buildings	0.1
5 Utilities and communications	0.4
6 Education (includes school playing fields)	1.8
7 Sports and leisure	2.7
8 Minerals	1.2
9 Transport (railways, motorways and principal roads)	1.3
10 Agriculture and forestry	130.8
11 Central areas (in towns)	0.7
12 Other	0.3
	Total: 163.4

*Local, minor and access roads are included in each category

Despite the increases in population and developed areas Hertfordshire remains a primarily rural and agricultural county. In 1982 some 104 500 ha (net of roads) or 64 per cent of the county was being farmed. Over 80 per cent of farmland is arable and is on the boulder clay in the north-east, the chalk, and clay-with-flints in the west. Nearly 80 per cent of cultivated land is used for growing cereals, mostly wheat and barley. Rape is now the third commonest crop. Most of the farmed grassland is either transient or has been 'improved'.

Figure 2.4   *The 'prairie-like' cereal landscapes on the chalk contain some scarce species. Similar areas on the boulder clay are relatively barren.*   Photo: © *Trevor James*

2.2 Geology

The underlying or solid geology of the county is relatively simple. Most of the solid formations found in Hertfordshire were originally deposited as sediments on an ancient sea floor: some were later transformed into fairly hard rock as a result of compaction beneath very thick deposits of younger sediments.

The oldest deposit (approximately 100 million years old) which can be seen at the surface in Hertfordshire is of restricted distribution, appearing in only two north-western extremities — one near Tring and the other near Ashwell. This is the Gault Clay which was laid down in the Upper Cretaceous. It forms a continuous strata of low-lying ground all along the north-western foot of the Chiltern Hills, and occurs at even greater depth in the south-east of the county. Most of the Gault consists of a grey calcareous clay, but beneath south-east Hertfordshire the uppermost strata are sandy and are known as the Upper Greensand. Next, and of somewhat greater extent, is the Chalk (divided into Lower, Middle and Upper Chalk) which forms the scarp of the Chiltern Hills then dips downwards to the south-east. The Chalk was deposited over a time-span of 20–30 million years in the last part of the Cretaceous period, and overlies most of the Gault Clay and Upper Greensand.

At the end of the Cretaceous period (about 65 million years ago), the Chalk and the underlying deposits were tilted and uplifted above sea level to form land. There then followed an extensive period (10–15 million years duration) during which there was widespread erosion of this land by rivers. During the Eocene period (53–38 million years ago) there was a westwards transgression of the sea across southern England which trimmed the already substantially eroded Chalk. It was on this relatively flat surface that the next deposits, the Reading Beds, were laid down in shallow brackish water. A further cycle of uplift and erosion, followed by yet another transgression of the sea, occurred before the next Eocene formation (the London Clay) was deposited. Finally, the youngest solid deposits in the county are the Claygate Beds which overlie the London Clay in small patches in the southern part of the county.

7

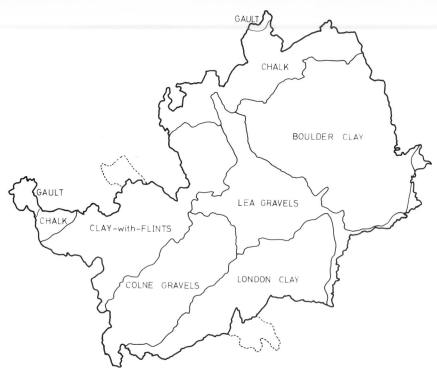

Figure 2.5   *County of Hertford – Geological regions*

Following the depositional sequences of the Eocene, there was an extended period of erosion which removed the Claygate Beds, London Clay and much of the Reading Beds from the north-western parts of the county, thereby re-exposing much of the Chalk to form the Chiltern Hills. Some remnant patches of Reading Beds do, however, remain on the south-eastern slopes of the Chilterns.

Most of the superficial drift deposits were laid down much more recently in the Pleistocene period which began about 1.5 million years ago. The superficial geology of the county is shown in simplified form in Figure 2.5. Much of the Chalk of the Chilterns is covered by the distinctive reddish-brown Clay-with-Flints, the flints being derived from the Upper Chalk. The

Figure 2.6   *River Beane near Waterford. A lowland river with natural banks and one of the few remaining uncanalised sections.*   Photo: © Trevor James

Figure 2.7 *Stockers Lake NR. The chain of gravel pits in the Colne valley includes a wide variety of wet habitats and aquatic birds.* *Photo: © Trevor James*

Pleistocene brought many rapid climatic changes, which were the main causes for the subdivision of the superficial deposits. Relatively long, cold glacial periods of about 100 000 years were separated by shorter and warmer interglacial periods. The four most recent glacial periods were so extremely cold that ice-sheets were able to spread from montane areas across parts of lowland Britain. However, it was only in the first two of these glacial periods that the ice sheets actually penetrated into Hertfordshire.

The main deposits laid down by these glaciers were clays (usually referred to as tills) and gravels. The earlier of the two glaciations referred to left a band of till to the south-west of St. Albans, and some pockets in the south-east of the county. These deposits, however, are of somewhat less significance than those left by the second glaciation. The primary deposit at this time was the Chalky Boulder Clay which covers extensive areas of north and east Hertfordshire, and has outliers in the Vale of St. Albans and over the London Clay in the south-east. During its steady advance across Hertfordshire (basically from north-east to south-west) this ice-sheet deposited large quantities of gravels, and more were left when it finally melted. These gravels lie in the Vale of St. Albans, in the valleys of the Colne and Lea and the lesser rivers in eastern Hertfordshire. It is in these areas that gravel extraction is today a major industry. Deposits of fine alluvium have of course been laid down by the present rivers as they flow through their respective valleys.

It must be emphasised that this is a somewhat simplified account of Hertfordshire's geology. In southern Hertfordshire, particularly on the London Clay, the local surface geology can be quite complicated. Furthermore, not all the gravels in the Colne and Lea valleys, and in the Vale of St. Albans, are of glacial origin. Many of them were deposited by a prototype of the present River Thames which, in those earlier times, followed a more northerly course eastwards through the Vale of St. Albans to enter the North Sea off what is now Suffolk. The erosive action of this river, as it cut lower and lower, has left remnant gravel terraces on either side of the valley through which it flowed.

9

2.3 Weather

Climate may be defined as the summary of daily changes in the weather. The climate of Hertfordshire has been subject to little significant change in the past century (1883 to 1982) its weather remains particularly variable and changeable.

The weather in the county is predominantly westerly in origin. Situated on the western seaboard of Europe, the English climate and dependent environment benefit from the relative warm ocean currents, especially the Gulf Stream, and moist Atlantic winds.

Continuous weather records kept at Rothamsted Experimental Station, Harpenden, for many years are regularly reported in the Transactions of the Hertfordshire Natural History Society. A summary of some of these records is provided in Table 2.1.

The wide year-to-year variations in weather are readily apparent from Table 2.1. For example, nearly twice as much rain falls in some years as in others, e.g. 924mm in 1960 compared with 540mm in 1973. In 1976, the year of the summer drought, it rained on only 141 days compared with 215 in 1960; and in 1968 only 1149 hours of sunshine were recorded compared with 1777 hours in 1959. In addition to the year-to year variations there are significant and consistent differences in the weather experienced at different locations within the county. For example, at Odsey on the north side of the Chilterns, the average rainfall between 1916 and 1950 was 592mm compared with 721mm at Rothamsted. On average it rains on 20 days fewer per annum at Odsey than at Rothamsted (Fordham 1965).

Equally wide variations in rainfall and average mean temperature are evident if year by year analyses are carried out on a monthly basis. In 1963, for example, the average mean temperature at Rothamsted in January was −3.5°C, 6.5°C lower than the January average of 3°C, whilst the average

TABLE 2.1 *Summary of certain weather records from Rothamsted Experimental Station, 1916 to 1982*

Period (years)	Rainfall (mm/year)		Number of Rain Days	
	Average	Range	Average	Range
1916–50	721	not known	187	not known
1950–59	742	626–914	185	164–208
1960–69	734	541–924	186	161–215
1970–79	704	540–909	178*	141–201
1980–82	747	652–836	181	173–186

Period (years)	Hours Sunshine		Average Mean Temp.°C	
	Average	Range	Average	Range
1916–50	1538	not known	9.0	not known
1950–59	1473	1304–1777	9.2	8.4–10.0
1960–69	1371	1149–1583	8.9	7.9–9.7
1970–79	1485	1388–1629	9.2	8.5–9.8
1980–82	1427	1286–1533	9.0	8.7–9.5

*Based on figures for 1974 to 1979 only; 1970 to 1973 not available

mean temperature for June 1976 at 17°C was 3°C higher than the long term average of 14°C.

In recent years there has been a trend towards colder, wetter springs, often extending throughout May, which have, on occasions, delayed the arrival of some summer visitors and reduced the breeding success of others.

Summers have been variable. Hot summers in 1959 and 1976 are, for example, reflected in Average Mean Temperatures for those years of 10°C and 9.8°C respectively compared with the long term average of 9.0°C. Also in those years there were 1777 and 1629 hours of sunshine respectively. Hot dry summers can also disadvantage bird populations and mortality was particularly high during the summer drought of 1976.

In contrast to the spring, autumns have generally been warmer with fewer frosts before December, and an increasing dominance of westerly weather. The east winds, associated with 'falls' of Scandinavian and scarce migrants of easterly origin along the North Sea and Channel coasts in September and October, have been relatively scarce.

Winters have also been very variable. During the past 25 years (1958 to 1982) the county has experienced several relatively severe winters. These are mostly due to anticyclones passing over Scandinavia, much further north than is the norm, and subjecting Britain to north to north-easterly arctic airstreams. The 1962/63 winter was prolonged with frosts from 26 December to 5 March. However, the frosts were not as intense as in 1968 and 1981/82, when temperatures fell to −13°C. The onset of cold weather involving glazing usually triggers large movements of birds south and south-west towards the continent as well as causing high mortality.

2.4 Wetlands

As can be seen from Figure 2.8 Hertfordshire forms a large part of the northern quadrant of the London Basin. Shallow chalk streams originating along the foot of dip slope of the Chilterns flow south-east to feed into the slow lowland rivers Colne and Lea. The division of the river systems is determined by the plateau of relatively high ground known as the Hatfield Divide (*see* Geography). Thus the Bulbourne, Chess, Gade and Ver run into the Colne which rises near Hatfield. The Mimram, Beane, Rib, Quin and Ash feed the Lea which originates near Luton and which is joined by another lowland river, the Stort, near Hoddesdon. All of these eventually drain into the Thames.

The northern belt of the county, particularly to the north of the Chilterns, is drained into the Ouse by the Ouzel, Oughton, Purwell, Hiz, Ivel, Cat Ditch, and Cam (or Rhee).

The Grand Union Canal passes down the west side of the county following the valleys of the Bulbourne, Gade and Colne from Tring to Rickmansworth.

Permanent open still water habitats in Hertfordshire comprise a series of ponds, artificial lakes, flooded gravel pits and reservoirs.

Although ponds exist in all parts of the county the greatest concentration is on the London clay in the south. During the period 1958–82 many farm ponds and a few village ponds were lost, mostly by infilling. In the two 10 km

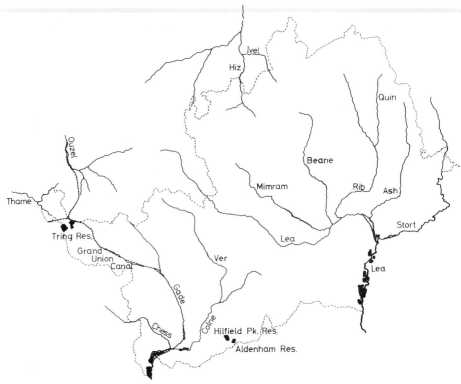

Figure 2.8   *County of Hertford – The rivers, canals and lakes*

Ordnance Survey squares TL2l and TL3l, for example, Gladwin (1983) found that over 80 per cent of farm ponds were infilled between 1947 and 1980.

Lake habitats include the important chains of flooded gravel pits in the Colne and Lea valleys (*see* Appendices M and N) and a number of artificial lakes such as in Brocket Park, the Broadwater in Hatfield Park, and at Panshanger. Although some lakes and flooded gravel pits have poorly vegetated margins due to their steep banks, many provide a wide range of

Figure 2.9   *Great Hard Mead Lake, Amwell. One of the flooded gravel pits in the Lea valley attractive to migrants and wildfowl and, in this case, being developed as a conservation area as excavation proceeds.*   Photo: © Tom Gladwin

(Top) Figure 2.10   *Hilfield Park Reservoir LNR. An important site for winter wildfowl and gulls.*   Photo: © Tom Gladwin.

(Centre) Figure 2.11   *Wilstone Reservoir, Tring. Important for aquatic and migrant birds, and part of Hertfordshire's only National Nature Reserve.*

Photo: © Bryan Sage

(Lower) Figure 2.12   *The Lagoons at Rye Meads; one of the most important migration stations in inland Britain.*   Photo: © Tom Gladwin

aquatic habitats with shallow as well as deep water, islands, spits, bays and rich aquatic vegetation.

The county contains three major reservoirs one of which, Aldenham Reservoir situated in Aldenham Country Park, is used for leisure. Hilfield Park Reservoir, also at Aldenham, is a Local Nature Reserve, largely due to its important winter wildfowl population. Tring Reservoirs, Hertfordshire's sole National Nature Reserve, are relatively shallow with well established reed-beds and extensive muddy shores which appear at times of low water levels. This site holds important breeding and wintering bird populations. Strategically located in the line of the Chiltern Hills it is also an important migration station. Set in the Lea valley, Rye Meads with its lagoons, reed-beds and other wet habitats is of equal importance.

Other important shallow water habitats include existing and former watercress beds. Of the latter, Lemsford Springs NR is of national importance for wintering Green Sandpipers.

Only very small remnants of true marsh now remain in the county. However, most river valleys still contain meadows which are normally flooded or saturated in winter. The King's Meads, Hertford, meadows at Rye Meads, and Sawbridgeworth Marsh NR are particularly important.

Major reed-beds in the county are few and include those at Rye Meads, Stanborough Reedmarsh NR, Tewinbury NR, and Tring Reservoirs NNR.

2.5 Grasslands, Commons and Heathlands

Most of the old established rough grazings found in the county are the remnants of former sheep-walks and land over which there were or are common rights. Much has been lost by ploughing. Further, as a result of the breakdown of common rights since the beginning of the twentieth century there has been a serious reduction, and in some cases almost complete removal, of grazing. Most of what remains has deteriorated having been invaded by scrub. The reduction in sheep and cattle, and in the rabbit population due to myxomatosis, are other major factors.

Few of Hertfordshire's old grasslands are on calcareous soils, particularly the chalk. Important areas are Albury Nowers, Sheethanger and Roughdown Commons, Therfield Heath, and Tring Park.

A few peaty calcareous pastures remain both on wet calcareous clays and in the river valleys. In the first category these include Purwell Meadows and Oughtonhead, Hitchin; Rushy Meadow, Tring; meadows at Sandon Green End and Wateringplace Green, Ardeley. Important river valley sites are found in the Chess and Stort valleys and in the Mimram valley at Tewinbury

On facing page
(Top) Figure 2.13   *Lemsford Springs NR. Old spring-fed watercress beds support diverse and dense bird populations.*   *Photo: © Barry Trevis*

(Centre) Figure 2.14   *King's Meads, Hertford. One of the last flood-plain meadows in the Lea valley with wildfowl and Snipe in winter and Yellow Wagtails in summer.*
Photo: © Trevor James

(Lower) Figure 2.15   *Stanborough Reedmarsh. One of the few large reed marshes in Hertfordshire.*   *Photo: © Tom Gladwin*

Figure 2.16 *Wateringplace Green. One of Hertfordshire's few remaining ancient wet boulder clay pastures.* *Photo: © Trevor James*

and Poplars Green. Isolated sites, often on less calcareous soils include Braughing Meads, King's Meads (Hertford), Standon Lordship and Rye Meads.

In the west and centre of the county on sands, gravels and the clay-with-flints, there are a number of dry heathy commons typified by bracken, gorse and heather. Such sites, which are not found in adjacent counties, include Berkhamsted Common, Chorleywood Common, Colney Heath, Gustardwood Common and Nomansland Common.

Wet heathy grasslands which are now very localised include Burleigh Meadow, Knebworth; parts of Croxley Common Moor; and the very acid commons at Patmore Heath, Albury, and Hertford Heath. These are remnants of vast areas of similar habitats that have disappeared from south-east Hertfordshire since 1800.

Many of Hertfordshires' rarer or lost breeding species e.g. Stone Curlew,

Figure 2.17 *Nomandsland Common. Dry heather heath in central Hertfordshire and the habitat of the Meadow Pipit.* *Photo: © Trevor James*

Plate 1:   *Night Heron at Lemsford Springs NR in January 1972.*   *Photo:* © *P. Waterton*

Plate 2:   *Stone Curlew, a rare but annual breeding species in the north-east of Hertfordshire.*
Photo:© Bryan Sage

Figure 2.18 *Patmore Heath –*
One of Hertfordshire's few
remaining wet acid heaths with
a characteristic bird fauna.
        Photo: © Trevor James

Snipe, Redshank, Wheatear, Meadow Pipit and perhaps Dartford Warbler are species of primary unenclosed rough grazing.

Ancient enclosed permanent pastures were once widespread on all soil types except perhaps the chalk. There is evidence that in North Hertfordshire up to 92 per cent of such pasture has been lost since 1940 (North Hertfordshire Museums Services, unpublished information).

Other grasslands, not used for agricultural purposes, which are important to bird populations are found in parks, playing fields — particularly golf courses, roadside verges and garden lawns.

2.6 Woodlands

Hertfordshire was once mostly forested. The Forest of Middlesex covered most of the area between the valleys of the rivers Colne and Lea and a large part of the Chiltern Forest extended into the western part of the county. The forests in most of Hertfordshire were naturally dominated by oak; pedunculate oak on the heavy clays, sessile oak on the lighter loams and sandy soils, oak–hazel and oak–birch in the west and sessile and pedunculate oak–hornbeam in the south and south–east. Ash–maple was probably the typical woodland on the boulder clay of north-east Hertfordshire and beech along the Chilterns. Traditional management of most small woodlands into the the present century involved coppicing the shrub layer every 14 years or more, and successive removal of the standards at 80 to 100 years old. Many of the larger woods owe their existence to wood pasture systems which have succeeded to scrub or been converted to high forest. These latter woodlands are typified by Redstarts, Tree Pipits and Wood Warblers for example.

The Forestry Commission inventory of Hertfordshire woodlands obtained between 1921 and 1926 found 10 486ha (25 912 acres) of woodlands of 2 acres or more including 3692ha (9123 acres) of broad-leaved high forest and

Figure 2.19 *Wormley Wood – A sessile oak–hornbeam woodland and the only major primary high forest in Hertfordshire.* Photo: © Trevor James

4891ha (12 086 acres) of coppice. This represented 6.4 per cent of the county area at that time. High forest was defined as being comprised of trees of uneven age which had not been formed by planting.

In 1982 Hertfordshire contained some 11 331ha (28 500 acres) of woodland of 1 ha (2.47 acres) or more. However, cessation of traditional management practises and reafforestation of large areas with exotic coniferous species and hybrids has significantly changed its character. With a few exceptions only relatively small remnants, totalling some 4000ha (9884 acres) of the ancient broad-leaved woodlands remain.

In 1977 the Nature Conservancy Council carried out a limited desk-top survey to list the ancient woodlands in Hertfordshire of 2ha (4.94 acres) or more. The results of this survey (Bowley 1979) listed 490 woodlands divided into 3 categories as follows:

Figure 2.20 *Young conifer plantations provide transitional habitats for Nightjars and Grasshopper Warblers.* Photo: © Chris James

Category/Description	Number of woodlands	Total Area of woodlands (ha)
I Ancient broad-leaved woodlands of semi-natural structure which may contain up to 50% coniferous plantation	418	4165
II Older secondary woodlands including 18th and early 19th century plantations and some parkland	57	442
III Recent plantations on ancient sites, including over 50% coniferous plantation	15	625
Total:	490	5232 ha (12 928 acres)

Bowley (1979) found that 22 per cent of all extant woodland in the county is of 'ancient' origin (i.e. likely to be pre-1600). However, this ancient woodland is very fragmented. Hinton (1978) reports on the results of The Hertfordshire Woodland Survey carried out in 1978. The primary object of this survey of the woodlands placed in Category I by Bowley, was to define and classify biologically important woodlands in the county. The survey found the following eighteen main-stand types as defined by Peterkin (1977):

Group	Type
1 Ash–Wych Elm woods	1B Lowland wet Ash–Elm woods
2 Maple–Ash woods	2A Wet Ash–Maple woods
	2B Maple woods
	2C Dry Ash–Maple woods
3 Ash–Hazel woods	3A Acid Ash–Hazel woods
	3B Basic Ash–Hazel woods
6 Acid Birch–Oak woods	6A Sessile Oak–Birch woods
	6B Western Sessile Oak–Ash woods
	6D Lowland mixed Oak woods
	6E Pedunculate Oak–Birch woods
8 Beech woods	8A Acid Sessile Oak–Beech woods
	8B Calcareous Pedunculate Oak–Beech woods
	8C Calcareous Ash–Beech woods
	8D Acid Beech–Oak–Ash woods
	8E Acid Pedunculate Oak–Beech woods
9 Hornbeam woods	9A Pedunculate Oak–Hornbeam woods
	9B Sessile Oak–Hornbeam woods
10 Suckering Elm woods	10A Invasive Elm woods

Ancient woodland in Hertfordshire is very fragmented, 75 per cent being in units of less than 10 ha and only 1 per cent in continuous stands of 100 ha or more. The most widespread ancient woodlands are of the oak–hornbeam

(Top) Figure 2.21 *Small oak–hornbeam coppiced woodlands are a feature of central and southern Hertfordshire and if maintained on a coppice cycle provide rich habitats for Nightingales and Warblers.*   *Photo: © Chris James*
(Lower) Figure 2.22 *Ancient wood pasture with pollarded beeches and the habitat of Redstart and Wood Warbler.*   *Photo: © Trevor James*

types mainly found in the SE. of the county. These include many of the larger woodlands such as Northaw Great Wood and Balls Wood of Type 9A, and Wormley, Hoddesdon Park and Sherrards Park woods of Type 9B. Such woodland is widespread on the acid clays and gravels. Acid Birch–Oak woods (Group 6) are mostly found on the lighter acid soils in the southern half of the county. Good examples are present in parts of Northaw Great Wood, Oxhey Woods and Sherrards Park Wood. In the south and west of the county, oak is often found in association with hazel coppice. Beech woods occur typically along the edge of the chalk such as at Aldbury Common, Ashridge and Frithsden Beeches, and on the clay-with-flints. The chalky boulder clay in the north-east of the county is typified by Maple–Ash woods (Group 2) mostly, with a few exceptions, reduced to small fragments.

(Top) Figure 2.23 *Oughtonhead. Alder woodland, one of a variety of habitats associated with the chalk springs, important for Siskins and other finches.* Photo: © *Trevor James*

(Lower) Figure 2.24 *Hedgerows in association with improved pasture provide feeding and nest sites for many farmland species.* Photo: © *Trevor James*

Many of the woodlands are enriched by the presence of other tree species such as Cherry, Holly and Midland Hawthorn which in turn encourage a greater diversity of birds.

With the cessation of traditional management practises much of the Hornbeam coppice in Hertfordshire has become tall, excessively shading the woodland floor, and reducing the ground and shrub layer vegetation.

Semi-natural wet woodlands dominated by Alder or Willow were not considered by Hinton (1978). Mostly found in the Colne and Lea valleys and around Hitchin, these important habitats were significantly reduced between 1956 and 1982.

Many of Hertfordshire's woodlands are now dominated by coniferous plantations which include Larch (some hybrids), Norway Spruce, and

Corsican Pine. The diversity and density of bird populations in these plantations is generally much lower than in the native broad-leaved woodlands.

Hertfordshire also contains a few old apple and other orchards which are important ornithological habitats.

Hedgerows are important linear woodland habitats. In Hertfordshire many hedgerows have been cleared from land in agricultural use in the 25 years to 1982. Gladwin (1983) calculated that 43 per cent of hedgerows were removed in the area covered by the two 10 km Ordnance Survey squares TL2l and TL3l between 1956 and 1980. Proportionally greater losses have occurred elsewhere and particularly on the boulder clay farms in the north-east of the county. Mechanical cutting has resulted in a significant change in the structure of many hedgerows and a reduction in the number of standard trees found in them.

Stands of Yew of ornamental origin are found in some older churchyards.

2.7 Urban

During the 25-year period 1958 to 1982 major changes occurred in the urban environment. Some of these changes have had a major effect on bird populations.

A feature of new residential and many urban developments has been the incorporation of ornamental trees and short grasslands in the form of verges, playing fields and other open spaces. Similarly, the gardens of most houses built in the late 1950s and 1960s now contain established lawns and mature shrubs and trees. These have become important habitats providing food, shelter and nest sites for many species. In addition urban bird populations have been increasingly encouraged and supported by the provision of nestboxes and food at bird tables. Some idea of the scale of these activities is provided by Gladwin (1983). During the 1980/81 winter three pet food shops

Figure 2.25   *Garden habitats provide food and nest sites for many species.*
Photo: © Tom Gladwin

in two central Hertfordshire towns sold 21½ tons of seed and peanuts for use as bird food. In the very cold winter of 1981/82 the weight sold increased to 35½ tons. In a sample survey of 500 new houses in low density housing estates Gladwin found that in 1980 30 per cent contained commercially manufactured bird feeders filled at least once every two days in winter. In the same sample 57 per cent of the gardens contained 462 nestboxes of which at least 229 were occupied in 1980.

The period 1958 to 1982 saw the demolition of many old buildings with shuttered or open towers, or roofs with tiles that provided access and nest sites for Swifts and other species. In contrast the eaves of many new houses have proved suitable nest sites for House Martins.

Although not restricted to urban areas, traffic speeds, both on railways and roads, have increased and as a result there is a greater mortality of birds due to collision with high-speed vehicles.

No major open irrigation sewage farms, once important feeding sites for many species, remain in the county.

3
Migration and Movement

Hertfordshire is an inland county through and within which large numbers of birds are moving and migrating at all times of year. Some are regular seasonal movements such as migrations between breeding and rest or wintering areas. Others are a spontaneous response to a change in circumstances such as the onset of cold weather, failure of the food crop or a successful breeding season producing more surviving birds than can be supported by normal food supplies (eruptions and irruptions). Many of these journeys involve distances of several hundred miles or more. In contrast, and equally important to the welfare of the birds, there are local movements which include seasonal shifts from one habitat type to another, and daily roosting–feeding flights. Whatever the cause or objective, the fact is that widely differing and sometimes complex patterns of travel are taking place at all seasons. Birds, it may be said, are never still and the purpose of this short chapter is to provide a general account of this readily observed and fascinating behaviour. Detailed descriptions of the major movements made by each species are provided in Chapter 6, The Systematic List.

Strictly defined, migrations are the regular seasonal, normally annual, movements of a bird to and from the area in which it breeds and that which it normally occupies outside the breeding season. In Hertfordshire the most obvious migrations are due to the arrival, departure and passage of birds which are primarily summer or winter visitors. By the end of February in a normal year, wildfowl, waders and gulls have started moving back to continental Europe. As the spring exodus gains momentum, huge numbers of thrushes, starlings and finches pass through and leave the county. By mid-April only the stragglers remain. As the winter birds depart some of the resident species, such as Robins, Dunnocks and Wrens, move back into the woodlands having established winter territories in gardens and other more favourable habitats. At the same time the winter flocks of resident finches start to disperse and the partial migrants return. Partial migrants are species in which only a proportion of the population migrates from a given area. Species in this category include Pied Wagtail, Robin, Song Thrush, Goldfinch and Linnet.

The end of March sees the arrival of the first summer visitors. These include birds which go no further south than Iberia or North Africa, e.g. Willow Warblers, Chiffchaffs and some Blackcaps, and a few Trans-Saharan migrants such as Sand Martins and Wheatear. Thereafter whilst the first representatives of other species, such as Swallow, Yellow Wagtail and Sedge Warbler, have usually been seen by mid-April, the main arrival of these and other summer birds occurs in late April and early May. In recent years the drought in the Sahel and its effect on food there, is thought to be the cause of a disastrous decline in the numbers of Trans-Saharan species such as Sand Martin, Whitethroat and Garden Warbler. Many observers now look for the arrival of these and other affected species with genuine concern.

Some species such as Swift, Turtle Dove and Reed Warbler are rarely seen before early May when a second wave of Wheatears includes 'larger and brighter' birds of the Greenland race.

Weather is a major influence at all times of the year and migration may be substantially delayed by unfavourable conditions. In recent years the weather associated with a series of long cold springs, extending well into May and sometimes early June, has caused major hold-ups. Thus the arrival of most House Martins and Swifts has occasionally been as late as the first ten days of June.

Small numbers of waders pass through the county in the spring but largely go unnoticed, unless conditions at one or more reservoirs or gravel pits are sufficiently attractive to cause the birds to interrupt their journey to rest and feed. Some of the rarer birds that pass through the county are more likely to be seen in spring than autumn. These include Osprey, Marsh Harrier, Dotterel, Avocet, Little Gull, Arctic Tern, Hoopoe, Blue-headed Wagtail, Ring Ouzel and Golden Oriole. However, there is a much greater urgency about spring than autumn migration and birds with destinations outside Hertfordshire rarely remain for more than a day or so, moving on as soon as energy and weather permit.

In mid-June many Lapwing start arriving back from eastern Europe. Few observers can have failed to notice the Lapwing flocks passing westwards on fine summer days.

At the end of the breeding season, i.e. from the end of June, and prior to the commencement of autumn migration; the young and some adults of long distance migrant species disperse in various directions, often opposite to that in which they will eventually migrate; sometimes covering quite large distances even up to several hundred miles. The young of most resident species also disperse at this time but many will never, even through their adult lives, move more than a few kilometres from their birthplace.

Small numbers of waders appear in July including Common Sandpipers which reach a peak in mid-August, and the first returning Green Sandpipers. Black-headed Gulls also start to reappear in early July. Late July and early August sees the departure of most Turtle Doves, Cuckoos and Swifts. For most species, however, there seems to be, at least initially, less urgency about the autumn than spring migration. The departure and passage periods may extend over two months, and rare birds tend to remain longer, in some cases for several weeks. The main departure and autumn passage of the summer visitors ends suddenly in the last decade of September although a few warblers and moderate numbers of Swallows and House Martins are usually seen well into October. Most summer visitors are nocturnal migrants. As in spring, certain species are more likely to be seen in autumn than at other seasons. These include Whinchats, still common in autumn, and rare species such as Wryneck and Pied Flycatcher. Small numbers of common and sometimes scarce waders occur wherever conditions are suitable.

October and November sees the main return of the winter birds. The huge diurnal westward movements of lapwings, skylarks, thrushes, starlings, finches and many others are obvious to all. These broad front movements studied over London in 1960 are well described in *Four Million Birds!* (Gibbs and Wallace 1961). Not all such movements are diurnal and the night skies sometimes seem to be full of calling Redwings. The winter populations of wildfowl, snipe and gulls also arrive during this period when scarce birds which might be seen include Long-eared and Short-eared Owl, Rock Pipit, Stonechat and Great Grey Shrike. Weather has a major effect on these movements which can be quite spectacular following a period of delay caused by high winds and rain. These readily observed movements are usually at their peak for up to five hours after dawn.

Some specialist feeders, particularly those occupying the northern forests of Europe, are forced to migrate whenever their population levels exceed that which can be supported by available food supplies. These irregular migrations or irruptions usually occur in late summer or autumn following a food crop failure. Species which have occurred in Hertfordshire (and their preferred foods) as a result of irruptions include Pallas's Sandgrouse (seeds), Slender-billed Nutcracker (Arolla Pine), Waxwing (Rowan) and Crossbill (Spruce and Pine). Other specialist feeders from the northern forests winter regularly in Hertfordshire. A characteristic of these species which include Siskin (Alder and Birch), Redpoll (Birch) and Brambling (Beech), are wide winter to winter variations in numbers which may well reflect food levels on the continent. Common in some years, Bramblings and Siskins can be scarce in others. Rare irruptive birds to have reached Hertfordshire include Northern Great Spotted Woodpecker (Spruce and Pine) and Two-barred Crossbill (Larch).

Within Britain some local breeding species periodically irrupt. Perhaps the best known of these in Hertfordshire is the Bearded Tit which has reached the county in 22 of the 24 winters up to 1982/83.

Late autumn also finds many resident species making relatively short movements as they leave woodlands to establish winter territories in more suitable habitats nearby. These include Robins, Dunnocks, Wrens and some thrushes, tits and finches.

Many birds such as gulls, wagtails, thrushes, starlings, crows, finches and buntings roost communally throughout the winter. The morning and evening flights of these birds between roosts and feeding areas are a well studied feature of Hertfordshire's ornithology.

As stated earlier some species will undertake long distance movements in a spontaneous response to the onset of adverse weather. Undoubtedly the most spectacular of these movements are to be seen as cold weather spreads down the country, sometimes 'forcing' millions of birds to move south or south west, even to France and Spain, to avoid death through cold and starvation. Lapwings, Skylarks, thrushes and finches are the most numerous birds to be so affected.

Migration through the county is on a broad front although concentrations, particularly of diurnal migrants, are associated with particular linear features of the landscape such as the Chiltern Hills and the main river valleys. Many birds traditionally follow these features often benefiting by minimising the effect of head winds. Sage (1959) described the flight-lines followed by migrating gulls through Hertfordshire. As the status of species like the Lesser Black-backed Gull has changed so have the flight-lines which need to be resurveyed. Despite the enormous contribution made to our knowledge by the work of the Maple Cross and Rye Meads Ringing Groups much remains to be researched.

4
Changes in the Status of Hertfordshire Birds

Even during the relatively short time span of 25 years covered by this book a number of interesting changes in the status of various species have been noted. Full details of these will be found in the species accounts, but the main points of interest are summarised below. New species added to the county list are discussed in Chapter 5.

Many of the changes concern non-breeding species, most of which are winter visitors. The Cormorant, formerly a fairly regular passage migrant and occasional winter visitor, is now common. The 11-year period from 1972–82 saw an increase of almost 600 per cent in the number of records compared with the 14 years from 1950–71. Both the Bittern and Whooper Swan are now of more frequent occurrence in winter, the former particularly in the Lea valley. The status of the Gadwall has changed from that of an uncommon to a common winter visitor, and since 1967 it has been recorded almost annually in the Colne and Lea valleys, but particularly in the latter where numbers in excess of 100 have been seen. In the case of the Shoveler, numbers present in winter have also increased markedly in the last 10 years, particularly in the Colne and Lea valleys. The status of the Common Scoter has altered from that of an irregular to a regular winter visitor and passage migrant, with records for 23 of the 25 years. Two species of wader also deserve mention here. The Oystercatcher, classed by Sage (1959) as an irregular passage migrant, shows a clear change in status and is now a regular visitor, and the Dunlin is now of much more frequent occurrence in winter.

Changes are also evident in the number of some species of gulls that use the two main winter roosts at Hilfield Park Reservoir and Tring Reservoirs. The main species affected is the Black-headed Gull which, in January 1958, totalled c.8000 at the Tring Reservoirs roost, but had increased to about 12 000 in January 1980 and 13 900 in January 1982. At Hilfield Park Reservoir this species totalled c.9000 in January 1958, but c.17 400 in January 1980 and 25 000 in January 1983. Two other species using the Hilfield Park Reservoir roost have exhibited more erratic changes. Common Gull numbers in January 1958 were c.1850, but had increased to c.3000 by January 1969. However, January 1980 saw only 900 present, but by January 1983 the numbers were c.2750. The Herring Gull, however, after a rise from c.4000 in January 1958 to c.7250 in January 1969, had declined to only about 100 in January 1983 (although c.2200 had been present in January 1980).

The winter populations of a few species of duck have declined. This has been most noticeable in the case of the Pochard whose numbers exhibited a steady decline in the 10 winters from 1973/74 to 1982/83. The winter population of Goosander at Tring Reservoirs has declined drastically since the winter of 1970/71. From 1972–74 it increased in the Colne valley below Rickmansworth, but then declined there also.

Two migrant raptors have undergone a marked change of status. The Marsh Harrier was regarded as a scarce spring migrant by Sage (1959) but this situation has changed considerably since the late 1950s, and there were 27 records in the 25 years covered by this book: it has been recorded annually since 1973. Even more striking has been the change in the status of the Osprey from that of a rare to an almost regular visitor, particularly in the spring.

There is clear evidence of a considerable improvement in the breeding populations of at least 19 species. Following the establishment by the Grey Heron of a regular breeding population at Tring Reservoirs in 1957, additional smaller heronries subsequently appeared in Brocket Park, the Panshanger, and at Stockers Lake. The Greylag Goose bred at Tring Reservoirs from 1963–75 (but not thereafter), while in the Colne valley it first bred in 1973 and again from 1976 to date: this is now the main centre of their distribution. Similarly, the Canada Goose first bred successfully in the Colne valley in 1969 and at Tring Reservoirs in 1970. It began to expand its range in 1974 and by 1982 was nesting in about a dozen localities. The Rickmansworth GPs are now the main population centre with high numbers present in autumn and winter. Substantial numbers have also been reported from the Lea valley. One other species of waterfowl, the Tufted Duck, has increased its breeding population, particularly in the Colne and Lea valleys, and has also colonised the valleys of a number of smaller rivers.

There has been a welcome improvement in the status of some birds of prey in the county. Following the pesticide problems of the 1960s, the Sparrowhawk has shown a clear increase in numbers both in the breeding season and at other times. The Hobby has returned as a breeding species with the first confirmed instance in 1967, and there is now a small annual nesting population. There is evidence of attempts by the Buzzard to re-establish itself as a breeding species, but irrefutable evidence of successful nesting has yet to materialise.

The Little Ringed Plover has continued to maintain a healthy population, and from 1958 to 1982 there were seven attempts (successful or otherwise) at breeding by the Ringed Plover.

Two striking examples concerning breeding species involve the Common Tern and the Collared Dove. The former, previously just a regular passage migrant, has now firmly established itself as a breeding species in the Lea valley where it first nested in 1963. The Collared Dove nested in the county for the first time in 1958, then expanded rapidly to become a common and widely distributed breeding species, whose population has probably now stabilised. Stock Dove populations also increased rapidly during the same period. The readily overlooked Lesser Spotted Woodpecker is now only a little less numerous than the Great Spotted Woodpecker.

Several passerine species also require mention. The Black Redstart first bred in 1958 and has done so again in most subsequent years. Twenty years later, in 1978, Cetti's Warbler bred for the first time (at Rye Meads), and has subsequently done so at other sites. The Reed Warbler appears to have expanded its range and numbers as a nesting species in the county, probably as a result of an increase in suitable habitat. Bearded Tits nested or attempted to do so on several occasions between 1966 and 1973. Although Firecrests have been of increasing occurrence and there are several breeding season records, no nest has yet been found or breeding suspected in the county. Other species whose breeding populations have increased significantly in the last 25 years include Blackcap, Goldcrest, Blue Tit, Magpie, Carrion Crow, Tree Sparrow and Redpoll.

On the debit side are a number of species which have either disappeared or substantially declined as breeding species. In the former category are the Corncrake (an odd pair may still nest occasionally), and the Whinchat and Stonechat whose loss may be due to adverse climatic conditions. Other species which have not bred for some years are mentioned below in the section on breeding species in Chapter 5, Analysis of the County List. The breeding population of the Mute Swan has declined since the late 1950s and early 1960s. The Grey Partridge remains scarce and does not seem to have recovered from the effects of the earlier widespread use of pesticides. Changes to woodland habitats are probably the main cause in the decrease of the breeding population of the Woodcock that has been evident in the last 10 years, and it is certainly the loss of wet meadows that has adversely affected the Redshank.

Barn Owls have declined to the point where they are now very rare, and Nightjars also are fewer. Five species of summer visitor — Sand Martin, Redstart, Whitethroat, Garden Warbler and Spotted Flycatcher – have been particularly affected by the severe droughts in the Sahel in Africa which commenced in 1968/69. The drastic decline of the Redstart seems to have been reversed in some parts of Britain but not, evidently, in Hertfordshire. The decline in the breeding status of the Nightingale recorded by Sage (1959) has continued, mainly due to losses of suitable woodland habitat. There is strong evidence of a decline in the breeding population of the Song Thrush, possibly as a result of a succession of cold winters. Tree Pipits, Yellow Wagtails and Chiffchaffs are other summer visitors whose populations have been significantly reduced.

The decline of the Rook population on a national scale has been well documented, and in Hertfordshire there was a 44.82 per cent drop in the total number of nests from 1960/61 to 1975, although from 1980 to 1983 there was some evidence of a slight recovery.

5
Analysis of the County List

At the time of publication of Sage (1959) the total number of species and subspecies recorded in the county was 258 (245 species and 13 additional subspecies) excluding 21 species that were placed in square brackets. This total was made up approximately as follows:

Species which breed or have bred	118
Winter visitors only	52
Passage migrants only	32
Vagrants	56
Total:	**258**

TABLE 5.1   *Additions to the county list since the publication of Sage (1959), listed in chronological order*

Fulmar	1956	Bishops Stortford
Purple Sandpiper	1959	Tring Reservoirs
Aquatic Warbler	1960	Hilfield Park Reservoir
Little Bunting	1960	Hilfield Park Reservoir
Eider	1961	Hilfield Park Reservoir
Sociable Plover	1961	Tring Reservoirs
Melodious Warbler	1961	Rye Meads
Iceland Gull	1963	Panshanger
Kentish Plover	1964	Tring Reservoirs
Alpine Swift	1965	West Hyde and St. Albans
Solitary Sandpiper	1967	Rye Meads
Goshawk	1967	Wareside
Nutcracker	1968	10 records in irruption year
Roseate Tern	1969	Tring Reservoirs
Night Heron	1970	Stockers Lake
Mandarin	1970	Maple Cross and Hamper Mill
American Wigeon	1971	Tring Reservoirs
Ruddy Duck	1971	Hilfield Park Reservoir
Barred Warbler	1972	Rye Meads
Avocet	1973	Tring Reservoirs
Serin	1973	Near Hilfield Park Reservoir
Egyptian Goose	1974	Rickmansworth
Ring-necked Duck	1974	Broxbourne GPs
Golden Pheasant	1974	Watery Grove
Ring-necked Parakeet	1974	Bragbury End, Stevenage
Cetti's Warbler	1975	Rickmansworth
Long-billed Dowitcher	1975	Tring Reservoirs
Bean Goose	1979	Maple Cross
Squacco Heron	1979	Rye Meads
Savi's Warbler	1979	Stanstead Abbots GP
Paddyfield Warbler	1981	Tring Reservoirs
Mediterranean Gull	1982	Stanstead Abbots GP

Total species 34

In addition: (a) Lady Amherst's Pheasant has also been added to the county list, but the date of the first record is uncertain although it was between 1967 and 1973.

(b) The Feral Rock Dove is also now included since it has bred in the wild for many years.

The breakdown given above is a rough guide only, since some species fall into more than one category. At that time the Pink-footed Goose was considered to be conspecific with the Bean Goose and the Common Sandpiper with the Spotted Sandpiper. Subsequently both were accorded full specific status. A record of Blue-winged Teal at Woodhall Park in 1938 was placed in square brackets, but in the light of current knowledge it is considered that the record probably referred to a genuine wild bird: in the present work this record is removed from brackets. In addition, the record of breeding by the Pied Flycatcher near Hitchin prior to 1917 is now considered unacceptable for the reasons given in the text. The most recent discussion of the county list was by Sage (1980).

In addition to the changes mentioned above, a number of species have since been added to the list. From 1958–82 there were only six years (1958, 1962, 1966, 1976, 1978 and 1980) in which no additions to the list were made, and by the end of 1982 the total number of species recorded in the county was 281.

Those species added to the county list since Sage (1959) are listed in Table 5.1. In 1970 and subsequently, several species owing their origins to escapes from captivity, such as the Egyptian Goose, Mandarin, Ruddy Duck, Golden Pheasant, Lady Amherst's Pheasant and Ring-necked Parakeet, which have established self-supporting feral populations in this country, were added to the official British List. Those which have been recorded in the county are dealt with in the appropriate place in the text. Additionally, it is now recognised that the Feral Rock Dove must be included since it has bred in the wild for many years.

5.1   Subspecies

With a few exceptions, such as the American Green-winged Teal, White Wagtail, Black-bellied Dipper, White-spotted Bluethroat (in the right stage

TABLE 5.2   *Subspecies recorded in Hertfordshire*

(a)   *Sage (1959)*

Arctic Ringed Plover	Greenland Wheatear
Northern Golden Plover	Northern Willow Warbler
Spotted Sandpiper	Water Pipit
Continental Redshank	White Wagtail
Scandinavian Lesser Black-backed Gull	Blue-headed Wagtail
Hooded Crow	Mealy Redpoll
Scandinavian Jackdaw	

(b)   *Subsequent additions*

American Green-winged Teal (1961)	White-spotted Bluethroat (1978)
Northern Great Spotted Woodpecker (1968)	Icelandic Redwing (1963)
Eastern Skylark (1963)	Continental Song Thrush (1980)
Atlantic Meadow Pipit (1961)	Northern Chiffchaff (1971)
Scandinavian Rock Pipit (1962)	Northern Bullfinch (1968)
Black-bellied Dipper (1962)	

of plumage), and Hooded Crow, many subspecies are not recognisable in the field with certainty. All the subspecies so far definitively recorded in the county are dealt with in the appropriate place in the text where their scientific names will be found, but a few clarifying comments may be helpful at this point. In Sage (1959) a total of 13 subspecies were listed, together with two others that were included in square brackets. The elevation of the Bean Goose and Spotted Sandpiper to full specific status was mentioned above, and it should also be noted that the race formerly known as the British Redshank *Tringa totanus britannica* is no longer recognised and British birds are regarded as belonging to the nominate race. All the subspecies listed by Sage (op. cit.) and those added subsequently are shown in Table 5.2.

5.2 Frequency of Occurrence

There are 20 species which have only been recorded in the county on one occasion, and these are listed in Table 5.3. It may be noted that the Table lists four species that have not been recorded at all during the present century.

TABLE 5.3 *Species recorded in Hertfordshire once only, listed in chronological order*

Rock Thrush	1843	Little Bunting	1960
Rustic Bunting	1882	Sociable Plover	1961
Marsh Sandpiper	1887	Solitary Sandpiper	1967
Baillon's Crake	1891	Roseate Tern	1969
Razorbill	1934	American Wigeon	1971
Great Reed Warbler	1946	Long-billed Dowitcher	1977
Lesser Yellowlegs	1953	Bean Goose	1979
Ortolan Bunting	1953	Squacco Heron	1979
White-winged Lark	1955	Paddyfield Warbler	1981
Spotted Sandpiper	1956	Mediterranean Gull	1982

TABLE 5.4 *Species recorded in Hertfordshire between two and five occasions, listed in taxonomic order*

Fulmar	Pectoral Sandpiper	Roller
Night Heron	Purple Sandpiper	Red-rumped Swallow
Little Egret	Broad-billed Sandpiper	Bluethroat
Glossy Ibis	Red-necked Phalarope	Savi's Warbler
Spoonbill	Pomarine Skua	Aquatic Warbler
Blue-winged Teal	Great Skua	Melodious Warbler
Ring-necked Duck	Long-tailed Skua	Barred Warbler
Eider	Iceland Gull	Woodchat Shrike
White-tailed Eagle	White-winged Black Tern	Rose-coloured Starling
Goshawk	Guillemot	Serin
Little Crake	Alpine Swift	Two-barred Crossbill
Kentish Plover	Bee-eater	

Plate 3: *Little Ringed Plover, a scarce but regular breeding species at the nest.*
Photo: © *Dr R. Ransome*

Plate 4:   *Wheatear, a common spring and autumn migrant.*   *Photo:© Bryan Sage*

Still within the category of rare vagrants are 35 species which have occurred in the county on two to five occasions, and these are listed in Table 5.4.

5.3   Breeding Species

The total number of species which currently breed in the county, or have done so at sometime in the past, is 130 and these are listed in Appendix K. Twelve of these species were added to the list after the publication of Sage (1959), these being Canada Goose, Greylag Goose, Mandarin, Ruddy Duck, Spotted Crake, Common Tern, Collared Dove, Cetti's Warbler, Bearded Tit and Siskin. The Black-headed Gull bred at Watford SF in 1950, but the information concerning this fact did not come to light until 1963. The Feral Rock Dove is also now included for the reason given earlier. Five species – Red Kite, Montagu's Harrier (but *see* Appendix K), Great Bustard, Golden Oriole, and Raven, have not bred at all in the present century. In the case of the Buzzard it should be noted that there has not been any *definitive* evidence of nesting in the west of the county in recent years, although the *circumstantial* evidence is strong.

On the basis of present knowledge is seems that up to the end of 1982 there were seven species which have only bred once in the county. These are Bittern, Mandarin, Montagu's Harrier, Spotted Crake, Dipper, Ring Ouzel and Siskin. In the case of the latter species, although birds were holding territories in Bramfield Forest in the early 1970s, there was no actual evidence of nesting in the county until the 1982 Hemel Hempstead record. As a matter of historical interest it may be noted that, as pointed out in Appendix A in Sage (1959), the Egyptian Goose made abortive attempts to breed at Hamper Mill in 1936 and 1937, and was successful in 1938.

Other species which can probably now be considered 'lost' in so far as breeding is concerned are the Black-necked Grebe (last nested in 1928), Garganey (last nested in 1959), Corncrake (last known instances 1967 and 1968), Common Sandpiper (last nested in 1967), Black-headed Gull (last bred in 1964), Wryneck (last bred in 1977), Whinchat (last bred in 1972), Stonechat (last bred in 1973), Wheatear (last bred in 1967), Bearded Tit (last bred successfully in 1968), Red-backed Shrike (last bred in 1968), Crossbill (last bred in 1974), and the Cirl Bunting which has probably not nested in the 25 years covered by this book.

Some comment is necessary on certain of the species included in Mead and Smith (1982). The single instance of breeding for the Mandarin was at a location which, at the time, was in Middlesex. In the case of Lady Amherst's Pheasant, the one proven record of breeding was at Luton Hoo in Bedfordshire. The Curlew, as the authors rightly state, has not yet been proved to nest in the county. The statement that the Whinchat still breeds in the Lea valley and on the Chiltern scarp is no longer borne out by the recent records. The solitary proven record for the Wheatear was just over the border in Bedfordshire. Finally, the case of the Siskin was dealt with in a preceding paragraph.

6
Systematic List

Note

The map references in the margins of the following pages are against breeding species; the relevant maps will be found in the atlas section to Chapter 7 between pages 292 and 310.

Red-throated Diver

Gavia stellata

A very rare winter visitor, but with one April record.

In Sage (1959) it was classed as a rare winter visitor with 13 records listed, all in January or February, but with two March records and one at Tring Reservoirs on the very unusual date of 3 July 1910. An additional record of this species is given in Sage (1962) and refers to one seen on the River Lea between St. Margarets and Rye House on 13 October 1927.

Recent records (with the exception of the one in April) all fall within the period November to early March are as follows:

1958　A male made a forced landing in thick fog near Hitchin on 29 November and was released at Tring Reservoirs the following day; this may have been the bird found dead there on 6 December.

1959　Another dead bird was found at these reservoirs on 22 November.

1962　One present at Little Tring from 28 February to 3 March.

1965　Single birds were seen at Hilfield Park Reservoir on 24 and 30 January.

1975　Single bird at Tring Reservoirs on 28 April.

1979　Single birds at Stanborough Lake on 1 January and on lake at Fairlands Valley, Stevenage, from 14 to 22 February. One that was believed to be this species flew over Troy Mill in the Colne valley on 11 February.

The records for 1979 no doubt resulted from the unusual influx of divers and grebes into the British Isles during the winter of 1978/79, discussed by Chandler (1981).

It should be noted that the record of one at Dobbs Weir GP on 17 February 1974, (*London Bird Report* No.39:11), although listed under Hertfordshire should refer to Essex.

Black-throated Diver

Gavia arctica

A very rare winter visitor, but with one May record.

Classed as a rare winter visitor by Sage (1959) with eight records as follows:

1910　One at Tring Reservoirs on 27 December.

1947　Three at Tring on 30 and 31 January, one from 12 to 28 February, and an immature on several occasions from 21 to 30 March.

1949   One on the Aquadrome at Rickmansworth from 1 to 4 January.
1955   One present at Tring Reservoirs from 8 to 11 January; a sickly bird
        at Rye Meads on 6 March was killed by a workman on
        8 March; one present at West Hyde GP near Rickmansworth from
        2 to 8 January.

The 10 recent records (with the exception of the one in May) all fall within
the period late October to early March and are detailed as follows:

1959   One at Tring Reservoirs on 19, 24 and 25 December was probably
        the same individual noted there on (24 January 1960).
1962   No less than three occurred — one at Rye Meads on 8 February,
        one at Hilfield Park Reservoir from 11 to 25 February, and one at
        Stockers Lake on 4 March.
1967   One seen at Hilfield Park Reservoir on 29 October.
1976   One at Tring Reservoirs on 12 and 13 November.
1978   One at Tring on 14 May was believed to be of this species.
1979   In late February, three individuals were recorded — one at
        Holwell, near Hitchin on 15th was badly oiled; one at Amwell GP
        on 17th and 18th was probably the one seen at Stanstead Abbots
        GP from 19th to 24th, lastly there was one at Rickmansworth from
        17 to 25 February.

The remarks made under the preceding species concerning the 1979
records apply here also.

Great Northern Diver

Gavia immer

A very rare winter visitor, but with one record in late March.

The 13 records listed in Sage (1959) extend from late October to mid-
February.
There are only seven further records, five of which are from Tring
Reservoirs, and they are as follows:

1960   One, in almost complete summer plumage, was present at West
        Hyde GP in the Colne valley from 10 to 20 November.
1967   At Hilfield Park Reservoir, one with a large orange fishing float
        attached to one of the primaries of one wing, was present from 11
        November until at least (11 February 1968).
1972   Single birds were seen at Tring Reservoirs on 11 November.
1974   Another single bird at Tring on 7 and 8 December.
1977   A further single bird, same location, from 31 October to 24
        November.
1978   A single bird at Tring Reservoirs on 29 March.
1982   Lastly, a single a bird at Tring from 9 to 14 November.

Little Grebe

Tachybaptus ruficollis

MAP 1 A resident breeding species, winter visitor, and passage migrant. The status of this species has remained basically unchanged since Sage (1959), although the breeding population may have increased slightly.

The Little Grebe breeds primarily on lakes and large ponds, providing that there is adequate marginal vegetation. However, some pairs also nest along the wider stretches of the larger rivers, on canals, and occasionally even on watercress beds, as for example at Water End on the River Gade. In Mead and Smith (1982) breeding was recorded from 64 tetrads (73 per cent of the Hertfordshire total) and probably occurred in eight more. The most recent comprehensive data on the size of the breeding population was obtained from 1980 to 1982, although not all sites were covered in all years. However, on the basis of all available data for these three years it would seem that the minimum breeding population for the county was in the range 190–200 pairs at 38 to 40 different sites. These figures include about 22 pairs along the River Stort (Hertfordshire section only), an area not normally censused.

The autumn build-up in numbers which used to be such a feature at Tring Reservoirs has, in recent years, not reached the levels previously recorded. The general pattern was that numbers would start to increase about the end of July and reach a peak in September or October. For example, Sage (1959) quoted sample maximum counts of 76 in September 1937, 60 in August 1938 and 79 in August 1952. During the period 1958–82, however, the highest counts at Tring were 51 in October 1974 and 17 in September 1982. The phenomenon has, however, been evident at other localities from time to time. For example, some of the maximum counts from Rye Meads are shown below:

1959	44 in September	1966	22 in October
1960	37 in August	1978	20 in October
1961	69 in September	1980	25 in October
1962	41 in September	1982	16 in October
1964	16 in October		

Other examples include 17 at Brocket Park in October 1972 and at Hilfield Park Reservoir, maxima of 15 in August 1977, 26 in October 1978, 26 in September and 38 in October 1980, with 23 in October 1981.

Higher than usual numbers at some sites in March and April provide evidence of a spring movement through or within the county. Some sample counts are — Broxbourne GP: 20 in March 1969 and 1970, 26 in April 1970. Amwell GP: 20 in March 1979, 24 in March 1980, 35 in March 1981.

The numbers present at any one locality in winter are rarely very high. Some examples of maximum winter counts in recent years are — Amwell GP: 28 in February and 32 in November 1980, 53 (probably the highest winter count ever made in the county) in January and 26 in February 1981. Broxbourne GP: 20 in January 1969, and 30 in January 1970. Chesunt GPs: 33 in December 1975. Hilfield Park Reservoir: 28 in November 1978, and 42 in November 1982.

Great Crested Grebe

Podiceps cristatus

A common breeding species, passage migrant and winter visitor. Its status **MAP 2** has remained basically unchanged since Sage (1959).

This species requires fairly large bodies of water on which to nest, so it is more sparsely distributed than the Little Grebe, the main concentrations being found on the flooded gravel pits of the Colne and Lea valleys. The breeding population at Tring Reservoirs has decreased considerably since 1965. According to Mead and Smith (1982), during the period 1967–73 the absolute maximum number of territories in the county was 69. There is a considerable amount of data concerning the breeding season population of this species in the county; complete surveys were carried out in 1960, 1965 and 1973 (Sage 1973), 1975 (Hughes, Bacon and Flegg 1979 and Oliver 1977), and in 1982. The results of these surveys are shown in Table 6.1. Although the Table shows the number of pairs present, not all of these were necessarily breeding.

It can be seen that overall the increase in the breeding season population

TABLE 6.1   *Breeding season surveys of the Great Crested Grebe in Hertfordshire (figures refer to the number of pairs present in May–June)*

	1960	*1965*	*1973*	*1975*	*1982*
Aldenham Reservoir	2	2	1	—	—
Hilfield Park Reservoir	—	—	2	3	—
Tring Reservoirs	7	14–20	1[a]	7[b]	4
Coopers Green Lane (St. Albans)	—	—	—	—	1
Old Parkbury GP	1	1	—	—	2
Frogmore (Moor Mill)	1	—	—	—	—
Hamper Mill	3	1	—	—	[c]
Rickmansworth GPs	26	15	16[d]	26[e]	21
Croxley Hall	—	—	—	—	3
Kings Langley GP	—	1	1	—	1
Brocket Park	1	1	1	1	1
Stanborough Lake	—	—	—	—	1
Hatfield Park	—	1	—	—	1
Water Hall (Essendon)	1	—	—	—	—
Amwell GP	—	—	—	—	3
Stanstead Abbots GP	—	—	2	3[f]	5
Rye Meads	3	1	3	4	5
Broxbourne GP	1	6	4	6	6
Cheshunt GPs	8	9	14	9	15
Brookfield Lane Reservoirs (Cheshunt)	1	—	—	—	—
Gilston Park	—	1	1	1	1
Welwyn Garden City	—	—	—	—	1
Total number of pairs	**55**	**53–59**	**46**	**60**	**71**

NOTES: (a) water levels very low this year

(b) in addition there were 13 non-breeding birds on Startops End Reservoir

(c) included in the total for Rickmansworth GPs

(d) figures from Stockers Lake and Springwell GP only

(e) in addition there was one bird on the Rickmansworth Aquadrome

(f) one additional bird was also present on this pit

from 1965–82 was between 12 and 18 pairs (20–24 per cent). The 1973 figure
for Tring Reservoirs was clearly abnormal due to the very low water levels
prevailing in that year. If we exclude the figures for the five sites (Amwell
GP, Coopers Green Lane, Croxley Hall, Stanborough Lake and Welwyn
Garden City) which were included in the 1982 survey, but were either not
covered or not in existence in 1965, then the increase between these two years
was not marked. It should be pointed out that the total number of birds
recorded in Hertfordshire in 1975, as shown in Appendix 2 to Hughes, Bacon
and Flegg (1979), is incorrect due to the inclusion of 22 birds for a site which
is in Essex.

Hilfield Park Reservoir is not a regular breeding site. One pair attempted
to nest in 1959, two pairs probably bred in 1970, about 11 pairs (21 young
fledged) bred in 1971, two pairs in 1973, but none from 1974–82.

The main winter concentrations occur at four localities – Cheshunt GPs,
Rickmansworth GPs, Hilfield Park Reservoir, and Tring Reservoirs. Due to
incompleteness of the available data for the past 25 years analysis is
difficult. From 1958–66 there were no winter counts at Cheshunt GPs.
Between 1967 and 1979 there were only three January counts: 70 on 19
January 1975, 40 on 15 January 1978, and nine in January 1979. Three
February counts are also available – 49 on 13 February 1972, 52 on 17
February 1974, and 45 on 12 February 1978. Data for November and
December are no better: 35 in November 1975 and 1977, with 33 on 20
December 1970.

There is a similar lack of data for the Rickmansworth GPs where
maximum numbers reported were 46 at Troy Mill GP on 21 February 1960;
on all the pits, 33 in January and 24 in February 1975; 48 at Troy Mill GP
alone in December 1976; and again on all the pits, 46 in February and
November 1977; 43 in January and 50 in December 1978.

The situation at Hilfield Park Reservoir is interesting. There were counts
of 20 on 28 December 1958; 53 on 27 November, and 55 on 4 December 1959;
64 on 6 February 1960. But from 1961–70 winter numbers did not exceed 24.
The situation improved in 1971 with maxima of 48 in November and 49 in
December, while in 1972 there were 50 in November. Unprecedented
numbers were recorded in 1973 – 90 on 25 November, 112 on 30 November,
and 135+ on 15 December. From 1974–79 the maximum winter numbers
varied from two to 53.

At Tring Reservoirs for the period 1958–79 (where data are available) the maximum winter numbers ranged from 12 to 80.

Regular winter counts at the four principal localities mentioned above have been carried out annually from 1980–2, and the results are shown in Table 6.2.

Both spring (peak numbers appear in March) and autumn see a movement of this species through the county, with maximum

TABLE 6.2 *Maximum winter counts of Great Crested Grebes at four localities*

		January	February	November	December
Cheshunt GPs	1980	17	59	45	6
	1981	35	60	32	25
	1982	6	20	30	13
Rickmansworth GPs	1980	4	37	26	18
	1981	19	60	54	23
	1982	24	47	27	nc
Hilfield Park Reservoir	1980	14	2	38	16
	1981	2	12	70	13
	1982	11	9	82	60
Tring Reservoirs	1980	11	22	34	28
	1981	23	23	30	32
	1982	11	26	26	23

nc = No count

concentrations occurring at the same four localities as in winter. There are no relevant data from the Cheshunt GPs for the years 1958–66 inclusive. From 1967–82 maximum numbers in March (when recorded) varied from 20 to 71. In September/October the maxima for the same period range from 25 to 65. There are also no data for the Rickmansworth GPs from 1958–64 inclusive. From 1965–82 the information is fragmentary, but March maxima varied from 19 to 76, and for September/October from 18 to 56. In the case of Hilfield Park Reservoir, figures are available for the entire period 1958–82, and show March maxima ranging from nil to 130 (the latter in 1972), whilst the September/October maxima vary from three to 92 (the latter in October 1976).

Red-necked Grebe

Podiceps grisegena

A scarce winter visitor and passage migrant.

It was classed as a rare winter visitor by Sage (1959) who listed 23 records,

41

of which 15 were from Tring Reservoirs. With three exceptions these records were all within the months November to March.

There have been 42 subsequent records of which no less than 17 refer to 1979, the majority of them resulting from a major influx following easterly blizzards on 14 and 15 February. The influx of this species into the British Isles in the winter of 1978/79 is discussed in detail by Chandler (1981). These later records are of single birds at Rye Meads on 24 October 1963, Hilfield Park Reservoir on 25 December 1964, on the River Lea near Broxbourne on 22 February 1965, one in full breeding plumage at Cheshunt GPs from 6-27 October 1967, one (probably the same bird) also at Cheshunt GPs from 12 October to 15 December 1968, another at the same locality from 31 January to 2 February 1970; at Tring Reservoirs from 21-25 October 1970, at Tring again on 14 October 1971; at Hilfield Park Reservoir, a juvenile from 8 October to 18 November, an adult on 3 November, and two from 5-29 November 1978; one at Rye Meads on 5 January remained until 11 February, and on 16 February two more were present, one of which remained until 18 February 1979; at Hilfield Park Reservoir on 14 October 1979; in 1980 single birds at Batchworth Lake on 23 January, Bury Lake on 27 January, Hilfield Park Reservoir from 13-25 October, and Tring Reservoirs from 9-25 November, and at Springwell GP in the Colne valley in November and December. There were no records in 1981, but in 1982 there were single birds at Cheshunt GPs from 10-13 January, and 6 March; at Hilfield Park Reservoir on 5 and 29 March, and 25 May; at Tring Reservoirs on 26 March, and from 4 December until the end of the year.

The influx which commenced in mid-February 1979 was unprecedented in the annals of Hertfordshire ornithology. Eight birds were recorded in the Lea valley — up to two at Rye Meads from 16-18 February, two at Amwell GP from 17 February to 4 April, one at Stanstead Abbots GP on 24-25 February, one at Rye House from 4-10 March, one at Cheshunt GPs from 3 March to 1 April, and another at Broxbourne GP from 18 February to 26 March. Elsewhere two were seen at Tring Reservoirs on 16-17 February, one of which was found dead on the 24th. There were two at Hilfield Park Reservoir from 15-17 February and one on 9 April. In the Colne valley one was seen at Bury Lake and Rickmansworth Aquadrome from 20-23 February, and one at Batchworth Lake on 24 February.

Slavonian Grebe

Podiceps auritus

A rare visitor, primarily in winter, but with a few spring records and one in late June.

In Sage (1959), who listed about 30 records, it was classed as an irregular winter visitor and passage migrant. The records included five in spring and two in the autumn.

Within the 25 years covered by this book there were eight years in which the species was not recorded at all, but it was noted annually from 1976 to 1981. There are 24 records, all of single birds — Rye Meads on 17 December 1961, Hilfield Park Reservoir on 11 February 1962, St. Ippollits on 2 February 1963, Aldenham Reservoir from 8–28 February 1964; on the canal in Cassiobury Park on 1 January 1965, Tring Reservoirs on 20 October 1965, Hilfield Park Reservoir on 30 January 1966, at Cheshunt GPs on 25 and 31 January 1970 (probably the same bird). A bird in breeding plumage at Tring Reservoirs on 27 May and 29 June 1972; Stockers Lake from 23 February to 24 March 1974, and another in breeding plumage at Hilfield Park Reservoir on 15 April; Rickmansworth GPs on 15 February 1975; Troy Mill GP on 15 February and at Hilfield Park Reservoir on 4 April 1976; at Hamper Mill on 16 December 1977; Tring Reservoirs on 2 November 1978. The 1979 records were associated with the influx of Red-necked Grebes; single birds were reported from Tring Reservoirs from 17–21 February, Hilfield Park Reservoir from 15–24 February, and Cheshunt GPs from 17 February to 16 April. The most recent records are of single birds at Hilfield Park Reservoir on 14–15 October and from 25 October to 12 November 1980, Tring Reservoirs on 22 November 1980, and at Cheshunt GPs from 24 April to 13 May 1981.

Black-necked Grebe

Podiceps nigricollis

A scarce winter visitor and passage migrant, whose status has remained basically unchanged since Sage (1959) who listed about 48 records, excluding those relating to breeding birds.

This species formerly bred in the county at Tring Reservoirs, as detailed by Sage (op. cit.). The nesting of three pairs in 1918 was the first *proven* record for England. Further instances of definite or probable breeding occurred at the reservoirs in 1919, 1920, 1921, 1922 and 1928, and pairs were present in the summers of 1929 and 1930.

During the period under review there have been 46 further records, mostly from Tring Reservoirs (17), Hilfield Park Reservoir (13), and the Lea valley (12). There were no reports at all for the years 1958, 1963, 1964, 1966, 1968, 1974 or 1975. The majority of these records are for the months of September and October (18), and the period November to February (13), with nine records for April and May. One was present at Tring Reservoirs on 3 June 1965, another at Stockers Lake on 8 August 1969. The only other records for the Colne valley are of single birds at Hamper Mill on 17 May 1967, Troy Mill GP on 18–19 February 1972, and at Stockers Lake on 15 October 1977.

Only three of the 47 records refer to more than two birds at any one time. These are three at Tring Reservoirs on 14 May 1972, up to three there between 8 and 24 September 1979, and four at Hilfield Park Reservoir on 10 August 1982.

Fulmar

Fulmarus glacialis

A very rare vagrant.

There are three records; the first for the county was one seen at the Meads rubbish tip, Bishops Stortford, by A. Darlington, D. E. Pressland and A. S. Murray on 30 October 1956. Details of this record were not received until 1960 so it was not included in Sage (1959), but was published in Sage (1962). One was seen at Wilstone Reservoir on 19 September 1959, and was picked up moribund on the 20th and taken to Tring Museum where it was found to be a female. The only subsequent record is that of one seen at Bushey on the unusual date of 16 June 1974.

Manx Shearwater

Puffinus puffinus

A very rare vagrant whose status has remained unchanged since Sage (1959), who listed four records:

    1887 One caught at St. Albans on 30 August.
    1924 A male bird picked up in Tring on 12 September.
    1929 One caught alive at Ardeley on 4 July.
    1930 One found dead at Royston on 22 September

There are eight further records of this species. On the night of 4–5 September 1967, a intense depression moved rapidly from Ireland to southern Scotland and finally centred on the Shetland Isles. The resultant strong circulation round this depression caused gales and storm-force winds in many places, and as a result many shearwaters were blown inland, two appearing in Hertfordshire. These and the other six are as follows:

    1967 One found alive in Welwyn Garden City on 8 September, another
          found on Brookmans Park golf course on 10 September had been
          dead for about three days.
    1974 One was found alive in Stevenage on 12 September and later
          released in Wales.
    1977 A similar event to that of 1974 when another was found in
          Stevenage on 22 July and released on the Welsh coast the
          following day.
    1978 One was picked up alive at Bengeo, Hertford.
    1980 The latest records are of single birds found at Baldock on 12
          September, at Shephall, Stevenage, on 20 September, and near
          Bishops Stortford also in September (date unknown).

Storm Petrel

Hydrobates pelagicus

A very rare vagrant. Its status has remained unchanged since Sage (1959) who listed four records as follows:

  1876 One caught near Royston about November.
  1881 A male and female picked up near East Lodge, Hemel Hempstead, on 15 December.
  1886 One caught near St. Albans on 11 December.
  1907 One found dead at Whitwell.

There are two subsequent records:

  1963 One was seen at Tring Reservoirs on 18 November.
  1980 Another found near Cottered in April (date unknown) survived for two days.

Leach's Petrel

Oceanodroma leucorhoa

A very rare vagrant.

The status of this species has remained unchanged since Sage (1959) who gave seven records. These were:

  1823 One killed in December.
  1896 One shot at Croxley Green on 26 September.
  1905 One found dead in Cassiobury Park, Watford, in late November.
  1931 A bird found at Poynders End, Hitchin, on 12 November.
  1952 In the 'wreck' of this species in 1952, three appeared in the county — one at Hemel Hempstead on 30 October, one at Royston on 31 October, and another at Bishops Stortford on 1 November.

Following the 1952 'wreck' just mentioned, the species was not recorded in the county again until 1963, since when there have been a further seven records as follows:

  1963 At 1515 hours on 21 September, one flew low over the lagoons at Rye Meads heading north.
  1964 One was seen being chased by gulls at Tring Reservoirs on 22 November.
  1969 On 19 October, one was picked up in Stevenage.
  1977 One was at Hilfield Park Reservoir on 8 May, and another at Tring Reservoirs on 15 November.

1978 One, found on 14 December at Stevenage, subsequently died.
1982 The latest record concerns one at Stanstead Abbots GP on 3 October.

Gannet

Sula bassana

A rare vagrant whose status has remained unchanged since Sage (1959), who listed five records.

The earlier records comprise:

1875 One found near Baldock in late November.
1884 One caught at Cromer Hyde, near Sandridge, in August.
1885 A bird picked up near Brocket Park on 29 September.
c.1890 One found alive at Weston, near Stevenage.
1937 An adult shot at Barnet in March.

There have been 11 subsequent records:

1960 An immature landed at Barkway on 14 September, where it was captured, fed on whiting and released at Dover the following day.
1967 One found dead at Lemsford on 11 May, and another picked up alive at Royston on 13 October.
1970 One seen at Broxbourne GPs on 12 September.
1971 A bird was found at Childwickbury, near St. Albans, on 4 October and released on the lake at Verulamium where it remained for about a week.
1972 An adult flew over Foxholes, near Hertford, on 28 May.
1974 One was seen at Stevenage on 6 April.
1976 One found in Buckinghamshire was released at Tring Reservoirs on 4 December.
1980 One seen flying west over Codicote on 12 October.
1981 On 27 April, one flew over the B1000 near the Panshanger, and one released at Rye Meads on 29 April had earlier been found at Roydon GP in Essex.
1982 The latest record was one flying over Hadham Hall, Little Hadham, on 26 September.

Cormorant

Phalacrocorax carbo

A common non-breeding visitor which may be seen in any month of the year, but primarily in winter, and during the spring and autumn migration periods.

This species was classed by Sage (1959) as a fairly regular passage migrant and occasional winter visitor.

The status of this species has changed markedly during the period covered by this book with over 600 records. For the 14-year period from 1958–71 inclusive there were at least 76 records, while for the 11 years from 1972–82 there were at least 528 records, an increase of 595 per cent. Analysis of these records by month of occurrence clearly indicates the changes that occurred between the two periods (*see* Table 6.3).

TABLE 6.3   *Analysis of Cormorant records by month of occurrence 1958–82*

	1958–71	*1972–82*		*1958–71*	*1972–82*
January	1	55	July	3	5
February	2	40	August	3	20
March	6	50	September	8	44
April	9	66	October	14	64
May	13	45	November	8	72
June	2	3	December	7	64

From Table 6.3 it can be seen that winter records (November–February) account for just over 40 per cent of the total number of records, spring records (March–May) for 31 per cent, and autumn records (September–October) for 22 per cent.

The change in the actual numbers occurring in the county has been dramatic. At Rye Meads, for example, prior to the provision of tern nesting rafts in 1972 there had been only four records of single birds. From 1958–72 the maximum number recorded at any one time anywhere in the county was 20 at Tring Reservoirs on 18 May 1968. Between 1973 and 1982 the highest counts at these reservoirs was 15–20 on 23 February 1975.

From 1973 to 1982 the Colne and Lea valleys have been the main centres for this species. In the former case there is an island roost at Broadwater GP in Middlesex, from which birds range northwards up the valley. The highest counts for Stockers Lake are 40 on 15 January 1978; in 1980, 20 on 24 February, 24 on 30 March, and 15 on 26 December; in 1981, 20 on 11 January, 16 in February, 14 in March, 23 in November, and 40 in December; and in 1982, up to 20 from January–April, 15 in November, and 13 in December. Maximum counts for Maple Cross are 35 on 15 January 1978; 17 on 21 February and 15 on 17 October 1981; 20 on 7 March and 14 November 1982. In 1980 there were 25 at Troy Mill GP on 6 January.

Numbers appearing in the Lea valley are considerably higher, many originating from the roost at Walthamstow Reservoir in Essex, and others from another roost at Holyfield Marsh GP on the Hertfordshire/Essex

TABLE 6.4   *Maximum counts of Cormorants at Rye Meads 1974–82*

	Jan.	Feb.	Mar.	Oct.	Nov.	Dec.
1974	21	38	25	26	41	50
1975	52	38	30	5	30	20
1976	33	43	46	42	22	40
1977	40	36	17	20	29	38
1978	24	18	18	3	nc	11
1979	40	6	14	6	5	9
1980	9	12	5	13	25	14
1981	16	15	11	11	11	5
1982	11	9	9	12	12	14

nc = No count available

border. The maximum numbers recorded at Rye Meads are shown in Table 6.4 in so far as data are available.

In the case of Broxbourne GPs the highest counts have been 26 on 17 March 1974, and 18 on 23 December 1976. Similar data for Cheshunt GPs are 14 on 16 February, 13 on 5 April, and 33 on 13 December 1975; 20 on 17 October 1976; 30 on 6 January 1979; 13 on 11 January, 17 on 14 March, 14 on 12 October, and 20 on 31 December 1980; 35 on 18 January, 23 on 17 October, and 26 in November and December 1981; in 1982, 25 on 6 February, 33 on 14 March, 22 on 14 November, and 26 on 11 December. On 27 July 1981 a flock of 42 were seen flying north over Stanstead Abbots GP.

Shag

Phalacrocorax aristotelis

An occasional winter visitor and passage migrant.

It was classed by Sage (1959) as a rare winter visitor and passage migrant; 18 records were listed. An additional record, given in Sage (1962), is that of one ringed on the Farne Islands on 11 June 1957 and recovered at Bishops Stortford on 21 December the same year, a movement of 270 miles SSE.

There are some 66 records for the period 1958–82, but 14 of these refer to the 'wreck' of March 1962. In normal years the majority of records fall within the period September to March.

The 'wreck' in the second week of March 1962 occurred when the weather was very cold with strong NE. winds and most of the records involved immature birds. The numbers involved (about 51 individuals) were unprecedented in the Hertfordshire context. In the Lea valley one was seen on the river at Ware on 10 March, and from 12–18 March up to two were seen at Hertford, Cheshunt and Broxbourne. There were seven on the River Beane between Hertford and Waterford on 13 March. In the Colne valley there were two at Old Parkbury GP on 18 March. At Wilstone Reservoir,

Tring, a flock of 28 immatures was present on 11 March, and at Hilfield Park Reservoir up to two were present from 12–18 March. Other March records included single birds at Hitchin, Codicote, Redbourn, Kings Langley, and the Panshanger estate, and two at Smallford GP near St. Albans on the 18th. Later records, probably related to the March influx, were — one at Hilfield Park Reservoir on 22 and two on 28 April, and one at Troy Mill GP on 5 May.

Most records for the other years under review involve less than five birds at any one time, and the great majority are from Tring Reservoirs, and the Colne and Lea valleys. Unusual numbers were up to 15 at Tring Reservoirs from 15 January to 15 February 1974, and up to 15 at Hilfield Park Reservoir from 29 November to 14 December the same year.

Bittern

Botaurus stellaris

An occasional but now fairly regular visitor. It has been recorded annually since 1966.

In Sage (1959) it was classed as probably a regular winter visitor. The only definitive record of breeding was at Tring Reservoirs in 1849. However, James and Sawford (1979) give details of a suspected case of breeding in osier beds at Bayfordbury Park Farm between 1890 and 1894. There are three additional early records of this species not given in Sage (1959) — one was shot near Bayfordbury in February 1889 by W. R. Baker (manuscript note in the 1888 edition of the *Fauna and Flora of Haileybury,* in the Sage library); one seen at Broxbourne Mill on 26 December 1906, and another in osier beds at Roxford (i.e. Bayfordbury) in January 1907 (manuscript note in the 1902 edition of the above publication in the Sage library).

During the 25-year period under review here there were approximately 100 records. Due to the difficulty, on occasion, of knowing how many individual birds are concerned in records from areas such as Rye Meads and the nearby gravel pits, greater precision is not possible. Although there are records for all months of the year, the great majority fall within the period December to February, but odd individuals often remain in an area until March or April. There is great disparity in the geographical distribution of these records within the county. There is only one for the Colne valley, 15 or so for Tring Reservoirs, but about 66 from the Lea valley gravel pits and Rye Meads. In all cases most records refer to single birds, but there have been some exceptions. In 1969 there were up to three at Rye Meads from early January until 28 March, and on 8 November there were at least four in an adjacent field. Two, probably the same birds in each case, were seen in 1978 at Stanstead Abbots GP on 13 August, at Rye Meads on 14 August, and at Rye House on 15 August. In 1979 there were up to four in the Rye Meads–Stanstead Abbots GP area from early January until 31 March, and two at Cheshunt GPs during February. There were also two at the latter locality on

17 December 1981. In 1982 up to three were present at Cheshunt GPs during January, with up to two throughout February. In 1973 and 1974 single birds were present at Rye Meads throughout the summer.

The only records away from Tring Reservoirs and the Lea valley were — Cassiobury Park, one from 19–22 January 1963, later found dead; one, first noticed on 30 October 1967 was still present early in 1968, and one on 16 February 1979; Bushey, one picked up after a storm on 19 December 1971; Water End (River Gade), one present from mid-February until 19th of the month in 1976; Ashwell, one flying SW. on 3 December 1976; Aldbury, one on 29 December 1981; Stockers Lake, one on 30 December 1981 was probably the same bird seen there on 8 January and 9 February 1982.

Little Bittern

Ixobrychus minutus

A very rare vagrant.

This is the same status accorded it by Sage (1959) who listed four records as follows:

> 1840   One obtained at Aldenham Reservoir.
> 1884   A female was shot at Broxbourne on 13 October.
> 1890   Another shot at Oughtonhead Common, near Hitchin.

The statement that one was shot near Broxbourne Station in 1898 must be incorrect, since in the 1888 edition of the *Fauna and Flora of Haileybury* it states 'One shot the other side of Broxbourne railway station a few autumns ago'. Research has failed to find any evidence that there were two different records from that location.

There are three further records, all referring to males:

> 1965   One seen at a pond by the River Beane at Walkern on 10 June, (*British Birds* 59:285, 1966).
> 1968   One at Wilstone Reservoir, Tring, on 17 August (ibid. 62:463, 1969).
> 1979   The latest record is one by the river at Oughtonhead Common, Hitchin, on 9 June (ibid. 73:493, 1980).

Night Heron

Nycticorax nycticorax

A very rare vagrant.

In Sage (1959) the only record was of a known escape from captivity seen at Watford in April 1936. In James and Sawford (1979) mention is made of a pre-1878 specimen from Royston that was sold to a collector. Since there is no further supporting data this simply cannot be claimed as the first county record.

There are now three definitive records:

    1970   An adult was present at Stockers Lake on 6 September (*British Birds* 64:345, 1971).

    1971   At Lemsford Springs NR, near Welwyn, an immature bird was present from 28 November until (19 February 1972) (ibid. 65:326, 1972 and 66:335, 1973).

    1972   At Archers Green in the Mimram valley another immature was seen on 3, 5 and 19 January.

Squacco Heron

Ardeola ralloides

A very rare vagrant.

The first record for the county was one at Rye Meads which was watched for two hours on 1 July 1979 (*British Birds* 73:494, 1980).

Little Egret

Egretta garzetta

A very rare vagrant.

The first county record, given in Sage (1959), was one at Old Parkbury GP from 1–3 July 1956.

The only subsequent record is that of one seen by the River Mimram at Poplars Green, Tewin, on 8 June 1979 (*British Birds* 73:495, 1980).

Grey Heron

Ardea cinerea

MAP 3 A resident breeding species, and non-breeding visitor.

Classed as a scarce resident breeding species by Sage (1959), the numbers nesting have increased in recent years. An additional record, given in Sage (1962), is that of a pair that bred by the River Beane at Waterford in 1955, but the site was not used the following year.

The heronry at Tring Reservoirs had its beginnings in 1957 when two pairs bred at Marsworth Reservoir, followed by three pairs in 1958. From 1959–62 inclusive, four or five pairs bred annually. Following the hard winter of 1962/63, none bred in 1963, only one pair in 1964, and two pairs in 1965. By 1966 there were eight nests (possibly only five or six occupied), and in 1967 a total of 21–25 young were reared by 9–12 pairs. In 1968 the number of nesting pairs had risen to 14 but only 18 young were reared. Twelve pairs bred in 1969. The subsequent history of this heronry, for those years for which data are available, is shown in Table 6.5. The Tring Reservoirs heronry is one of the very few in the country where the nests are primarily in reed beds.

TABLE 6.5   *Number of pairs of Grey Herons at Tring Reservoirs from 1970–82*

Year	No. of pairs	Year	No. of pairs
1970	10	1976	11
1971	8	1977	5
1972	11	1978	9
1973	12	1980	8–10
1974	13*	1981	6– 7
1975	14	1982	7

*Three pairs failed

In 1950 a heronry, size and age unknown, was reported in Brocket Park (Sage 1959). There was no further evidence of nesting at this site until 1972 when three pairs bred. There were four nests from 1973–75, three nests in 1976 and 1977, one in 1980, two in 1981 and three in 1982.

In the Panshanger estate in the Mimram valley, breeding had been suspected in the early 1960s but no nests were actually located, although a pair with two juveniles were seen on 22 June 1965. Finally, in 1972, three nests were found, and in 1973 there were no less than 10 nests. The subsequent history of this heronry has been — 1974 seven nests, 1975 10 nests, 1976–80 no reports received, 1981 five nests, 1982 no count made but at least one pair bred.

The only other regular breeding site is at Stockers Lake in the Colne valley, where the first evidence was in 1977 when a pair reared three young. There were three nests there in 1978, five in 1979 (but only two or three young reared), and three nests in 1980, 1981 and 1982.

On 21 April 1960 two nests, one empty and the other containing three young, were found in Whippendell Woods near Watford. Between 1967 and 1973 one or two pairs were reported nesting at Batchwood (near St. Albans), Knebworth Park, and at Goldings near Waterford. The latter was close to the site used in 1955 that was mentioned above. Other isolated breeding records were a pair by the River Ver at Gorhambury in1971, a pair at Waltham Cross in 1976, and four pairs at Cheshunt GPs in 1979.

Variable numbers of herons occur at numerous localities throughout the county outside the breeding season. The maximum counts at Tring Reservoirs were 43 on 27 September 1959, 30 on 1 August 1964, 28 on 20 August 1965, 30+ on 30 August 1967, 25 on 29 August 1971, 20 on 28 July 1976, 17 on 22 August 1977, 16 in March 1979 and 13 in January 1981. The highest count at Hilfield Park Reservoir was 12 on 23 November 1963. In the Colne valley there were 18 at Hamper Mill on 20 October 1961 an 15 on 27 September 1971. At the Rickmansworth GPs the maxima were 16 in 1972, 1974 and 1979 (all in the period January to May), 13 in January 1981, and at Stockers Lake 14 on 11 January and 20 on 20 February 1982. Selective maximum counts at Rye Meads are: 40 on 13 October 1968, 26 in September 1971, 24 on 9 January 1977, 20+ on 12–13 January 1978, but only 11–12 in 1980 and 1981. Three counts from other localities that deserve mention are — Tewinbury, 12 on 4 September 1980; Ickleford, 14 on 13 February and 15 March 1982; and 14 in the Panshanger on 20 January 1982.

Purple Heron

Ardea purpurea

A very rare vagrant.

The status of this species has remained unchanged since (Sage) 1959 who listed one record — an immature bird shot at some watercress beds at Castle Farm, near Harpenden, in November 1902.

There are six additional records listed below:

1958   An immature first noted at Wilstone Reservoir on 30 July, remained until 11 August (*British Birds* 53:158, 1960).

1967   Another immature bird frequented the sewage field by Marsworth Reservoir from at least 3 August to 8 September (ibid. 61:333, 1968).

1972   An adult was seen at Tring Reservoirs on 7 May, and another at Rye Meads from 2 September to 3 October (ibid. 66:334, 1973 and 67:342, 1974).

1973   One was present at a lake in Nyn Park, Northaw, on 11 and 14 August (*Trans. Herts. Nat. Hist. Soc.* 27:2, 1974).

1978   The latest record is of a juvenile at Little Tring Reservoir on 30 August (*British Birds* 72:510, 1979).

[White Stork]

Ciconia ciconia

A rare vagrant, but since none of the records can unequivocally be accepted as referring to wild birds, the species must remain in square brackets.

The only record given by Sage (1959) — one shot at Hatfield, about the end of July 1883 — was undoubtedly an escaped bird. An additional early record subsequently came to light concerning three shot near Hertford in July 1891 (Sage 1962).

In 1960 one was reported from Broxbourne, Cheshunt and Wormley, between 6–26 December, and on 15 January 1961 (*British Birds* 54:180, 1961). The latest record concerns one flying SSW. over Marden Hill in the Mimram valley on 9 July 1978 (*Trans. Herts. Nat. Hist. Soc.* 28:38, 1980).

Glossy Ibis

Plegadis falcinellus

A very rare vagrant. The three occurrences listed by Sage (1959) remain the only records — one killed at Tring Reservoirs in 1826, another at Hertford in 1881, and the last near Waterford in 1887.

Spoonbill

Platalea leucorodia

A very rare vagrant.

Only two records were listed by Sage (1959), these being single birds at Tring Reservoirs on 9 May 1947, and on 27 October 1957.

The only subsequent record is of two which flew over Wilstone Reservoir on 5 June 1982.

Wildfowl

Regular wildfowl counts for the months September–March inclusive have been carried out for many years at all the important wildfowl wintering sites in the county, as part of the National Wildfowl Counts organised by the Wildfowl Trust. With the exception of Canada Geese in the Colne valley below Rickmansworth, it is various species of duck that are an important feature of the winter wildfowl population of the county. One species, the Wigeon, now winters in significant numbers only at Tring Reservoirs and the population statistics over a period of 25 years are shown in Appendix A. There was formerly a regular wintering flock at Hilfield Park Reservoir (*see* Appendix B), but this ceased after the winter of 1977/78 for reasons that are not clear. In the case of the Teal, the four most important localities are Hilfield Park and Tring Reservoirs, Broxbourne GP, and Rye Meads; the maximum numbers at these sites in January and November of the years 1973–82 are shown in Figure 6.1.

The remaining important wintering species — Mallard, Shoveler, Pochard, and Tufted Duck — occur in significant numbers at nine main localities (only six in the case of the Shoveler); the numbers involved are shown in Figures 6.2, 6.3, 6.4, 6.5 respectively. It should be pointed out that for the purpose of analysis 'winter' has been taken as the period November–February inclusive.

The National Wildfowl Counts are carried out on the Sunday nearest the 15th of each month and thus record only the numbers present on that day, although higher numbers may be present on one or more other dates in the month. For the purposes of this book we have been concerned with the *maximum* numbers of the various species. Therefore, the histograms for each species have been based on the maximum numbers recorded in any one month and not just those present on the day of the official wildfowl count. The winter population of each species is taken as the mean of the counts over the four month period (November–February). In practice the majority of the figures used have been those obtained on the official wildfowl count date since the number of additional counts available has been limited, the main exceptions being Hilfield Park Reservoir and the Rickmansworth GPs. In the latter case not all the pits have always been covered on the official wildfowl count date.

Mute Swan

Cygnus olor

MAP 4   A widespread resident breeding species which has declined in numbers since the late 1950s and early 1960s.

In Sage (1959) it was classed as a common resident and non-breeding visitor at all seasons.

This swan nests by most water bodies of suitable size, including many in urban areas, as well as at flooded gravel pits, and the banks of rivers and canals. The breeding population has undoubtedly declined since the mid-1950s to the mid-1960s. In 1961 a survey was carried out in April and May to ascertain the number of breeding and non-breeding birds in the area covered by the London Natural History Society, that is to say within 20 miles (32 kilometres) of St. Paul's Cathedral. The results of this survey were discussed by Cramp (1963) who recorded a total of 31 nests, to which should be added a further nest at Northaw, bringing the total to 32. In terms of distribution, 13 of these nests were in the Lea valley (to which may be added a further three just outside the LNHS boundary), 11 in the Colne valley and eight at miscellaneous sites elsewhere. A similar survey of the same area in 1978 resulted in a total of 20 breeding pairs at 15 different sites (*London Bird Report*, 1978:13), a decrease of 12 pairs or 37 per cent.

Between these two surveys came the fieldwork from 1967–73 culminating in the publication of Mead and Smith (1982) wherein it is stated that the total number of different territories occupied during this seven-year period was about 120. The 1978 survey referred to above was in fact a national survey the results of which were discussed by Ogilvie (1981) who gives the total number of breeding adults in the county as 128 (i.e. 64 pairs). Even allowing for incomplete coverage, this suggests a considerable decrease since 1967–73, but not that much difference from the total of about 60 nests reported in 1956 (*see* Sage 1959). However, this is understandable since it is known on a national basis that the population continued to increase after 1956, and probably reached a peak in 1959. In all these surveys there were additional pairs holding territories but not breeding.

The number of non-breeding birds present in the county during the breeding season may be considerable. In 1961, for example, there were 84 on the River Lea between Hertford and Ware on 12 May. Previous counts on the same stretch of river gave totals of 66 in 1958, 62 in 1959, and 70 in 1960. The total number of non-breeding birds present in the LNHS area of Hertfordshire in April/May 1961 was 104–122, which included 40 on the

Year	Rickmansworth GPs	Rye Meads	Amwell GP	Tring Rsvrs.
1973	44 in November	29 in Oct./Nov. 33 in December	—	—
1974	39 in December	30 in January 34 in February 25 in October 35 in November	—	45 in October
1975	65 In Nov./Dec.[a]	—	—	21 in November
1976	Maple Cross 70 on 18 January Troy Mill 63 on 31 January and 72 in February	—	—	37 in September 23 in Oct./Nov. 24 in December
1977	14 in January	144 in November	—	31 in January
1978	19 in January 15 in October	30 in January 32 in February 47 in December	11 in January 13 in December	27 in September 26 in November 15 in December
1979	43 in October[b] 47 in November[b] 63 in December[c]	50 in January 28 in September 30 in November	29 in March 24 in April 58 in December	32 in July/Aug.
1980	80 in January[c]	16 in February 33 in November	102 in February 54 in December	26 in Aug./Sept.
1981	17 in January 50 in December[a]	111 in November	51 in January 42 in February	35 in July/Aug. 38 in September
1982	53 in January[a] 53 in February 43 in September 32 in October	13 in November	55 in January 58 in February 43 in March 41 in November 52 in December	19 in Sept./Oct. 17 in November

NOTES: (a) Troy Mill GP only
(b) Stockers Lake only
(c) Bury Lake only

Lea between Hertford and Ware. According to Ogilvie (op. cit.) there were about 121 non-breeding birds in the county in 1978, compared to about 134 in 1956. The large non-breeding herds formerly seen on the Lea at Hertford and Ware are now a thing of the past. Further down the Lea valley some losses are known to have been caused by lead poisoning.

Maximum winter counts for the 10 years 1973–82 are summarised in Table 6.6, from which it can be seen that quite high numbers occur in the Colne and Lea valleys, but rather fewer at Tring Reservoirs.

Bewick's Swan

Cygnus columbianus

An occasional winter visitor which has occurred annually since 1967.

It was classed by Sage (1959) as a rare winter visitor, with less than 20 records listed.

There are about 76 records for the period dealt with in this book and all fall within the period October to March inclusive, but with the majority (about 49) in November and December. About half the records come from Tring Reservoirs where the maximum counts have been — 16 on 26–27 December 1962, 13 from 27–29 December 1965, 11 on 5 March 1968, 13 on 16 January 1972, 14 on 26 November 1975, and 28 on 1 January 1979. The eight records for Hilfield Park Reservoir comprise two on 2 March 1958, one on 7 November 1964, five on 5 December 1970, five on 1 December 1973, six on 21 December 1975, two on 1 January 1976, three on 29 November 1978, and two from 1–6 December 1980. The Colne valley records are of three at Troy Mill GP on 24 February and four on 21 December 1963; a flock of 15 at Stockers Lake on 31 December 1964, and one there from 3–6 November 1979; two other records are discussed below. In the east of the county Rye Meads accounts for seven records, with the maximum counts being 18 on 26 December 1961, and 10 on 1–2 January 1971. Other Lea valley counts of note are 11 at Stanstead Abbots GP on 9 December 1978, and 13 at Broxbourne GPs on 27 December 1980. The highest counts of all for the period reviewed here were a flock of 42 flying ENE. over Bramfield Forest on 30 March 1964, and a flock of 35 flying north over Spellbrook, near Bishops Stortford, on 1 January 1979.

In 1981 a spell of cold weather in mid-December resulted in the following records — seven at Troy Mill GP on 12 and eight on 13 December, 14 flying west over Pitstone on 12th, one at Ickleford SF on 12th, 14 flying west over Rabley Heath on 12th, two at Stanstead Abbots GP on 18th, and three at Tring Reservoirs on 31 December.

Whooper Swan

Cygnus cygnus

An occasional winter visitor and possibly also a passage migrant.

This represents a change of status since Sage (1959) who classed it as a rare winter visitor, and listed about a dozen records. Two additional earlier records are given in Sage (1962), these being one at Hertford on 6 March 1955, and four on the River Mimram in the Panshanger on 4 March 1956.

There are a total of 26 records for 10 of the 25 years reviewed here. These fall within the period 30 October to 24 March, but the majority are in December (10), January (5) and March (7). Fourteen of these records are from localities in the Lea valley, six from Tring Reservoirs, and only two from the Colne valley. The records are mostly of less than five birds at any one time, but numbers in excess of this were 12 flying NE. over Marsworth Reservoir on 15 March, and 14 at Ware on 17 March 1960; eight at Cheshunt GPs on 23 March 1963; a flock of 48 (almost certainly this species rather than Bewick's Swans) at Hilfield Park Reservoir on 30 October 1974. This latter record represents the largest flock ever seen in Hertfordshire. A flock of 11 flying north over Stanstead Abbots GP on 19th December 1981 were considered to be of this species.

The two Colne valley records are from Stockers Lake where there were two on 25 December, and four flying west on 27 December 1970.

Bean Goose

Anser fabalis

A very rare winter visitor.

The two records in Sage (1959) were placed in square brackets since it was uncertain whether or not they referred to wild birds. These records were a flock of 15 said to have been seen near Royston on 15 January 1881, and one shot in Munden Park, near Watford, during the winter of 1890/91.

The two seen at Maple Cross in the Colne valley on 16 February 1979 (*London Bird Report* 44:19; *Trans. Herts. Nat. Hist. Soc.* 28 Pt 5:4) thus constitute the first county record. They are considered to have been wild birds since small parties of this species were noted along the east and south coasts at this time, together with flocks of Pink-footed and Barnacle Geese moving in from colder wintering areas on the continent. One seen at Hooks Marsh, Cheshunt, at intervals between 31 March and 2 May 1981 was considered to be an escape from captivity.

Pink-footed Goose

Anser brachyrhynchus

A rare winter visitor and passage migrant.

Seven records were listed by Sage (1959) who classed it as a rare visitor. Five were seen at Radwell Mill during the winter of 1912/13. At Tring

Reservoirs one was seen on 16 January 1926, two from 13 October to the end of December 1928 (considered to be escapes), and two from January–March 1929 were also taken to be escaped birds. A flock of nine passed over Moor Mill, Radlett, on 5 November 1950, and a flock of 11 were seen there on 14 January 1953. Four flew SW. over St. Albans on 11 November 1954.

There are a total of 25 subsequent records for nine different years, one or two of which again, probably refer to escapes from captivity. A few of the observations refer to birds flying northwards in the spring. For example, four over Rye Meads on 11 May 1960, and two over Cheshunt GPs on 21 April 1965. Nine of the records are from Lea valley localities, six from Tring Reservoirs, three from the Colne valley, two from Woodhall Park, and one from the Panshanger. The majority of records involve from one to four birds; the highest numbers recorded were 22 flying NNW. over Panshanger airfield on 13 February 1966, and 73 flying north over Tring SF on 28 January 1979.

White-fronted Goose

Anser albifrons

A scarce winter visitor and passage migrant.

This goose was classed as a rare winter visitor by Sage (1959) who listed eight records considered to apply to wild birds. The acceptable records comprised a skein (number unknown) at Wilstone Reservoir on 1 February 1924; two there on 19 January 1928; a flock of 40 flying over Tring on 24 January 1929; three flying NW. over Tring Reservoirs on 16 February 1934; single birds over Tring on 21 March and 1 April 1942; a flock of about 50 flying NE. over Tring Reservoirs on 18 January 1953; and a party of eight at Wilstone Reservoir from 12–14, and one until 17 December 1953.

Excluding 13 occurrences attributed to escapes from captivity, there were 36 records during the period 1958–82, but none for the years 1959, 1960, 1966, 1967, and 1971–74. The records fall within the months October to April, with one September and one May record, and often refer to flocks flying over. The maximum numbers for this period are — about 50 flying eastwards over Tring Reservoirs on 12 March 1963; 20 and later 10 flying NW. over Tring on 29 December 1968; 42 flying over Old Parkbury GP on 5 January, and 25 over Watford on 20 December 1969; 35 flying SE. over Hamper Mill GP on 25 January 1970; 20 flying north over West Hyde GP on 24 December 1976; 60 feeding in a field at Ayot St. Lawrence on 26 January, and 50 flying NE. over Cheshunt GPs on 28 January 1979; 48 flying south over Stanstead Abbots GP on 22 October, and about 20 circling in fog over Ashwell on 24 January 1982.

Grey Lag Goose

Anser anser

Status not easy to define due to the establishment of a resident feral **MAP 5**
population during the period under review, but probably also a rare winter
visitor and passage migrant.

It was regarded by Sage (1959) as a rare visitor. He listed eight records of
which, in the light of present knowledge, five were of genuinely wild birds —
one shot at Tring Reservoirs in September 1886; one shot from a skein at
Hitchin on 29 December 1923; one at Tring Reservoirs on 13 October 1942;
one at Radwell on 4 April 1948; an immature at Ickleford Common in the
autumn of 1952, and one at Hilfield Park Reservoir on 26 February 1956.
   The breeding population within the county owes its origin to birds released
during the last 20 years or so. Breeding occurred first at Tring Reservoirs
where a party of five arrived in mid-April 1963 and remained for several
months, during which time one pair reared three young. The subsequent
history was — 1964 one pair, 1965 one pair, 1966 three or four pairs, 1967 one
pair, 1968 three pairs, 1969 one pair, 1970 two pairs, 1971 one pair, 1972 the
number of pairs was not recorded but 10 young were reared, in 1974 and 1975
single pairs bred, but none in subsequent years.
   In 1969 a pair bred at Stanstead Abbots GP, and this remains the only
breeding record for the east of the county.
   The feral breeding population is currently centred in the Colne valley
below Rickmansworth where, in 1973, single pairs bred at West Hyde GP,
Pynesfield GP and Royal Oak GP. There were no further records until 1976
when single pairs nested at Stockers Lake and Royal Oak GP. Thereafter
breeding occurred at Stockers Lake in 1977 (two pairs), 1978 and 1979 (one
pair), 1980 (two pairs), and in 1981 (one pair). In 1982 two pairs bred at
Stockers Lake, another two pairs at Maple Cross, and one pair at Bury Lake.
   In 1979 the species made its first appearance in Brocket Park when five
were present in March and April. A flock was present regularly in 1980
reaching a maximum of 13 in September and October. A feral flock is now
resident and in 1981 and 1982 were interbreeding with domestic geese.
   From 1961 to 1973 maximum numbers at Tring Reservoirs varied from
eight to 20, some being present during most months of the year. Slightly
higher maxima 24–43 were recorded from 1974 to 1978, but in recent years
numbers have declined with maxima of 24 in 1979, 16 in 1980, 24 in 1981,
and only one in 1982. They are now present in the Colne valley throughout
the year and quite high numbers are recorded at certain times, as for
example 34 on 26 October 1977; 31 at West Hyde GP on 14 January and 25 at
Maple Cross SF on 3 December 1978; 29 at West Hyde GP on 7 January, 65
at Maple Cross on 16 February and 55 there on 26 December 1979; in 1980
up to 38 below Rickmansworth; in 1981 about 35 from January–April, 40 on
25 June, 35 from August–December; in 1982 the maximum counts were 44
at Stockers Lake on 13 September, 40 at Maple Cross in February, June and
October, 39 flying over Pynesfield GP on 27 October, and 44 at Batchworth
Lake on 13 November.
   Two other records of interest were 150 flying over Letchworth on 29

61

January 1967 (the highest number ever seen in the county), and 43 flying over Amwell GP on 30 September 1980.

$\left[\begin{array}{l}\text{Snow Goose} \\ \textit{Anser caerulescens}\end{array}\right]$

There are about 13 occurrences of this species in the county in addition to the one given in Sage (1959); they are given here as a matter of record although all must remain in the category of possible escapes from captivity.

At Cheshunt GPs in 1974, what was known to be an escaped bird paired with a Grey Lag Goose and produced a juvenile. One was present at Waverley GP, Cheshunt, from 12 January to 16 February, and what may have been another individual was seen on 16 March 1975. In the Colne valley one was seen at Stockers Lake in April 1978. In 1979 there was one at Tring SF on 26 April, three at Stevenage during April, and one at Ickleford Common on 19 August. There were even more records in 1980 with one flying north over Cheshunt GPs on 1 March, two at Holyfield Marsh (mostly in Essex) at Cheshunt from 2 March until April, one at Stevenage between 5 and 9 March, and three at Stanborough Lakes from 3–16 March. Six flew north over Rye House on 12 April, and what were probably the same group were seen at Amwell GP on 14 April 1981. In 1982 one was present at Stanstead Abbots GP from April to October, and it was no doubt this bird that was seen at Rye Meads on 23 May.

In connection with the 1980 records, it is of interest to note that a flock of 18 wild Snow Geese, including one that had been ringed in Canada, occurred in Holland in April of that year.

Canada Goose

Branta canadensis

MAP 6 A resident breeding species well established in several areas.

There has been a considerable change in the status of this species since Sage (1959) classed it as a rare visitor, and listed 21 records.

The present breeding population in the county has probably originated from two sources, the first being the natural spread of the species into Hertfordshire from elsewhere, and the second local releases. The first breeding attempt was at Pynesfield GP in the Colne valley in 1965, but the eggs were taken. The second, this time successful attempt, was a pair at Stockers Lake in 1969. The first record of breeding at Tring Reservoirs was a pair in 1970. The species began to spread in 1974 and by 1982 some 44 pairs were nesting in about a dozen localities. The history of breeding in seven areas is shown in Table 6.7. Breeding records not included in the Table are — a pair in Woodhall Park in 1978; single pairs at Aldenham Reservoir, Drop Lane GP (Colney Street), and St. Pauls Walden in 1980; in 1981 two pairs at Drop Lane GP, and single pairs at Holwell GP (near Hitchin), Ickleford and Pirton; in 1982 three pairs probably bred at Codicote, single pairs at

TABLE 6.7   *Number of pairs of Canada Geese breeding at seven localities, 1970–82*

	Tring Reservoirs	Rickmansworth GPs	Lea Valley	Brocket Park	Stanborough Lakes	Panshanger	Knebworth Park
1970	1						
1971	1	1					
1972	2	3					
1973		6	1				
1974	1-2	6		3		3	
1975	2	8			1		1
1976		5	3		2		
1977		12					
1978	2	7	2			6	1
1979		12+(a)	3	1	2		1
1980	1	13	4				
1981	5	22	5 (b)	1		1-2	
1982	1	19	5 (c)		7	2	

NOTES: (a) 10 young were also reared at Maple Cross
(b) A pair also bred on Hertford Meads
(c) Two pairs also bred at Lemsford Springs

Kimpton Mill and Kings Langley GP, two pairs at Park Street GP (St. Albans), and a pair in Woodhall Park.

It is only since 1970 that high numbers have been recorded in the county. During the twelve years from 1958–69 there were over 40 records from various localities, but nearly half were from the Colne valley. A previously unpublished record concerns 12 flying over Cuffley on 4 September 1961. The highest counts in 1970 were 13 at Hoddesdon on 16 April, 24 at Hilfield Park Reservoir on 13 September, and 24 in the Colne valley below Rickmansworth on the same date. At Tring Reservoirs from 1971–81 the maximum numbers occurred between September and February, varying from 18 to 57, but in 1982 there was a sudden increase with 154 on 21 September, and 90 in December.

At the Rickmansworth GPs, the headquarters of the species in Hertfordshire, numbers increased steadily with maxima of 35 in August 1971, 90 in October 1972, 80 in November 1973 and 140 in December 1974. In 1975 there were high counts: 130 in January, 225 in September, 280 in October, 157 in November, and 134 in December. The 1976 maximum was 225 in September, and in 1977 about 175 were present all summer. From 1978–82 the maximum counts varied from 300–450; from 1980 onwards about 100 have been consistently present all year. On 17 January 1982 at least 320 were present at West Hyde GP alone.

In the Lea valley there were single records from Rye Meads in November 1965 and December 1967, then none until 1970 when there were reports from three localities, including 13 at Hoddesdon on 26 April. In 1971 some were present at Rye Meads most months with maxima of 53 on 5 September and 48 on 2 October. The subsequent Rye Meads records of note were 60 on 22 October 1977, 90 on 21 October 1978 (and 60 at Rye House power station in September the same year), 100 in September 1979, 160 in August 1980, and 92 flying over on 5 September 1981. High counts from elsewhere in the Lea valley include 71 at Broxbourne GP on 16 December 1976, 200 at Stanstead Abbots GP on 10 October 1978; in 1979 there were 165 at the latter locality on 16 September, 148 at Broxbourne GP from 26–29 September, and 172 at Holyfield Marsh GP on 25 November; 300 at Mill End (Hatfield) in August, 240 at Stanstead Abbots GP on 31 August, and 230 at Broxbourne GP on 12 September 1980; 325 at Broxbourne GP on 29 August 1981; and 451 at Stanstead Abbots GP on 4 January 1982. Numbers in Brocket Park have increased in recent years, and on 5 January 1980 there were 82 present.

Elsewhere in the county it is seen regularly at a number of localities including Woodhall Park in the Beane valley where the highest count so far has been 80 on 19 September 1980. At Gilston Park there were 99 in March 1981 and 150 in March 1982.

[Barnacle Goose]

Branta leucopsis

A rare winter visitor and passage migrant, but it is probable that most of the records refer to birds escaped from captivity, so the species has been retained in square brackets. However, it should be borne in mind that some Siberian breeding birds now winter regularly in SE. England, from where they depart between March and May.

In Sage (1959) three records were listed — two at Aldenham Reservoir on 30 April 1941, one at Hamper Mill from 5 February to 26 March 1950, and one at Tring Reservoirs on 27 October 1957.

The 27 subsequent records are as follows: one at Hamper Mill on 18 October 1959; one at Stockers Lake on 5 and 31 March 1960; one at Rickmansworth GPs from July 1974 until April 1975; two in the same area on 23 February 1975; one at Maple Cross on 11 April, and up to three at Stockers Lake from 23 April to 5 May 1976; singles at Tring Reservoirs on 27 February, and at Stockers Lake on 7 and 21 April, and 29 May 1977; in 1978 there was one at West Hyde GP on 14 January, at Tring Reservoirs from 17–19 March and 15 October, at Frogmore GP, Radlett, on 9 April, two at Rye Meads on 8 July, two in Brocket Park on 18 October, and one at Stanborough Lakes on 23 November; there were singles at Tring Reservoirs on 25 February and on nine dates from 27 August to 13 October, and at Stockers Lake on 22 May 1979; a flock of seven landed at Hilfield Park Reservoir on

15 April, and at Stockers Lake two were seen on 29 April and one on 3 May 1980; the latest records are of singles at Stockers Lake from 24 March to 8 April and on 21 May, two at Maple Cross on 9 April, and two at Rye Meads on 31 August 1982.

Brent Goose

Branta bernicla

A very rare winter visitor and passage migrant.

Status has remained unchanged since Sage (1959) who listed four records as follows:

1905   One shot at Preston in December.
1910   One found dead near Tring Reservoirs on 10 March.
1941   A flock of seven at Wilstone Reservoir on 26 January.
1950   Over Hamper Mill on 23 December, a flock of five flying south.

There are eight records for the period under review, of which two almost certainly refer to escaped birds. The six acceptable records are:

1962   Two very wary birds at Hilfield Park Reservoir on 11 December.
1963   Two at Tring Reservoirs on 16 March.
1974   One seen at Hilfield Park Reservoir on 22 March.
1976   At Troy Mill GP on 18 April, a flock of 15 flying east.
1977   Six flying SW. over Kimpton on 6 February.
1978   Three flying NE. over Maple Cross on 7 March.

The two records assigned to escaped birds were one at Rye Meads on 21 September 1961, and one feeding with Canada Geese at Stockers Farm on 4 April 1980.

Egyptian Goose

Alopochen aegypticus

A very rare visitor.

In Appendix A to Sage (1959) a number of records of this species are listed, including a case of the successful breeding of a pair at Hamper Mill in 1938.
Prior to being added to the British List in 1970, there was a record of two flying south over Rye Meads on 20 August 1966. Subsequent records are as follows:

1974 One at Stockers Lake on 18 and 29 September.
1978 Two at Maple Cross SF on 10 and 17 December, and one at Woodhall Park also on 17 December.
1979 Up to five birds in the Lea valley from 14 March until the end of the year, and single birds at Rickmansworth GPs on 13 September and 14 October.
1981 A pair at Cheshunt GPs on 12 March.
1982 One flew SE. over Rye Meads on 6 February.

[Ruddy Shelduck]

Tadorna ferruginea

The species is retained in square brackets since all the recent records refer, without much doubt, to feral birds.

The only recent records refer to Tring Reservoirs where one was seen on 2 September 1967 (K. J. Hall and S. G. Banks, pers. com.), one on 23 July 1977, and two on 25 February 1979.

A recent study by Rogers (1982) concluded that no record of this species in Britain during the past 50 years can certainly be regarded as other than an escape from captivity.

Shelduck

Tadorna tadorna

A common winter visitor and passage migrant.

In Sage (1959) it was classed as a regular visitor at all seasons, but mainly in winter and early spring.

There were over 200 records during the period under review, and this excludes the period 25 April to 11 May 1978 at Tring Reservoirs, during which time some 38 different individuals were recorded. An analysis of 204 records by month of occurrence is given in Table 6.8. The data shows that about one third of the records fall within the winter period, and about 42 per cent during the spring migration.

Most records refer to between one and four birds, but numbers in excess of this are seven at Tring Reservoirs on 5 January 1966, five there on 10 January 1967, the same number again on 25 November 1970, five at Rye Meads on 29 January 1972, five at Tring Reservoirs in May 1976, a flock of 12 there on 1 May 1978 and, in 1979, nine on 3 May and six on 25 September.

66

TABLE 6.8 *Analysis of Shelduck records by month of occurrence 1958–82*

Jan.	Feb.	Mar.	Apr.	May	June
21	17	32	35	19	1
10.29%	8.33%	15.69%	17.16%	9.36%	0.49%
July	Aug.	Sep.	Oct.	Nov.	Dec.
4	24	12	9	8	22
1.96%	11.76%	5.88%	4.41%	3.92%	10.78%

In terms of distribution, Tring Reservoirs account for about 92 records (excluding those mentioned above), the Lea valley for 51, Hilfield Park Reservoir for 29, and the Colne valley for only 10. The remainder of the records are from miscellaneous localities. There are very few reports for the north of the county: these comprise Radwell Lake in 1967; Royston SF in 1969, 1975 and 1976; Walkern in 1974; Willian in 1975; Ickleford in 1979; and Holwell GP, Hitchin, in 1981.

Mandarin

Aix galericulata

A scarce visitor. There has been one attempt at breeding. **MAP 7**

Two records of this species were given in Appendix A to Sage (1959), these being one shot at Radwell Mill on 21 December 1916, and another near Royston in June 1941.

There are 44 records for the period covered by this book and all are quoted here in order that there may be a complete historical record. Three of these records pre-date the addition of the species to the official British List in 1970. These records were — an attempt at breeding by a pair at Harmer Green, near Welwyn, in 1961; a male near Mimms Wood on 11 April 1964, and a pair at Clay End, near Walkern, on 15 May 1966.

The remaining records comprise a male at Maple Cross on 21 June, and another at Hamper Mill on 15 September 1970. In 1971 there was a male at Maple Cross on 31 August, and what was probably the same bird on 1 and 3 September, and a female at Tring Reservoirs on 17 October. One at Hemel Hempstead from 2 October to 31 December 1973. Two males at Stevenage on 30 March, and an immature there on 20 July 1974. In 1975 there was one at Stevenage on 28 April, a male at Stanstead Abbots GP on 24–25 October, and two females at Rye House on 26 October. There was a spate of records in 1976 with a female at Stevenage on 1 March; a male at Stockers Lake on 26 May; at Tring Reservoirs there was a female from 8–9 August, a juvenile from 6 August until at least 3 September, a pair on 5 September, one on 12 September, and a female with a broken wing from 19 September until early December; a female was at Stanborough Lakes from 6–18 September; there were four at Rye Meads from 3 October until 28 November; and a male at

Hilfield Park Reservoir on 29 December. In 1977 there was a female on the River Ash at Blakesware on 28 July, and single birds at Tring Reservoirs on 26 October and 1–14 November. In 1979 a male was present in Cassiobury Park from 2–8 January, a pair at Hamper Mill on 13 January, a female at Tring Reservoirs on 5 May, and another at Boyers GP near Cheshunt on 25 December. The following year, 1980, there was a pair in Brocket Park on 20 January and 1 March, three males at Rye Meads on 12 February, one at Tring Reservoirs on 26 August had in fact been released there, and a male at Broxbourne GP on 11 October. In 1981 a male was in the Stockers Lake area from 6 March to 17 June (probably the same bird that was seen at Maple Cross on 15 March), with a female from 9–15 June; a male was seen at Stevenage from 29 May until September, and again on 8 November and 12 December; and there was a female at Amwell GP from 17–28 December. Finally, in 1982, a female was at Stevenage on 23 February and a male throughout April, a female at Lemsford Springs on 22 April, and up to five birds at Rye Meads between 10 October and 5 November.

In addition to the above records, Mead and Smith (1982) state that a pair were seen prospecting on the Ashridge Estate near Tring, 'one recent spring', but no details of this record have been forthcoming. Also, in order to avoid confusion, it should be pointed out that the definite record of breeding given by these authors refers to two broods that were reared in Wrotham Park, near Potters Bar, in 1972. At that time this locality was in Middlesex, but became part of Hertfordshire in the local government boundary changes of 1974.

Wigeon

Anas penelope

A regular but not abundant winter visitor, also occurring on passage in March. This is the same status as given in Sage (1959).

During the 25 winters reviewed here there have been only two localities where significant numbers of Wigeon have been present in winter, and during this period one of these has declined in importance. The main locality is Tring Reservoirs and the winter (November–February) population statistics are shown in Appendix A. It will be seen that the population has fluctuated somewhat with peaks occurring in 1968/69, 1978/79 and 1982/83. With few exceptions the maximum numbers are reached during January and February, and the highest counts during this 25-year period were 200 in February 1979, and 195 in February 1983. It may be noted that in December 1981 a flock of 300 were present nearby at Puttenham, although numbers at the reservoirs at that time were less than one-third of this figure.

At Hilfield Park Reservoir regular wintering began in 1955/56, and there was a count of 116 in February 1958. The subsequent history from the winters 1985/59 to 1977/78 is shown in Appendix B. Regular wintering ceased after the latter period and the species has been irregular in its appearances since, the highest counts being 15 in January 1979, and 25 in December 1981.

Although it appears regularly in winter in the Colne valley below Rickmansworth, the numbers involved are generally small (up to 10), but there have been some counts in excess of this figure, as for example 55 on 18 February 1973, 12 on 1 January and 18 on 18 November 1975, 20 on 15 February 1976, and 16 on 21 January 1979.

A somewhat similar comment applies also to the Lea valley where examples of counts in excess of 10 birds include 18 at Broxbourne GP on 25 February and 38 on 3 March 1963; at Rye Meads, 14 in January and 36 in February 1964; 12 at Broxbourne GP in January 1965, 13 in January 1971, 17 in January 1976, and 24 in December 1981; 40 at Rye Meads in February 1979; in December 1981 there were 25 at Amwell GP; in 1982 there were 11 at Cheshunt GPs in January and 12 in February, 21 at Rye Meads in January, and 54 at Stanstead Abbots GP in January.

Small numbers of Wigeon may occur irregularly in winter at other scattered localities, as for example in the Panshanger in the Mimram valley. In the north of the county, however, it is rare and records such as one at Radwell Lake on 23 December 1978, two at St. Pauls Walden on 30 January 1980, and one at Oughtonhead Common on 25–26 December 1981 are unusual.

There is evidence that additional birds pass through the county on passage in late February and March, one good example being a flock of 61 at Broxbourne GP on 16 March 1958 — still the highest number ever recorded in East Hertfordshire.

Summer records of this species are exceptional. A female at Woodhall Park in the Beane valley on 6 June 1960 was only the second summer record for the county at that time. A most unusual record was that of seven males at Tring Reservoirs on 29 June 1976. In 1980 a male remained at these reservoirs until 9 June, and in 1982 one was present until 23 July.

American Wigeon

Anas americana

A very rare vagrant.

As recorded by Sage (1959), a male, and possibly a female, were seen on Wilstone Reservoir on 5 April 1925, but were considered to be escapes from captivity so the record was square-bracketed.

A very wary male was seen at Tring Reservoirs on 26 January 1971 (*British Birds* 65:328, 1972), and is the first record for the county.

Gadwall

Anas strepera

MAP 8 A scarce and irregular breeding species, but a common winter visitor and passage migrant.

One instance of breeding (at Tring Reservoirs in 1928) was given by Sage (1959), who classed it as an uncommon winter visitor and passage migrant.

There has been one further definite record of breeding, and that was a pair that reared six young at Cheshunt GP in 1969. In 1968 a pair with a well-grown juvenile seen at this site may possibly have bred there. Another possible breeding record is that of a pair seen at Stockers Lake on 7 June, and a female with a juvenile on 17 July 1980. Despite the presence of pairs at some localities during the breeding season, as for example at Tring Reservoirs in 1967, Cheshunt GPs in 1970, at Rye Meads in 1980 (a pair on 6 June and 11 on 16 June), and at Stockers Lake in 1981 and 1982, no further evidence of breeding has been forthcoming.

There has been a marked change in the status of this species in Hertfordshire in recent years. From 1958–63 the majority of the records came from Tring Reservoirs and usually involved less than five birds at any one time, although 19 were noted on 17 December 1961. During this period there were a few records from Hilfield Park Reservoir, Aldenham Reservoir, and from two sites in the Colne valley. The second record for Rye Meads (the first was in 1957) was two on 18 April 1959. In 1964 there were records from seven localities, including Stockers Lake, Digswell and two sites in the Lea valley. Since 1967 the species has been recorded almost annually in both the Colne and Lea valleys. With the exception also of the reservoirs, records from elsewhere remain few, particularly in the north of the county where two at Radwell Lake on 28 December 1981 is the most recent record. There are nine records for Woodhall Park in the Beane valley — 11 on 5 and six on 15 February, two on 13 March, and one on 22 April 1978; two on 22 January, one on 4 and 11 February, and three on 18 February 1979; six on 2 January 1980; and a pair on 4 and 9 April 1982.

As recently as 1972 the highest number recorded in the county was 19 at Tring Reservoirs on 17 December 1961, but this was exceeded by a count of 36 at Tring Reservoirs on 8 November 1978. In recent years the main centre of distribution has been the Lea valley from Stanstead Abbots GP and Rye Meads, south to Cheshunt. High counts during the past four years include — 1979: Cheshunt GPs 22 on 24 February and 32 on 16 December; Rye Meads 32 on 28 January and 29 on 4 February; 1980: Cheshunt GPs 31 in January and 54 in November; Rye Meads/Stanstead Abbots GP, 45 in January and 39 in December; 1981: Cheshunt GPs 23 on 24 January, 55 on 15 November, and 65 on 12 December; Rye Meads, 30 on 15 February and 40 on 30 December; 1982: Cheshunt GPs 60 in February, 120 in October, 145 in November and 155 in December; Rye Meads 54 in January. During the same four years the maximum counts at Tring Reservoirs were 40 in November 1981, 48 in November and 33 in December 1982. Much lower numbers were reported from the Colne valley with maxima of 12 at the Rickmansworth GPs on 16 December 1979, and 13 in October 1982.

Teal

Anas crecca

The following two sub-species, separately described in the sub-sections that follow, are referred to by the Hertfordshire records.

    (*a*)   Teal, *Anas c. crecca*
    (*b*)   American Green-winged Teal, *Anas c. carolinensis*

(*a*)   Teal

    Anas crecca crecca

Formerly bred irregularly, but now very rarely does so. A common visitor **MAP 9** outside the breeding season, particularly in autumn and winter.

In Sage (1959) it was classed as an irregular breeding species and a common autumn and winter visitor.

In Mead and Smith (1982) breeding was proved in one tetrad, this being at Tring Reservoirs, and was considered probable at Beech Hill, Hadley, although this locality was removed from Hertfordshire in the 1974 local government boundary changes. A pair may have bred at Maple Cross SF in 1977. There have been no further breeding records from anywhere in the county despite the presence of birds at the right season. For example, there were two at Maple Cross SF on 9 June 1979, and in the summers of 1980 and 1981. In the latter year there were also four males at Tring Reservoirs on 26 June.

Outside the breeding season the species is found in suitable wetland sites throughout the county, with numbers reaching a peak from October to March. The January and November maximum counts of Teal at Broxbourne GPs, Rye Meads, Hilfield Park Reservoir, and Tring Reservoirs (the major localities), for the years 1973–82 are shown in the histogram, Figure 6.1. Since 1979 numbers at Broxbourne GPs have declined and Cheshunt GPs now attract modest numbers, as for example 36 in February 1979, 40 in January and October 1980, 45 in February and 115 in December 1981, and 80 in January 1982. Since 1980 Stanstead Abbots GP has attracted the species, as for example 34 in February and 85 in November 1980, 40 in January and 70 in December 1981, and 86 in January and 98 in December 1982. Numbers in the Colne valley below Rickmansworth have also been quite high over the past 10 years or so, for example 90 at Stockers Lake on 26 March 1970; 100 there on 10 January, and at Maple Cross 150 in January and 100 on 26 December 1971; 90 at Maple Cross on 9 January 1972; 85 at Maple Cross on 2 February and 100 at Stockers Lake on 18 February 1973; 150 at Stockers Lake on 11 December 1976; 100+ at Stockers Lake and 120 at Maple Cross on 27 February 1977; and 100 at Maple Cross in February 1982. Counts for the Rickmansworth GPs complex from 1980–82 have shown populations of up to 80 from January–March, and 130 from October–December but coverage has often been incomplete.

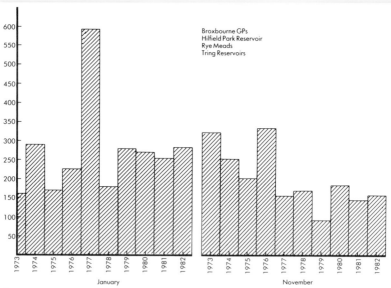

Figure 6.1   *Teal – January and November maximum counts at four localities 1973–82*

The Panshanger estate in the Mimram valley has long been a regular haunt, but numbers have generally been low during the period covered by this book, the maxima being 66 on 10 August 1967, and 55 on 17 January 1982. An unusually high count was obtained near Puttenham (on the Hertfordshire side of the county boundary) in December 1981 when 300 were seen. Quite high numbers sometimes occur at some localities outside the winter period, as for example *c.* 60 at Maple Cross in August–September 1970, 80 at Tring Reservoirs in April 1978, and 30 at Maple Cross in late August 1980.

(*b*)   American Green-winged Teal

Anas crecca carolinensis

A very rare vagrant. A drake was seen at Hilfield Park Reservoir by Bryan Sage on 11 and 15 November 1961 (*British Birds* 55:568, 1962).

Mallard

Anas platyrhynchos

MAP 10   A common resident breeding species and winter visitor whose status has remained unchanged since Sage (1959), although actual numbers have increased during the period covered by the present book.

In terms of numbers, the Mallard is exceeded only by the Moorhen as the most common aquatic breeding species in Hertfordshire, and Mead and Smith (1982) recorded definite breeding in 223 of the 504 tetrads in the county, and probable breeding in 27 more. There have been very few attempts to establish the actual number of pairs of Mallard nesting at any one locality. In 1965 it was estimated that 30 pairs bred at Tring Reservoirs. A study by Chesterman (1978) of the breeding birds of Stockers and Springwell Lakes in the Colne valley, from 1970–6, showed that the number of breeding pairs of this species averaged 28, with a low of 20 pairs in 1970 and a high of 41 pairs in 1973. In 1982 10 broods were reared at Amwell GP, 12 at Broxbourne GPs, and 42 at Cheshunt GPs. In his study of the breeding birds of central Hertfordshire, that is to say the area covered by Ordnance Survey 10 kilometre squares TL21 and TL31, Gladwin (1983) found that between 1956 and 1980 the breeding population of this species increased by some 300–400 per cent.

Quite high numbers of moulting adults and juveniles occur at some localities in late summer and early autumn, as for example at Tring Reservoirs where some sample counts include 573 on 30 August 1959, 732 on 27 August and 925 on 17 September 1961, 426 in September 1981, and 440 in September 1982. The numbers present at this time often exceed the winter population. Hilfield Park Reservoir has not proved of much importance in this context, but there were 286 there on 3 September 1961, and 278 on 25 August 1963. Another locality where this phenomenon has been noted is Woodhall Park where counts include 400 on 20 September 1975, 200 on 19 September 1976, 200 in September 1977, and 250 on 21 August 1979. At Stockers and Springwell Lakes in the Colne valley, an average of 120 were present in September 1976.

Very large numbers of Mallard are present in the county during the winter months with variable numbers at a wide range of sites. The total population in most winters being in the range 1000–2000 birds. Data for the winters 1973/74 to 1982/83 have been analysed and the population for each winter

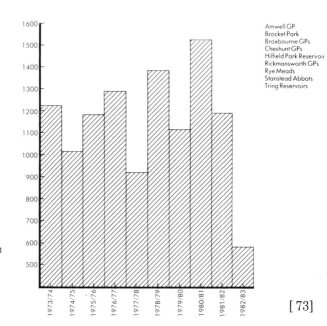

Figure 6.2   *Mallard – Mean of November to February counts 1973/74 to 1982/83*

arrived at by taking the mean of the cumulative maximum counts for each of the four months November–February inclusive, for Amwell GP, Brocket Park, Broxbourne GPs, Cheshunt GPs, Hilfield Park Reservoir, the Rickmansworth GPs, Rye Meads, Stanstead Abbots GP, and Tring Reservoirs, and the resultant figures are shown on the histogram, Figure 6.2. This represents only the minimum winter population since further birds are present at various other localities. Woodhall Park is one such site which occasionally holds significant numbers, for example 137 on 23 December 1975, 120 on 12 December 1976, 106 on 6 January 1977, 104 in January 1980, and 137 on 28 December 1982. Large numbers sometimes occur in unexpected localities, such as 200+ at Pirton in February 1981.

The Mimram valley in the Panshanger formerly held a fairly high population in winter, but this declined in the late 1960s and early 1970s. Table 6.9 shows the mean winter population in the Panshanger over 11 winters for which data are available, calculated on the same basis as the histogram.

TABLE 6.9   *Mean winter populations of Mallard in the Panshanger over eleven winters*

1958/59	192	1962/63	299	1967/68	23
1959/60	314	1963/64	201	1972/73	23
1960/61	260	1965/66	105	1976/77	31
1961/62	282	1966/67	98		

Pintail

Anas acuta

A regular non-breeding visitor mostly in the winter, but also on migration, and with a few records in August.

In Sage (1959) it was classed as a fairly regular winter visitor and passage migrant.

During the period under review the species has been recorded annually and there have been just over 200 records in that 25-year period. The distribution of these records is Tring Reservoirs 84 (40 per cent), Lea valley 61 (30 per cent), Hilfield Park Reservoir 34 (17 per cent), miscellaneous localities 17 (8 per cent), and the Colne valley 11 (5 per cent). In the case of the Lea valley, 39 of the records were from Rye Meads. The first records for East Hertfordshire were from Rye Meads in January and March 1958.

The maximum number recorded in the county at any one time is 29 which arrived at Rye Meads from the south on 1 March 1958. Other flocks in excess of 10 were 14 (10 males) at Tring Reservoirs on 3 January 1967, 15 at the same locality on 16 February 1969, 20 at Cheshunt GPs on 28 December 1974, 23 at Hilfield Park Reservoir on 2 and 13 September 1975, 14 at Tring

Reservoirs on 24 August and 27 October 1978, and 16 at Rye Meads on 3 January and 13 on 6 November 1982.

Records from miscellaneous localities include two in the Panshanger on 17 February, and one on 24 November, and one at Northaw on 6 November 1963; one at Archers Green on 22 January 1967; one at Tewinbury on 5 January and 23 February 1969; a pair at Oughtonhead Common on 21 May 1977; one at St. Pauls Walden on 4 January 1978; one on the River Hiz at Hitchin from 27 February to 22 March, and again on 9 June 1980; one at Ickleford on 4 March, and one in Brocket Park on 13 and 27 December 1981.

Garganey

Anas querquedula

A very rare breeding species, otherwise a regular but scarce spring and autumn passage migrant. There is one winter record.

In Sage (1959) a change in status was recorded from that of a rare visitor to a more or less regular spring and autumn passage migrant. Two instances of breeding were given — at Tring Reservoirs in 1928, and at Aldenham Reservoir in 1931.

Despite the not infrequent presence of birds at various localities in the breeding season, there have only been two further instances of nesting. In 1959 single pairs bred at Broxbourne GP and Broxbourne SF.

There have been approximately 189 records during the period 1958–82 of which 67 (36 per cent) are from the Lea valley, 56 (30 per cent) from Tring Reservoirs, 47 (25 per cent) from the Colne valley (mostly below Rickmansworth), 11 from Hilfield Park Reservoir, and seven from sundry other localities. The spring records fall within the period March to May, and those for autumn in August and September, although there have been occasional reports for early October. The species has occurred annually although in some years (i.e. 1980) there were no spring records. In 1959, an exceptional year for this species in the British Isles generally, there were about 21 records for the county, more than in any other year.

The few records away from the main localities comprise one in the Panshanger on 12 September 1960; one on the River Ivel between Baldock and Radwell on 29 March, one at Radwell Lake on 15 April, and one at Royston SF on 27 August 1967; one at Stevenage on 28 August 1974; a pair at Tednambury Marsh, Sawbridgeworth, on 24 May 1975; seven at Royston SF on 20 August 1977; and one at St. Albans GP in the Ver valley on 19 August 1979.

The only winter record is that of three at Hilfield Park Reservoir on 8 December 1962.

Generally only small numbers are seen at any one time, and the highest counts have been nine at Broxbourne GP on 18 April 1959, 11 at the same locality on 7 July 1967, and 11 at Tring Reservoirs on 26 August 1977.

Blue-winged Teal

Anas discors

A very rare vagrant.

One record of this species was listed by Sage (1959), and that was a female shot in Woodhall Park on 26 January 1938. This record was placed in square brackets although enquiries suggested that it was unlikely to have been an escape from captivity. In the light of present knowledge it seems likely that this was in fact a genuine wild bird.

There has been one subsequent record. A male was present at Tring Reservoirs from 2–5 April 1978 (*British Birds* 73:499, 1980).

Shoveler

Anas clypeata

MAP 11   An uncommon breeding species, but numerous winter visitor and passage migrant.

The status of this species has remained basically unchanged since Sage (1959) at which time it bred irregularly only at Tring Reservoirs, but its numbers and distribution within the county have increased in recent years.

It has never been numerous or regular as a breeding species. At Tring Reservoirs there was no report of breeding for the years 1958–65, but in 1966 two pairs may have nested, one (and possibly three) pairs bred in 1967, one pair in 1969, and one or two pairs in 1971. There were no reports of breeding in the intervening years, and none from 1972–82 although birds were often present all summer. The first record of nesting away from Tring Reservoirs was a pair at Rye Meads in 1959–61 inclusive. A pair may have bred at this locality again in 1965 and one, possibly two pairs did so in 1967, and a pair in 1978. Two pairs summered in 1980 and may have attempted to breed. Elsewhere, in the Lea valley a pair bred at Cheshunt GPs in 1976, and a pair at Stanstead Abbots GP in 1982. There was one instance of nesting in the Beane valley, this being a pair at Woodhall Park in 1960. Pairs may often be seen at various localities in the breeding season, as for example at Maple Cross, Stockers Lake, and Cheshunt GPs in 1979, but with no proof of nesting.

Outside the breeding season variable numbers may be seen at most suitable sites, and in recent years it has appeared in the Colne and Lea valleys in increasing numbers, and has also increased at Tring Reservoirs. At the latter locality a count of 42 on 16 October 1960 was the highest since 1937, but has been greatly exceeded since. Quite high numbers occasionally occur at these reservoirs in late summer, for example 99 on 7 August 1967, and 71

76

on 29 August 1981. A count of 111 at Tring on 2 October 1966 was the highest ever recorded anywhere in the county at that time. The maximum numbers of Shoveler at Tring Reservoirs for the months of January to March and September to December for the years 1958–82 inclusive are given in Appendix C and it can be seen that the maximum count at the reservoirs (and for the county) was 202 on 30 September 1973.

In the Colne valley the highest counts were 20 at Maple Cross on 21 October 1972, 63 at Stockers Lake on 14 December 1975 and, in 1977, the first three-figure counts (all at Stockers Lake) of 113 on 4 January, 130 on 8 February, and 110 on 4 March. The maximum count for the Rickmansworth GPs currently stands at 150 in November 1982. A count of 26 at Broxbourne GPs on 18 November 1962 was the highest for the Lea valley at that time, and was not exceeded until 50 were seen at the same site on 25 October 1970. In the last 10 years there have been numerous counts of between 50 and 100 at Broxbourne GPs, Cheshunt GPs, and Rye Meads. The mean winter (November–February) population of this species at the three localities just mentioned, and also Hilfield Park Reservoir, the Rickmansworth GPs, and Tring Reservoirs, for the winters 1973/74 to 1982/83 is shown in the histogram, Figure 6.3. Numbers at other localities are usually very small and it is of infrequent occurrence in the north of the county.

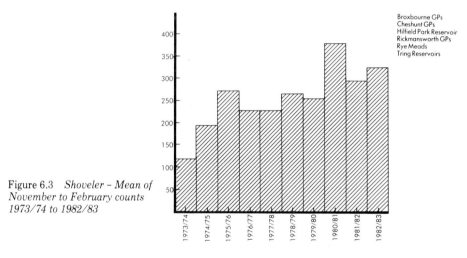

Figure 6.3   *Shoveler – Mean of November to February counts 1973/74 to 1982/83*

Red-crested Pochard

Netta rufina

An occasional winter visitor and passage migrant (mainly in autumn). It is thought that wild birds are involved as well as those that have escaped from captivity or have been deliberately released into the wild.

In Sage (1959) it was classed as a rare visitor and 14 records were quoted, all but one referring to Tring Reservoirs.

During the 25 years under review there were approximately 80 records, but none were recorded in 1958, 1962–4, 1966, or 1978. Of these 80 records, 30 are from the Lea valley, 24 from the Colne valley, 12 from Tring Reservoirs, and 10 from Hilfield Park Reservoir, the remainder being from sundry other sites.

Pochard

Aythya ferina

MAP 12 An uncommon breeding species, but abundant winter visitor and passage migrant whose status has changed little since Sage (1959).

During the period covered by Sage (op. cit.) breeding was known at Tring Reservoirs, from the Colne valley in 1947 (and possibly in 1946), and from two sites in the Lea valley in 1953 and 1954. During the period reviewed here the breeding population at Tring Reservoirs has varied from one to four pairs, although in some years no reports were received. In Mead and Smith (1982) breeding was recorded in eight tetrads, the localities being Tring Reservoirs, Hamper Mill, in the Lea valley on or near the Bedfordshire/Hertfordshire border, and in the same valley at three sites below Hertford, and a pair at Hexton. Breeding was also believed probable in six further tetrads.

A pair bred at Hamper Mill in 1967, four pairs summered at Stockers Lake in 1979 of which at least one pair bred, two pairs bred at this site in 1980, and a pair at Bury Lake GP in 1981. In the Lea valley two pairs bred at Broxbourne GP in 1965. In 1982 several reports of nesting were reported — single pairs at Amwell GP, Rye Meads, Maple Cross, and Stockers Lake where eight pairs summered. Pairs often summer at localities but proof of breeding is not found, as for example seven pairs in the Rickmansworth area in 1973 and 13 pairs in 1981.

During the ten winters 1973/74 to 1982/83 the average winter population at eight localities varied from 355 to 631 as shown in the histogram, Figure 6.4. This shows that from a peak in the winter of 1974/75 the population has declined. Hilfield Park Reservoir is an important winter haunt although numbers have decreased there in recent years. Some examples of high

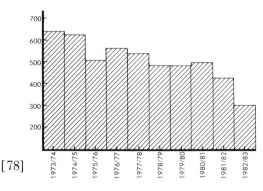

Amwell GP
Brocket Park
Broxbourne GPs
Cheshunt GPs
Hilfield Park Reservoir
Rickmansworth GPs
Rye Meads
Stanstead Abbots
Tring Reservoirs

Figure 6.4 *Pochard – Mean of November to February counts 1973/74 to 1982/83*

counts there are 330 on 2 October and 304 on 4 December 1960, 371 on 17 January and 282 on 20 December 1970, 425 on 24 January and 578 on 7 February 1971 (the highest count ever recorded at any single locality in Hertfordshire up to that date), 405 on 4 November 1973, and 378 on 23 February 1975. At Tring Reservoirs the maximum winter count between 1958 and 1982 was 372 on 2 January 1977. During the same 25-year period the highest counts in the Colne valley were 250 at Troy Mill GP on 26 December 1961, 320 at Hamper Mill on 25 December 1972, and at the Rickmansworth GPs as a whole 203 in January 1973 and 270 in December 1974. In the Lea valley the maxima were — Cheshunt GPs: 192 in November 1976 and 150 in December 1977; Broxbourne GPs: 172 in November 1978; and Rye Meads: 160 in January 1979.

Quite high numbers are sometimes present at certain localities in the summer months, as for example 172 at Hilfield Park Reservoir on 22 August 1964, 118 on 29 July and 261 on 26 August 1967, and 100 in July and 179 in August 1982. At Tring Reservoirs there were 131 in July and 145 in August 1982. Considerable numbers also occur often in spring and autumn, examples being — Hilfield Park Reservoir: 290 on 18 October 1959, 214 on 17 September and 330 on 2 October 1960, 369 on 16 September 1961, 261 on 26 August 1967, 274 on 15 September 1968, 316 on 12 October 1969, 630 on 28 October 1973 (currently the maximum number ever recorded in the county), and 365 on 15 March 1975; Stockers Lake: 200 on 14 March 1970; Tring Reservoirs: 240 on 26 September and 600 on 17 October 1971; and Broxbourne GPs: 300 on 5 October 1979.

Ring-necked Duck

Aythya collaris

A very rare vagrant.

There are five records and all refer to drakes. The first for the county was seen at Broxbourne GP from 28–30 April 1974 (*British Birds* 68:313, 1975). In 1977 there was one at Tring Reservoirs on 2 April, and another from 18–30 April (ibid. 71:494, 1978). One was present at Amwell GP from 17 April to 14 May, and another on 25–26 May 1981 (ibid. 75:493, 1982).

Ferruginous Duck

Aythya nyroca

A very rare vagrant.

Three records were listed by Sage (1959) and all were in 1953 — a male at

Hamper Mill on 13 January; a pair at Old Parkbury GP, Radlett, on 23 and 24 April, and one on 25 April and 2 May.

One that was present in the Cheshunt area almost continuously from June 1966 until late 1970 was considered to be an escape from captivity. If this bird is excluded then there are six acceptable records as follows:

1961 A male at Hilfield Park Reservoir on 26 November (*British Birds* 55:569, 1962).

1965 One at Tring Reservoirs on 3–4 January (ibid. 59:286, 1966); and a female at the same reservoirs from 7 to 9 November.

1971 Another female at Cheshunt GPs on 14 November.

1972 There was a female at Tring Reservoirs on 18 March, and two males and a female on 25 June and 2 July.

1982 Lastly, a female at Stockers Lake on 30 October.

Tufted Duck

Aythya fuligula

MAP 13 A common resident breeding species, passage migrant, and winter visitor.

Its status has remained unchanged since Sage (1959), but the breeding population has increased, as have the numbers present in winter.

Breeding sites include not only reservoirs, flooded gravel pits and large lakes, but also on smaller water bodies and rivers. In recent years it has colonised the valleys of several smaller rivers such as the Ash and the Beane where it now nests regularly. In Mead and Smith (1982) it was stated that during the period 1967–73 breeding was proved in 26 tetrads, and possibly occurred in four others. Despite the relatively widespread distribution of breeding records, the main centres are the valleys of the Colne and the Lea. Full coverage of all breeding sites in these two valleys in any one season is rarely achieved, particularly in the Colne valley below Rickmansworth. There is, however, little doubt that the breeding population has increased although it may fluctuate from year to year. During the 25 years under review the number of breeding pairs has varied from a low of four in 1962 to

80

maxima of 36 in 1971, 50 in 1974, and 38 in 1975. In a long term study of Stockers Lake and Springwell GPs, Chesterman (1978) recorded the number of breeding territories of this duck as follows:

1970	1971	1972	1973	1974	1975	1976	Mean
20	29	26	30	26	37	29	28

The growth of the breeding population at Rye Meads has been rapid, from six pairs in 1960, to a high of 46 pairs in 1981. The number of breeding pairs at this locality for those years from 1964–82 for which data are available is shown in Table 6.10. The 22 pairs which bred in 1964 reared a total of 110 young, and the 35 pairs in 1968 reared 183 young.

The maximum numbers recorded as breeding at Broxbourne GP were 15 pairs in 1975 and 14 in 1976; at Cheshunt GPs: 13–16 pairs in 1967, 21 in

TABLE 6.10   *Number of breeding pairs of Tufted Duck at Rye Meads, 1964–82*

1964	1965	1966	1967	1968	1969	1970
22	30–35	40	7	35	33	25

1972	1974	1975	1976	1980	1981	1982
31	34	35	11	42	46	35

1968, 12 in 1973, 10 in 1980, and 18 in 1982; Amwell GP had 15 breeding pairs in 1975, 13 in 1976, and six in 1980. Breeding has not been reported from Hilfield Park Reservoir; at Tring Reservoirs the maximum recorded was eight pairs in 1965, and five pairs in 1966, 1977 and 1982.

Despite the occurrence of high numbers at some localities during March, analysis of data from the six most important sites does not provide any evidence of a spring passage movement of any note. The numbers present in March at these localities being consistently lower than the February populations in each case, and also lower than the mean winter populations (November–February inclusive) in each case. There is, however, evidence of movement through the county in the summer and early autumn. The build-up usually commences in July (as for example at Hilfield Park and Tring Reservoirs), reaches a peak in August or early September, then declines prior to the winter influx. On 24 September 1961 a flock of 400 were seen flying southwards over Rye Meads.

The status of this species in winter has certainly changed during the 25 years with which we are concerned. In 1958 a count of 194 at Hilfield Park Reservoir was the highest recorded in the county up to that date. This figure was comfortably exceeded by counts at Hilfield Park Reservoir and elsewhere in subsequent years, particularly in the Colne and Lea valleys. For example, 410 at the Rickmansworth GPs in December 1970, 419 in January 1971, and 400 in November 1981 and January 1982, with 400 at Bury Lake GP alone on 4 November 1980. In the Lea valley there were 430 at Broxbourne GP in January 1968; 570 at Cheshunt GPs in October 1969; in 1970 at Cheshunt GPs: 581 in October, 639 in November, and 848 (currently the highest count ever made in the county) in December; at the same locality in 1971: 742 in November and 663 in December; and 607 at Broxbourne GP in November 1973. Counts in the Lea valley in subsequent years tended to be a little lower — 448 at Cheshunt GPs in December 1974, 485 at Rye Meads in December 1975, 462 at Broxbourne GP in November 1977, 547 at Rye Meads in February 1978, 431 in January 1981, and 625 in January 1982. At Hilfield Park Reservoir there were 420 in November and 450 in December 1972; 600 in November and 775 in December 1973; 600 in January, and 576 in February 1974; 580 in February 1975; and 500+ on 23 October and 490 in December 1976. The maximum winter count at Tring Reservoirs during the 10 winters from 1973/74 to 1982/83 was 367 in November 1978.

The mean winter populations of this species at the nine principal localities for the 10 winters 1973/74 to 1982/83 is shown in the histogram, Figure 6.5. This shows a peak of 1949 in the winter of 1973/74, with somewhat lower numbers subsequently, dropping to 1116 in the winter of 1982/83.

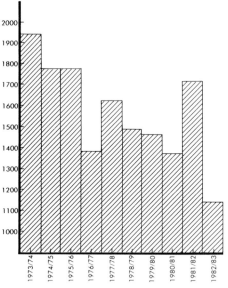

Figure 6.5   *Tufted Duck – Mean of November to February counts 1973/74 to 1982/83*

Scaup

Aythya marila

An occasional winter visitor and passage migrant which has occurred annually with the exception of 1964 and 1978. Some records of this species may be suspect due to the existence of *Aythya* hybrids, examples of which were, for instance, identified at Hamper Mill in December 1977 and January 1978, and at Hilfield Park Reservoir (a group of four) in April 1979.

In Sage (1959) this species was classified as an irregular winter visitor and passage migrant, but its appearances have become more frequent in the past 25 years.

There are approximately 80 records for the period under review of which over half refer to Tring (24) and Hilfield Park Reservoirs (23). The Lea valley accounts for 19 records, the Colne valley for nine (five from the pits south of Rickmansworth), and the remaining records are from miscellaneous sites. The latter records comprise four on the lake at Hilfield House on 5 January, and one at Aldenham Reservoir on 18 March 1960; five on the River Gade in Cassiobury Park on 24 January 1963 during arctic weather conditions; a male at Radwell Lake on 14 January 1968; and three records from Woodhall Park from March–May 1982. All records refer to betweeen one and five individuals, with the exception of a flock of eight at Tring Reservoirs on 16 April 1974.

The great majority of the records fall within the period November–February. A total of about 10 records for September–October, and 12 for March–April presumably reflect migratory movements. The only reports falling outside the months mentioned above are one at Hilfield Park Reservoir on 29 July 1960, one at Tring Reservoirs on 23 August 1977, and at Woodhall Park on 4 May 1982.

Eider

Somateria mollissima

A very rare winter visitor, but with one spring record.

This species was added to the county list in 1961 when a female was seen at Hilfield Park Reservoir on 17 December. There are four subsequent records as follows:

1963   A female again seen at Hilfield Park Reservoir on 5–6 January, and a drake at Tring Reservoirs on 3 May.

1975   A female seen at Lemsford Springs and later in Brocket Park on 23 November, may possibly have been an escape from captivity.

1977   The most recent record was a female at Rye Meads on 4 December.

Long-tailed Duck

Clangula hyemalis

A very rare visitor, primarily in winter, whose status has remained basically unchanged since Sage (1959).

There are eight records for the period under review, all but two of which refer to Tring Reservoirs. All the records refer to single birds. The Tring records are:

1966 From 13 to 19 February, and another from 18–31 December, remaining until (16 April 1967).
1972 From 14 May to 13 June (an unusual date).
1973 Seen on December 1st and 2nd.
1979 From 31 December to (20 January 1980).

The two remaining records are as follows:

1959 One at Hilfield Park Reservoir from 13 to 31 December.
1961 One at Stockers Lake from 10 to 12 December.

Common Scoter

Melanitta nigra

An occasional but regular passage migrant, and winter visitor, with records for all the 25 years under review except 1965 and 1968.

It was classed by Sage (1959) as an irregular winter visitor and passage migrant, so the change in status is evident.

There are about 55 records of which 29 refer to Tring Reservoirs and 10 to Hilfield Park Reservoir. The Colne valley can claim only three records — one at Hamper Mill on 8 April 1970, two at Stockers Lake on 28 June 1973 (an unusual date), and one at Helicon GP on 11 April 1981. In the Lea valley there are six records from Rye Meads and two from Stanstead Abbots GP. Elsewhere, one was present on the River Gade in Cassiobury Park, Watford, on 2–3 and 20 April 1962; and there were records of up to two in Fairlands Valley, Stevenage, in April–May 1979, 1980 and 1981. All records generally refer to between one and five birds, the exceptions being six at Hilfield Park Reservoir on 24 April 1972; and eight at Tring Reservoirs on 12 April, nine on 2 May, and 12 on 11 May 1978.

The species is predominantly a spring passage migrant with 80 per cent of the records falling within the period March–May. There are only four autumn records — three in September and one in October. In addition to the June record mentioned above, five were present at Tring Reservoirs on 4 June 1972. There is one record for July (three at Tring Reservoirs on 2 July 1978), and one for August (one at Hilfield Park Reservoir on 8 August 1959). There are only five winter records — one at Hilfield Park Reservoir on 23 February 1958; one at Rye Meads from 18–23 November 1961; one at Tring Reservoirs on 3 November 1963; one at Hilfield Park Reservoir on 24 December 1970, and one at Tring Reservoirs from 18–22 December 1982.

Velvet Scoter

Melanitta fusca

A very rare winter visitor. The only record listed by Sage (1959) was of two at Tring Reservoirs on 3-4 November 1930.

There have been five subsequent records as listed below:

1963   One at Rye Meads from 20 to 26 January, and a drake at Tring Reservoirs from 8 to 17 December.

1976   A female was seen at Hilfield Park Reservoir on 29 December.

1979   In the Colne valley, three were seen flying over Troy Mill GP on 23 January.

1982   The latest record was a pair at Cheshunt GPs on 9 January.

Goldeneye

Bucephala clangula

A common and regular winter visitor, and a spring passage migrant in small numbers in late March and April.

In Sage (1959) it was classed as a regular but not particularly numerous winter visitor.

The species has increased within the past 10 years and is of regular occurrence at Hilfield Park and Tring Reservoirs, and in the Colne and Lea valleys. In addition it periodically appears on various other waters around the county. The records (with a few exceptions mentioned below), all fall within the period October–April. In the 12 years from 1958–69 inclusive, the highest numbers recorded at any one time were seven on two occasions — at Hilfield Park Reservoir betwen 6-27 March 1960, and at Tring Reservoirs from 3 November to 19 December 1963. From 1970–82 the flooded gravel pits in the Colne valley below Rickmansworth have provided the highest single counts, the maxima being 17 in February 1970, 14 in November 1973 and December 1974, 15 in March 1976, 18 in February 1978 and March 1979, 24 in February 1980, 15 in January, February and again in April 1981, and 19 in January and 18 in February 1982.

At Tring Reservoirs in the same period the highest numbers recorded were up to 10 from January–April 1974, at least nine in February 1975, 11 in April 1976, March 1977, and March 1978, 20 in February 1979, 13 in February 1980, and 10 in February 1982. The highest count at Hilfield Park Reservoir within the period 1958–82 was 10 in March 1982. The Lea valley also usually holds only small numbers, the highest counts being 14 at Stanstead Abbots

GP in January 1973, seven at Broxbourne GPs in December 1977, and at Cheshunt GPs: 12 in February and seven in December 1982.

Few records fall outside the period October to April, the exceptions being a drake at Broxbourne GPs on 1 May 1965; one or two remained at Tring Reservoirs until 6 May 1967; there were two drakes at these reservoirs on 21 September 1969; two at Stockers Lake on 4 May 1971; a remarkable record of a drake in eclipse plumage at Rye Meads on 30 July 1978; and a female at the latter locality from 26 April until 26 September 1982.

Smew

Mergus albellus

A regular winter visitor, usually only in small numbers, with some individuals occasionally remaining into April. Its status has remained basically unchanged since Sage (1959).

From 1958–61 all the records, with one exception, emanated from Aldenham, Hilfield Park or Tring Reservoirs. The highest numbers ever recorded in the county appeared during the early 1960s. At Hilfield Park Reservoir in 1959 there were 27 (14 males) on 22 February, 28 (18 males) on 8 March, 26 (five males) on 20 December, and 30 (10 males) on 27 December. In 1960 at the same reservoir there were 24 on 31 January, and 20 on 20 February. High numbers occurred again in 1963 when 28 (eight males) were seen at Broxbourne GP on 27 February, and 30 (four males) at Rye Meads on 7 March. Since 1963 no flocks in excess of seven birds have been recorded in Hertfordshire.

During the 25 years under review the species has been recorded annually with the exception of 1972 and 1975. From 1958–73 there were only four records from the Colne valley below Rickmansworth, but from 1976–82 it was reported annually, the maximum at any one time being four. There have been no records from Aldenham Reservoir since five were seen there on 28 December 1973, and apparently none from Hilfield Park Reservoir since a single bird on 10–11 January 1971. During the last 10 years there have been very few reports in any one year, and most of those have been from the Colne or Lea valleys. An exception was 1979 when there were records from at least eight localities (all in the Colne or Lea valleys except for one at Tring Reservoirs on 18 February), with maxima of seven at Cheshunt GPs on 4 February, of which six remained until 18 February.

An unusual record, both for date and locality, was one on the lake in Nyn Park, Northaw, on 13 April 1965.

Red-breasted Merganser

Mergus serrator

A scarce winter visitor and spring passage migrant.

It was classed as a rare winter visitor by Sage (1959) who listed less than 20 records.

For the period 1958–82 there were a total of 36 records, but the species was not recorded at all in 1958, 1960, 1963-4, 1969, 1972, 1974, 1978 or 1980. Most of the records come from Tring Reservoirs (13) and the Lea valley (12), with six from Hilfield Park Reservoir, and five from the Colne valley. Analysis of these records by date gives the following result — October (2), November (6), December (5), January (3), February (9), March (7), and April (4). The maximum recorded at any one time was five at Cheshunt GPs on 24 February 1979, and a similar number at Hilfield Park Reservoir the same month (*see* below). This was in fact an exceptional year with reports of at least 15 individuals from seven sites.

The six Hilfield Park Reservoir records, all of single birds unless otherwise stated, were 10 January 1959, 29 December 1962, four on 15 January 1966, 23 December 1973, three on 20 November 1977 flew off to the SW., and five on 15 February 1979. The Colne valley records comprise one at Troy Mill GP on 27 November 1965; two at Maple Cross on 26 January, and one at Pynesfield GP on 10 April 1975; and four at West Hyde GP on 24 February 1979, and one at Pynesfield GP on the same date.

Goosander

Mergus merganser

A regular but not numerous winter visitor, and evidence also of occasional spring passage.

In Sage (1959) it was classed as an irregular winter visitor which had increased in numbers and frequency of visits since the beginning of the century.

With few exceptions, all records of this species fall within the months November–April. There are records from Tring Reservoirs for every winter from 1958/59 to 1979/80, but none for the winter 1980/81. The situation at these reservoirs has changed considerably during the period covered by this book. Some quite high numbers occurred in late 1959 and the early 1960s with maximum counts of 45 in December 1959; 52 in January (the highest count ever for Hertfordshire at that time), and 35 in February 1960; 65 in January and 71 in February 1961; 27 in January and 31 in March 1962; and 54 in March 1963. During the winters 1963/64 to 1968/69 numbers never exceeded 26 (in February 1966). In 1970 there were counts of 63 in January and 29 in February. Then from the winter of 1970/71 to 1977/78 the maximum count was only 12. The last reasonably high count was 28 in January 1979. It can, therefore, be seen that numbers have declined drastically during the period discussed here.

Equally interesting changes have taken place in the Colne valley below Rickmansworth for which area, from the winter of 1958/59 to 1970/71, there were only five records, the maximum being 11 at Stockers Lake on 11 January and nine at Troy Mill GP on 31 March 1970. In 1972 there were 30 at Troy Mill GP on 26 February and 18 on 13 March. In 1973 even higher numbers appeared in the valley — 44 on 22 February, 29 on 4 March, 32 on 4 April, 80 on 9 December and 109 on 21 December (the last two counts being the highest ever for the county). In 1974 there were 40 at Troy Mill GP on 20 February, after which year numbers fell markedly as at Tring Reservoirs. From 1975–82 the highest counts at these pits were 17 on 1 January 1975 and 18 (at West Hyde GP) on 11 March 1979.

Other localities in the county are relatively unimportant. Hilfield Park Reservoir provided 30 records in the 25-year period covered here, with a maximum of 12 from 5–16 January 1963 (the very hard winter). In the same period the Lea valley produced approximately 70 records (the majority from Rye Meads) with the maxima being 12 on 11 and 17 January 1970 (at Rye Meads), 12 at Broxbourne GP on 4 February 1979, and 13 flying over Rye Meads on 27 December 1981. There are records of one or two birds from sundry other sites in the county.

A most unusual record is that of a pair at Hilfield Park Reservoir on 15 August 1962. The only other Hertfordshire record for this month was one shot at Tring Reservoirs on 31 August 1903.

Ruddy Duck

Oxyura jamaicensis

MAP 14   An irregular breeding species, but regular non-breeding visitor. It may well be under-recorded due to its generally skulking habits, particularly in the breeding season.

This duck was officially added to the British list in 1971 since by then feral breeding populations were well established. Hertfordshire is in fact well separated from the other areas of feral breeding. There are conflicting statements in the literature concerning the nesting of this species in the county. In Hudson (1976) it is said that a pair bred at Tring Reservoirs in the four consecutive years 1965–8, which is correct although there was no definite proof in 1967. Mead and Smith (1982) state that it has bred regularly at Tring since 1965, but this is not the case. There was an increased incidence of records from the mid-1970s and breeding certainly occurred in 1981, and may have taken place in the three preceding years although no definite proof could be obtained.

There were no records at all for the county for 1962, 1963, 1970 or 1972, but it has occurred at Tring Reservoirs in all other years since 1960 (the record for that year undoubtedly referred to an escape from captivity) with the exception of 1971 and 1973. Numbers have always been small and did not reach double figures until 1982 when there were 13 in January, 10 in September, 13 in November, and 12 in December.

There have been a total of 21 records for Hilfield Park Reservoir, none involving more than two birds, and all within the period October to April. The Colne valley has produced about 17 records, all from the pits below Rickmansworth except for a drake at Hamper Mill on 15 October 1967. These records have never involved more than three birds at any one time. The Lea valley has 12 records (the first in 1975), all from the section from Rye Meads to Cheshunt, except for one on the river at Ware on 26 December 1981; all have been of single birds with the exception of two at Rye Meads on 7 January 1979.

Honey Buzzard

Pernis apivorus

A very rare vagrant.

This was classed as a very rare visitor by Sage (1959) who was able to quote only six nineteenth-century records. These were one shot near Munden between 1840 and 1850; one in Hamel's Park, near Puckeridge, in the first week of October 1874, and another in September 1875; one shot at Little Hadham on 23 September, and another near Buntingford on 29 September 1881; and one trapped at Hoddesdon on 2 October 1896. Two further records are mentioned by James and Sawford (1979), both apparently of immature birds. One was obtained at Baldock about 1830, and the other at Sandon in 1840, but in neither case is there any record of the exact date.

The only other records are of one seen at Offley on 20 June 1976 (*British Birds* 75:161, 1982), and one flying over Rye Meads on 24 May 1981.

Red Kite

Milvus milvus

A very rare vagrant.

Evidence of the previous breeding of this species in Hertfordshire was discussed by Sage (1959) who also listed three documented occurrences —

*c.*1840   One shot at Munden, near Watford.
late 1860s   Another shot near Wilstone Reservoir.
1872   One seen at Gallows Hill, near Hertford.

An additional item of evidence not given by Sage (op. cit.) is a statement by Miller Christy in *The Birds of Essex* (1890) that King James I once lost a valuable hawk whilst kite-hawking at Royston.

There are five recent records as follows:

1972   One seen in a thermal over Ashwell on 13 August.
1977   Two flew eastwards over Radlett on 23 August.
1981   One at Benington on 29 March and 4 April; one at Bulbourne near Tring, on 31 March; and one flying NW. over Tring Reservoirs on 20 April.

White-tailed Eagle

Haliaeetus albicilla

A very rare vagrant the only records being those quoted by Sage (1959). One shot at Sacombe prior to 1877, and an immature shot at Hitchin in 1880.

Marsh Harrier

Circus aeruginosus

A scarce non-breeding visitor, mainly as a spring passage migrant.

It was classed as a very rare visitor by Sage (1959) who quoted only one record, that of a male shot at Wilstone Reservoir on 21 May 1935. The Barkway specimen mentioned by James and Sawford (1979) is entirely without data and cannot be accepted as the first county record. A previously unpublished record concerns one seen at Tring Reservoirs on 14 August 1954 by A. J. Livett and M. D. Wortley.

The status of this species has changed considerably since the late 1950s and there are 27 records for the period with which we are concerned, 23 of them in April or May, and it has been reported annually since 1973. All but four of the records refer to Tring Reservoirs and are as follows — an immature flying over on 17 August 1958; a female on 3 May 1963; a male on 4 May 1965; one approached from the SW. and went off NE. on 30 May 1966; one on 27 April 1967; one on 10 June 1969; a female on 4 May 1973; one on 11 and 15 April 1974; one on 20 May 1975; three records in 1976: a female or immature on 20–21 April and 6 May, and an adult on 26 April; four records in 1977: a female or immature on 22, 26 and 29 April, and an immature male on 4 May; a female on 25 April, 13–14 and 27 May 1978; a female or immature on 6 May 1980; another flying south on 26 April 1981; and a female or immature on 7 May 1982.

Figure 6.6   *Immature Marsh Harrier in Hatfield Park on 4 August 1977.*

Photo: © F. R. Ivimey

The remaining four records are of one seen and photographed near Huntonbridge in June 1965, an immature seen and photographed in Hatfield Park on 4 August 1977 (this record has not previously been published), and a male at Rye Meads on 15 April and a female on 22 April 1979.

Hen Harrier

Circus cyaneus

A rare visitor, primarily in the winter months.

The status of this species has remained unchanged since Sage (1959) who listed about 13 records.

There are 20 further records of this species which has occurred in eight of the 25 years covered by this book. These comprise 14 winter, five spring, and one autumn record:

1959   A female at Burloes Hall, near Royston on 22 January.

1962   A female or immature in the Ashridge area from 24 November until (2 March 1963).
A male in the Ringshall area from November until (February 1963).

1970   One seen at Bramfield Forest on 15 February, and another at Tring Reservoirs from 1 to 7 February.

1975   One at Amwell on 11 October, and another at Rye Meads on 22 December.

1978   A male present at Graveley on 1 November.

1979   Seven records all of single birds:
a male at Tring Reservoirs on 1 January;
a female in the Pegsdon–Pirton area in January and February;
a male at Symondshyde on 2 and 3 February and at Lemsford on 2 and 4 February;
one in same area in April;
a male at Rye Meads on 4 March;
a female at Gorhambury from 7 to 21 March;
and one at Moor Park golf course on 4 April.

The records for 1978 and 1979 no doubt reflect the influx of this species into Britain in the winter of 1978/79 discussed by Davenport (1982). The remaining five records are as follows:

1981   A male near Gorhambury on 8 May.
A female at Wallingtonbury on 26 November.
Another female at Rye Meads on 16 December.
A male at Tring Reservoirs on 31 December.

1982   Four 'ringtails' were seen flying together near Barley on 14 November.

Montagu's Harrier

Circus pygargus

A very rare vagrant.

It was classed as a rare visitor by Sage (1959) who quoted one documented case of breeding and seven other records The latter were all of single birds as follows — at Hexton in 1875; Wigginton, near Tring, in 1891; Northchurch Common, Berkhamsted, on 8 April 1923; near Hitchin from May to July 1927, April 1929, and August 1932; and Northchurch Common on 21 September 1929. The sole breeding record was a nest with four eggs near Hitchin on 5 July 1809. However, as mentioned by Sage (1962), a group of four immature harriers seen near Hitchin in September and October 1944 may have been a locally bred brood of this species. A nest was in fact found just over the Bedfordshire border on the Pegsdon Hills in 1945.

There are four recent records as follows:

1977   A female seen flying NE. at Tring Reservoirs on 26 May.
1978   One at Tring Reservoirs on 13 May, and at Mimms Wood on 14 May.
1979   A male seen at Maple Cross on 18 May.

Goshawk

Accipiter gentilis

A very rare vagrant.

The status of this species has changed since Sage (1959) who listed only one record, in square brackets, of one said to have been shot at Northaw in September 1879.

There have been about five records in recent years. One was seen in the act of taking a Wood Pigeon at Mardock Mill, Wareside, on 11 July 1967, and what was probably the same bird was seen again on 12 and 19 August which suggests that it had summered in the area. In 1970 one was seen at Broxbourne Woods on 25 January. A female was seen near St. Albans on 24 September 1980. One was seen in the Digswell and Panshanger area on 3 March, and what was presumably the same bird, at the latter locality from 16–19 March 1981. In October of that year one was noted at Pirton on 26 September, followed by a pair in October and November, and one in December. At least one remained into 1982 since a male was seen on 6 January, followed by unconfirmed reports up until April.

Sparrowhawk

Accipiter nisus

MAP 15 Now increasing as a resident breeding species following the marked population decline of the late 1950s and early 1960s, due to the side effects of organochlorine pesticides, which brought the species to the verge of extinction in southern and eastern England.

It was classed by Sage (1959) as a scarce resident breeding species.

In the 10 years from 1958–67 the confirmed breeding records concerned single pairs at Scales Park, Nuthampstead, in 1959, and at Harmer Green in 1961. The number of actual sightings each year rose from a minimum of two in 1958 to nine in 1966, and about 23 (from 15 different sites) in 1967. The atlas published by Mead and Smith (1982) incorporates the results of breeding season surveys from 1967–73, during which period definite nesting was recorded in three tetrads, and considered probable in 10 more. A clear improvement in the status of this species is evident from the records for the 10 years from 1973–82. In 1975 in West Hertfordshire between Berkhamsted and Wendover one pair reared young, and there were April to July reports from seven other areas. A pair may have bred at Pirton in 1976, and five pairs (four successful) did so in West Hertfordshire. The improvement continued in 1977 with a pair nesting at North Mimms, seven nests found (14 young reared) in the west of the county, and April to July records from five other sites. The number of breeding pairs reported in West Hertfordshire in subsequent years was nine in 1978 (23 young reared from seven of the nests); a pair bred in the Tring area in 1979; in 1980 three pairs (at Wigginton, near Hastoe, and at Berkhamsted) reared nine young, and there was a nest with two young at Tring Reservoirs; a pair with dependent young were seen at Tring Reservoirs in 1982. Mead and Smith (1982) state that detailed studies in the Tring area (in the early 1980s) regularly revealed two dozen active nests over an area of about 100km^2, but the observers concerned did not see fit to provide information on these to the county bird recorder. Elsewhere, breeding was suspected near Stockers Lake in 1979, possibly near St. Albans in 1980, and a pair at Northaw Great Wood in 1982.

Breeding season reports subsequent to 1977 increased from seven sites in 1979, to 14 in 1980, 21 in 1981, and 18 in 1982.

Reports outside the breeding season have increased markedly in recent years from about 20 (from 12 sites) in 1978, to 30 (from 17 sites) in 1979, 22 sites in 1980, 30 sites in 1981, and 24 in 1982. In the Stevenage area alone there were 57 sightings in 1981 (all year), compared with only 10 in 1978 and 1979.

Buzzard

Buteo buteo

A regular visitor, and probably one or two pairs breeding at least intermittently.

A former breeding species, it was classed by Sage (1959) as a regular non-breeding visitor, mostly in the autumn.

The status of the Buzzard as a breeding species within the county rests very much on circumstantial evidence, although Mead and Smith (1982) state that breeding was proved in one tetrad in the west of the county. However, this statement presumably refers to 1972, for which year the records submitted for the county bird report state that up to four were seen in the west of the county in spring, and that a pair may have bred or attempted to do so. There were breeding season records from the same general area again in 1974, 1975, and 1977 (a pair summered but breeding was not suspected). In recent years there have been fairly persistent reports of a pair in the Pirton area in the breeding season, and of single birds from various other localities between April and July.

Between 1958 and 1982, and excluding records from West Hertfordshire in the breeding season, there have been approximately 116 records predominantly of single birds. In terms of the month of occurrence, the highest numbers were May (14), July (13), September (27), October (12), and November (11). The high number of September records suggests an autumn passage movement.

Rough-legged Buzzard

Buteo lagopus

A very rare vagrant.

This species was classed by Sage (1959) as a rare winter visitor, for which there were about 13 records.

There are only eight recent records as follows:

1963   One in the Panshanger on 15 April, and one at Bramfield Forest on 24 November which remained until 30 March 1964.
1966   One seen over Nyn Park, Northaw, on 28 October.
1967   One present on the Barton and Pegsdon Hills from 12 to 24 March.
1971   One at Pirton on the somewhat unusual date of 28 August.
1974   One on the Pegsdon Hills on 28 December, and another at

Kimpton on 14 December remained in the area until (26 January 1975).

1975   Lastly, two near Pegsdon on 19 January.

Both the Barton and Pegsdon Hills are in Bedfordshire but the birds are known to have crossed the county boundary on frequent occasions.

Osprey

Pandion haliaetus

A scarce but now almost regular visitor, primarily as a spring passage migrant.

In Sage (1959) it was classed as a rare visitor for which there were 18 records, of which six were in May.

There were a total of 41 records for the period 1958–82 and analysis of these by month of occurrence gives the following result:

Jan.	April	May	June	July	Aug.	Sept.	Oct.
1	4	20	6	1	1	7	2

The only years in which it did not occur were 1958, 1962, 1967, 1969, 1970 and 1975. The clear change in status, and in particular its now virtual annual appearance in May, is presumably a reflection of its increase as a breeding species in Scotland. The sole January record was of one at Moor Mill, Radlett, on 8 January 1959, whilst the July record was one at Tring Reservoirs on 14–15 July 1972. The two October records concern one at Tring Reservoirs on 3 October 1965, and another at Bedmond on 21–22 October 1976.

In so far as localities are concerned, 20 of the records refer to Tring Reservoirs, 16 to the Lea valley, three to the Colne valley, and two to other areas (one the Bedmond record mentioned above, and the other to one at Bourne End on 13 May 1978). The three Colne valley records are of single birds at Springwell GP on 18 September 1960, Royal Oak GP on 28 June 1973, and the Moor Mill record mentioned earlier. All the Lea valley records refer to the Amwell GP-Stanstead Abbots GP-Rye Meads-Broxbourne GP-Cheshunt GPs area, except for one in Brocket Park on 18 May 1971, and another at Waltham Cross on 19 June 1977.

Kestrel

Falco tinnunculus

A common resident breeding species, which was the status accorded it in Sage (1959). Immigrants from elsewhere occur outside the breeding season.

MAP 16

This species survived the pesticide era of the late 1950s and early 1960s much more successfully than did the Sparrowhawk. The records of this species given in the annual county bird reports have rarely reflected its true status. However, in 1960 there was evidence that it had much decreased in the NE. of the county, although a pair did breed at Buckland. In 1962 its status in the county was said to be reasonable, although it had probably deteriorated in the east. In that year a maximum of eight were seen along the crest of Pitstone Hill on 2 August. There was definite or suspected breeding at 16 localities in 1964, and at a minimum of eight additional areas in 1965, including five pairs between Digswell and Bramfield Forest.

The only really detailed survey of the breeding distribution of this species was provided by the fieldwork from 1967–73, which was published in Mead and Smith (1982). Records were received from 335 (66 per cent) of the 504 tetrads in the county, with breeding proved in 90 tetrads and probable in 87 more. Density in the predominantly arable north and north-east of the county was low.

It is probable that the species has continued to increase in recent years, although detailed data are lacking. In 1975, for example, there were 60 records in the Stevenage area alone, and in 1978 there were 14 pairs in the 10 kilometre square around that town. In 1980 breeding was reported from 15 areas in Hertfordshire involving some 35 pairs, including about 15 pairs in the Hitchin area. A study by Gladwin (1983) of the breeding birds of central Hertfordshire (i.e. the 10 kilometre squares TL 21 and TL 31) showed that from 1956–80 the population increased from 1–10 pairs in 1956 to 18 pairs in 1980.

Merlin

Falco columbarius

A rare visitor, mostly in the winter, but occasionally on passage.

In Sage (1959) it was classed as an irregular passage migrant and winter visitor.

There are 23 records for the period 1958–82 of which 16 refer to the winter months and are as follows — (all records refer to single birds), Stanborough 23 December 1962; near Tring on 17 November 1967; flying NE. over Stockers Lake on 30 November 1975; at Royston SF on 13 November 1977;

in 1979: at Tring Reservoirs on 9 January, near Wilstone village on 26 February, and at Hilfield Park Reservoir on 22 December; in 1980: at Tring Reservoirs on 21 February, flying west near Bramfield on 30 November and 12 December, and near Lilley on 30 December; at Frogmore, near Stevenage, on 24 January 1981; and in 1982: at Ickleford Common on 17 January, Benington on 24 January, Cheshunt GPs on 23 February, and near Baldock on 3 December.

The remaining records, again all of single birds, are at Tring Reservoirs on 25 April and 6 May 1978, and 16 October 1979; near Newnham on 19 October 1980; flying SE. over Tring Reservoirs on 8 March 1981; at Amwell GP on 5 March, and near Tring on 9 September 1982.

Hobby

Falco subbuteo

A summer visitor, now re-established as a breeding species. Also a regular and often widespread passage migrant.

In Sage (1959) the species was classed as a more or less regular visitor, particularly in spring and autumn. The last known instance of breeding at that time was at Stevenage in 1884.

Between 1958 and 1966 the species had on occasions been seen at a few localities in the breeding season. For example, a pair at Broad Riding Wood, Broxbourne, from mid-May to late July 1960; two pairs near Broxbourne again in 1961; a pair at Hertford Heath between 25 May and 24 July 1962. The first confirmed instances of breeding came in 1967, when a pair reared three young in Bramfield Forest, a pair bred at Gustardwood, near Wheathampstead, a third pair is believed to have nested at Stanborough, and two pairs were seen in the Broxbourne Woods area from May to July. Fieldwork from 1967–73 reported in Mead and Smith (1982) produced evidence of breeding in 10 tetrads, and probable cases in two more. These sites were in central Hertfordshire (Ayot St. Lawrence, Wheathampstead,

Lemsford, Knebworth, Bramfield areas), and the Broxbourne Woods complex further to the SE. From 1974–6 breeding was proved in the Ashridge, Lemsford, Redbourn and Rickmansworth areas. No definite reports of nesting were received from 1977–9, although birds were seen in the breeding season at various sites, and some probably bred. In 1980 there were 37 reports of Hobbies from about 21 different sites, a pair reared three young near Berkhamsted, and another pair may have bred at St. Pauls Walden. Data collected in 1982 suggests population of 9–13 pairs with a rather scattered distribution. Breeding was proved or considered probable by four pairs — in the north near Ashwell, in the Stevenage area, a pair in the east in the Stort valley, and another pair near Wigginton. A further five pairs were holding territories in the Gilston, Broxbourne, Cheshunt, Bricketwood, and Chorleywood areas. Additionally, there may have been a further four or five pairs at other sites.

Migrant individuals may occur at widely scattered locations throughout the county. At Tring Reservoirs in 1982, up to two appeared at the Swallow roost on numerous evenings from mid-August into September.

Peregrine

Falco peregrinus

A very rare winter visitor and passage migrant, with one July record.

Approximately 55 records were known at the time Sage (1959) was published, and he classed it as a regular non-breeding visitor, mainly in the autumn and winter.

Despite the recovery in the breeding population of this species in various parts of Britain, it has become rarer as a visitor to this county. Excluding a bird of known captive origin reported in 1982, there are a total of 12 further records, referring to only nine of the 25 years under review.

1959   Single bids at Easneye, near Ware, on 2 January, and at Rye Meads on 26 March.
1963   Two flying over Ashridge on 21 September.
1965   An immature found dead on Therfield Heath on 10 July.
1966   One circling over Bramfield Forest on 18 September,.
1967   Another at Therfield Heath on 18 April.
1969   A bird present in the Odsey area for some weeks at the beginning of the year, and at Ashridge on 30 October.
1976   One at Baldock on 8 September, another flying ENE. over Potters Bar on 21 November, and at St. Albans on 15 December.
1977   Stooping at Lapwings at Ashwell on 12 October.
1979   The latest record was one at Bourne End on 16 February.

Red-legged Partridge

Alectoris rufa

MAP 17 A common resident breeding species.

At the time of Sage (1959) it was considered to be a common resident breeding species, but rather more local and considerably less numerous than the Grey Partridge.

The status of this species does seem to have changed in the last two decades. Mead and Smith (1982) show records from 337 of the 504 tetrads in the county, with breeding proved in 141 and possible in 82 more. They found it to be by far the commoner of the two species over much of the northern part of the county. There is little evidence of any significant change since 1973, but 'marked declines' were reported in the Baldock–Clothall area, and around Ashwell in 1981. Data submitted for and published in the annual county bird reports rarely reflect the true status in any one year, and information on actual density in any given area is sparse. However, at Ayot St. Lawrence in 1965 only one pair was located on 290 acres (117 hectares) of farmland; about 20 breeding pairs were found in the Bygrave area in 1977; and about the same number in the Pirton area in 1982.

Most reports of coveys of course refer to the winter months, but there have been some exceptions — approximately 100 were counted on the old aerodrome at Nuthampstead in August 1960; a covey of 38 at Churchend Common, near Stevenage, on 25 August 1976; one of 72 at Ardeley on 10 August 1980; and 42 at Graveley on 25 August 1982. Other coveys in excess of 20 birds reported between 1958 and 1982 were as follows — 24 at Codicote on 19 September 1960; 30 at Northaw on 13 February 1963; 25 near Welwyn on 3 January 1970; 41 in two coveys at Kimpton on 26 January 1975; in 1976: 30 at Stanborough on 25 January, a maximum of 100 around Ashwell on 4 December, and one covey of 30 on 5 December; 21 at Turnford Marsh, Cheshunt, on 3 December 1977; 70+ near Royston on 21 January 1978; in 1979: *c.* 80 (largest covey of 28) in the Baldock–Wallington area on 3 January, 28 near Reed on 12 January, *c.* 35 in the Ashwell–Newnham area on 14 January, and 20–25 at Stanborough on 4 February; 35 at Graveley on 7 October 1980; in 1981: 25 near Wallington on 1 February, 24 near Pirton on 7 February, and 32 near Willian in February (date unknown); finally, in 1982: 37 at St. Albans on 28 November.

Grey Partridge

Perdix perdix

A scarce resident breeding species, which has only partly recovered from a **MAP 18**
significant decline in the early 1960s caused by the use of insecticides on
cereal crops. It still shows no sign of regaining the population level of 1963
(*see* graph in Mead and Smith (1982)).

It was classed by Sage (1959) as a very common and widely distributed
resident breeding species, occurring numerously in areas not favoured by
the Red-legged Partridge,.

Although geographically more widespread in the county than the Red-
legged Partridge, it is probably less numerous. In Mead and Smith (1982)
records are given for 376 tetrads (75 per cent of the Hertfordshire total
compared with 67 per cent for the Red-legged Partridge), with breeding
proved in 143 tetrads and probable in 105 more.

As with the preceding species, information submitted for the county bird
reports is usually of very limited value and often the species is not reported at
all. However, the annual reports do contain some data of interest. In 1958 it
was reported to have had a disastrous breeding season around Odsey on the
Cambridgeshire–Hertfordshire border, and another very bad year was
reported there again in 1964. In 1969 it was said to be scarce or absent from
areas in the south and west of the county, decreasing in the St. Albans and
Wheathampstead areas, but increasing considerably around Odsey. It was
recorded as apparently more numerous than the Red-legged Partridge in the
Baldock and Wallington areas in 1972. The 1982 county bird report
commented that it seemed to be considerably scarcer generally than the
latter species. Quantitative data on breeding density is scarce, but examples
are nine pairs in the Cuffley and Northaw area in 1964; in 1977 it was noted
that 20 pairs were present in the Bygrave area; and six to eight pairs in the
Pirton area in 1980.

In so far as the size of reported coveys is concered, there are fewer of more
than 20 birds than is the case for the Red-legged Partridge. At Stanborough
20–30 were seen from August to September 1967; 23 at Symondshyde on 12
January 1969; in 1970 in the Kings Langley area a total of 104 were killed in
two shoots; coveys of 22 and 23 were noted between Baldock and Wallington
on 27 February 1972; in 1976 it was estimated that there was a maximum of
50 around Ashwell, and a covey of 22 was seen on 18 December; about 90
were counted between Baldock and Wallington on 3 January 1979; a covey
of 30 at Graveley on 4 November 1980; one of 20+ on the Weston Hills,
Baldock, on 25 January 1981; and 29 at Pirton in December 1982.

Quail

Coturnix coturnix

MAP 19 A scarce summer visitor more numerous in some years than in others. It may breed annually, but this is difficult to prove.

The status accorded it in Sage (1959) was that of a regular but local summer visitor and passage migrant, and occasionally seen in winter.

During the 25-year period covered by this book no Quail were apparently recorded at all in 1958, 1962, 1973, 1974, 1978 or 1979. From 1959–61 inclusive there were seven reports from localities along the line of the Chiltern Hills, the favoured habitat of this species in Hertfordshire. A record of one at Old Parkbury GP, Radlett, on 10 May 1963, an unusual site, clearly referred to a migrant. In 1964 there was a widespread influx of Quail into the British Isles, and in Hertfordshire birds were heard calling between 28 June and 2 August from about 33 different sites on the Chilterns from Radwell, Therfield Heath, Wallington, and westwards to Kings Walden, Lilley, and Hexton. In addition there were a few further reports from more western localities, including one at Chorleywood on 26 May. Undoubtedly many pairs must have bred in that year although no definite evidence was forthcoming. However, in 1965 at least three pairs bred on Therfield Heath; approximately 17 were heard in the Lilley area during the course of the summer; and others at Hitchin and in the Tring area. In 1966 about 14 were heard at different sites in the Lilley area in July, one at Baldock on 3 June, and two in Knebworth Park on 6 June.

Based on fieldwork from 1967–73, Mead and Smith (1982) record reports from 34 tetrads in the county, with breeding proved in four (two near Tring, one on the Essex–Hertfordshire border near Sawbridgeworth, and a pair with young at Potters Bar in 1968), and suspected in a further 20. The majority of these records refer to 1970 which was a good year for this species. From 1975–81 (no reports in 1978 or 1979) there were only nine records, all from along the Chilterns except for one at Stevenage on 25 July 1976 and a pair with young near Symondshyde Great Wood on 19 July 1981. More recently, in 1982, a pair bred at Therfield, and others were heard calling near Therfield (two), Pirton (three), Baldock (two), south of Royston, Ayot St. Lawrence, and near Puttenham.

The only winter record is of one at Wheathampstead rubbish tip on 26 December 1971.

Pheasant

Phasianus colchicus

MAP 20 An abundant and widespread resident breeding species, whose status has remained unchanged since Sage (1959).

This species is still reared and released in considerable numbers for sporting purposes. In Hitch Wood, for example, no less than 115 were shot on 20 November 1982. In Mead and Smith (1982) records are shown for 459 (91 per cent) of the 504 tetrads in the county, with breeding proved in 250 and probable in 104 more.

Golden Pheasant

Chrysolophus pictus

Although this species was added to the official British list in 1970, there is no evidence of a feral breeding population in the county.

There are now six records in Hertfordshire, as follows:

1974   Male seen at Watery Grove, in Knebworth Park, on 30 September, the first record in the county.
1977   Another seen at Batchwood on 8 May.
1978   One at Amwell in May.
1981   Male at Holwell Hyde on 28 April, and another at Amwell GP on 1 November.
1982   A very tame female was present at Stockers Lake from 11 August to 20 September.

Lady Amherst's Pheasant

Chrysolophus amherstiae

Possibly established as a resident breeding species, but so far there has been no definite evidence of nesting.

MAP 21

In Mead and Smith (1982) there are records from four tetrads. The one instance of definite breeding was in fact over the border in Bedfordshire, at Luton Hoo. The two possible nesting sites were at Hoo Wood and Hudnall Common, and there was one sighting from the Whippendell Woods area. Subsequent records have been of a male in Hitch Wood on 16 August 1979; a male at Ashridge on 22 and 25 March, and four males at Chorleywood (date unknown) in 1980; and a male at Pirton on 15 February 1981.

Water Rail

Rallus aquaticus

MAP 22 A resident breeding species which has probably increased as such during the past 25 years. Also a winter visitor and passage migrant.

Sage (1959) regarded it as a fairly common but local winter visitor, probably resident in some localities. He was able to quote only one definitive record of breeding, and that was by the River Gade in Cassiobury Park in 1935.

Definite proof of the nesting of this species is remarkably difficult to obtain. Breeding season records from 1958–66 inclusive came from Cassiobury Park in 1958; Broxbourne GPs, Rye Meads, and Sawbridgeworth in 1959; in 1960: from Rye Meads (carrying nesting material), and an adult with juveniles by the River Gade at Great Gaddesden; 1961: Cheshunt GPs, Rye Meads, and Eastwick; and in 1966 breeding was suspected at Tewinbury and Tewinwater in the Mimram valley. In addition, from 1962–6 one or two pairs nested annually near Ashwell on the Cambridgeshire–Hertfordshire border. The fieldwork from 1967–73 which led to the publication of the atlas by Mead and Smith (1982) produced records from 30 (six per cent) of the 504 Hertfordshire tetrads, with breeding proved in five (at Tring Reservoirs, Maple Cross, Ashwell, on the Essex–Hertfordshire border near Bishops Stortford, and at Tewinbury).

Between 1974 and 1982 the species was reported from the following localities in the breeding season — the Colne valley below Rickmansworth (particularly at Maple Cross); Frogmore, near Stevenage; Ickleford and Oughtonhead Commons; the Lea valley (Cheshunt GPs, Rye House Marsh, and Rye Meads); and at Tring Reservoirs. Breeding was actually proved at Rye House Marsh in 1978, and in September 1979 a juvenile in downy plumage was seen at Cheshunt GPs.

Both on passage and in winter the Water Rail is much more widespread and may be found at almost any suitable location. Data on total numbers at any given site are not extensive. In 1959 seven were found along a three-quarters of a mile (1.21 kilometre) stretch of the River Hiz at Ickleford on 6 December. Between Kimpton Mill and the Panshanger, in the Mimram valley, a total of six were located on 27 December 1961. In 1969 there were eight on disused watercress beds in Cassiobury Park on 9 February, and nine there on 14 January 1979. The maximum winter count in 1970 was 10 at Cheshunt GPs on 31 January, and there were 11 there from January to March 1981. At Rye Meads the highest winter counts have been 15 on 25 November 1972, 10 in December 1975 and February 1976, 11 in January

1979, and 10 on 12 December 1981. The maximum count in the Rickmansworth area was at least nine at Maple Cross on 20 February 1972. At Tring Reservoirs the maximum were 10+ in January and February 1979, and 15 on 19 December 1981 when the reed beds were frozen. Up to eight were present on Oughtonhead Common in February 1981. In the Mimram valley a total of eight were counted between Digswell and the Panshanger on 17 January 1982.

A paper by Webb (1981) describes the results of an attempt to assess the numbers of this species in the Hitchin area during the winter of 1979/80. A minimum of 19 birds were found distributed as follows — Oughtonhead Common (five), Purwell Ninesprings (two), Ickleford Common (three), Hitchin Priory (two), Ickleford SF (one), Kimpton Mill (two), Cadwell Marsh (three), and Kimpton Hoo (one). It was considered that the total was an underestimate since some individuals probably went undetected at Kimpton Mill and along the River Mimram near Whitwell.

Within recent years the total number of sites from which birds have been reported in winter has been fairly consistent. For example, 20 in 1976, 1979 and 1980, and 24 in 1981.

Spotted Crake

Porzana porzana

A very rare breeding species (once only), and a rare non-breeding visitor with the majority of the records referring to the winter.

In Sage (1959) it was classed as a rare winter visitor and passage migrant and 17 records were listed.

A pair bred by the River Lea near Wheathampstead in 1967, an adult and young being seen by two very experienced observers.

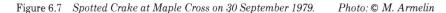

Figure 6.7   *Spotted Crake at Maple Cross on 30 September 1979.*   Photo: © *M. Armelin*

There are approximately 18 additional records for 11 of the 25 years covered by this book. The first occurrence since 1937 was at Cassiobury Park, Watford, in 1965. The records are detailed below:

1965   At Cassiobury Park, Watford, on disused watercress beds, four were seen on 4 January, two on 5 January, and one on 21, 28 and 30 January and on 4 March.

1966   One seen at Tewinbury in the Mimram valley on 1 December remained until (25 January 1967).

1967   One seen at Hilfield Park Reservoir on 31 December.

1968   One at Tewinbury from 20 October to 31 December.

1969   What may have been a different individual seen again at Tewinbury during February, remained until 17 March.

1972   One at Maple Cross in the Colne valley on 5 March.

1973   A summer record of one at Tring Reservoirs in mid-August which remained into November, one at Cassiobury Park from 31 March to 29 April, and another at Old Parkbury GP, Radlett, on 10 September.

1975   Another summer record was one at Maple Cross on 10 August.

1977   At Tring Reservoirs, one was noted on 3 November and then almost daily from 8 to 20 November.

1979   No less than four records of single birds — Cassiobury Park from 11 to 16 February, Stanstead Abbots GP and Rye Meads from 23 to 26 March, calling on Ickleford Common on 27 May, and at Maple Cross on 29 to 30 September.

1982   The latest record was one present at Amwell GP from 18 September to 2 October.

Little Crake

Porzana parva

A very rare vagrant for which there have been no records since Sage (1959). These comprised one said to have been shot at Tring Reservoirs on 5 January 1887, and one which was present on Oughtonhead Common from 22 January to 19 March 1953.

Baillon's Crake

Porzana pusilla

Another very rare vagrant for which the only record remains that cited by Sage (1959), of one shot at Cheshunt on 24 October 1891.

Corncrake

Crex crex

A rare and very irregular summer visitor which may occasionally still breed. **MAP 23**

It was classed as a very scarce summer visitor by Sage (1959), breeding in a few suitable localities but rather more numerous and widespread on passage.

Since then the status of this species has worsened still further, not only in Hertfordshire but over the whole of western Europe. From 1958–82 there were only about 16 records for the county, and it occurred in only some nine or ten of these 25 years; the records are listed as follows:

1959   One heard calling near Bishops Stortford from 2–5 May, and near Ware, two were heard and one seen on 27 June, and another heard on 5 July.

1961   One reported from Royston on 28 September.

1962   One heard at Kings Langley in late May was the first reported in that area for 40 years.

1963   Similarly, one heard in a hayfield at Watford on 7 July was the first since 1925.

Fieldwork for the *Breeding Bird Atlas* project (Mead and Smith 1982) from 1967–73 produced evidence of breeding in three tetrads, and probable cases in three more:

1967   A pair bred near Great Gaddesden, another pair possibly bred at Tewinbury; not included in the atlas data were one at MardockHill, Wareside, on 11 August, and two at Royston during harvesting on 31 August.

1968   A pair definitely bred near St. Pauls Walden.

1970   A pair possibly bred at Northchurch Common according to the atlas data.

1975   One at Munden Farm, Bricket Wood, on 28 September.

1976   One heard calling all summer at Gosmorebury, near Hitchin.

The *Breeding Bird Atlas* data also records that a pair bred near Offley, another pair near Cuffley and a further pair possibly bred near Preston during the period of fieldwork from 1967–73, but actual years unknown.

Moorhen

Gallinula chloropus

An abundant and widespread resident breeding species in all suitable **MAP 24**
habitats, with numbers probably augmented from outside the county in winter. This is essentially the same status accorded it by Sage (1959).

107

In Mead and Smith (1982) records are shown for 399 (79 per cent) of the 504 tetrads in the county, with breeding proved in 320 and probable in a further 18. This is a species which, in the normal course of events, most observers do not include in records submitted for the county bird report. As a consequence of this neglect it is difficult to establish population trends over a period of time, or to obtain data on the density of breeding pairs at any given site. There is, however, a modicum of information on the latter subject. In his study of the breeding birds of Stockers Lake and Springwell GP, Chesterman (1978) found that from 1970–6 the mean number of breeding pairs was 19, with a range of 14–21 pairs. In 1980 it was estimated that 65+ pairs bred in the Hitchin area (the size of the area was not stated), and in the same year 30–40 pairs bred at Amwell GP. An estimated 60 pairs bred at Rye Meads in 1982.

Counts outside the breeding season are available for a number of sites almost none of which receive regular coverage. All the counts quoted below are the maxima for the years concerned. There are, for example, only five such counts for Tring Reservoirs — 70 in November 1969; 73 on 9 December 1980; 57 in January and 60 in February 1981; and 170 on 30 September 1982. To these may be added a record of 60+ feeding on a ploughed field near Tring SF on 20 November 1966. In the Colne valley a series of 23 counts are available for Maple Cross for 14 different years, and these are listed in Table 6.11. There are some additional counts from elsewhere in the Colne valley. At Stockers Lake there were counts of c. 65 on 14 January 1973; 50 on 12

TABLE 6.11   *Maximum counts of Moorhens at Maple Cross, 1961–81*

1961	100+ on 24 May	1973	135 on 4 February
	250+ on 29 September		90 on 1 December
	250+ on 15 November	1974	100 on 30 December
1964	100–150 on 12 August	1975	100 on 7 December
1965	75 on 10 October	1976	130 in January/February
1967	150+ on 14 January	1978	90 on 10 December
	200 on 17 December	1979	60 on 14 January
1971	110 on 4 October		80 on 23 December
1972	120 on 19 January	1980	100 on 13 January
	100 on 22 October	1981	140 on 18 January
	100 in November/December		150 on 22 February
			80 on 25 October

February 1978; 50 on 1 March 1979; 60 on 6 January and 64 on 26 December 1980; 55 on 11 January, and 56 on 30 November 1981.

A few counts are available from the valley of the River Gade. On 18 December 1966 a total of 56 were counted along a 200 yard (183 m) stretch of the river bank at Water End. Also at Water End, in November 1970, a total of 60 were seen. In Cassiobury Park 70 were counted on 17 February 1979, and in 1982 there were 117 on 14 March.

Turning now to the Lea valley, there are five counts for the lake in Brocket Park — 44 on 10 January 1977, 69 on 15 December 1978, 64 on 10 February 1979, 48 on 21 December 1980, and 80 on 28 October 1981. In January and December 1972 maxima of 77 were present at Lemsford Springs. Further down the valley there are a few counts from Hatfield Park (The Broadwater) — 99 in October, 95 in November, and 86 in December 1979; 90 in January, 110 in October, 115 in November, and 110 in December 1980. A count of 58 was obtained at Hertford on 23 December 1981. Only three counts seem to be available for Rye Meads — 504 on 1 February 1964, 100+ on 7 January 1967, and 100–200 wintered in 1969. At Amwell GP it was estimated that 100 were present throughout 1981. Finally, there were 50 at Hooks Marsh, Cheshunt, on 2 January 1970, and 60 at Cheshunt GPs on 4 March 1973.

There are some data from certain of the minor river valleys. At Whitwell on the Mimram there were c. 50 on 13 December 1964, c. 60 on 14 March 1965, 70 on 3 January 1970, and 47 on 21 February 1981. During October to December 1969 there were 50 at Kimpton SF. About 70 were present at Tewinbury on various dates in 1970. In the Beane valley on 8 January 1973 a total of 82 were counted between Woodhall Park and Stapleford (a distance of just under one mile or 1.6 km), and in 1977 a total of 161 were counted between Aston and Waterford (a distance of about six miles, or 9.6 km) on 6 January. On 12 February 1977 there were 61 in Woodhall Park. The sole count from the Chess valley was 50 at Sarratt Mill on 3 March 1979.

In the north of the county, at Radwell Lake, there were 44 on 26 December 1966, 100 on 15 October 1967, 50 on 18 January 1970, and 30 on 30 December 1978. In the west, at Kings Langley GP, there were counts of c. 60 on 30 December 1967, and 33 (plus 46 on the adjacent canal) on 23 February 1969.

Coot

Fulica atra

A common resident breeding species, and also a winter visitor. This is **MAP 25** essentially the same status given in Sage (1959).

As a breeding species the Coot is primarily confined to water bodies exceeding 0.5 hectares in extent, but some pairs also nest along suitable stretches of various rivers. Breeding season surveys of this species were carried out in 1965 (Sage 1966), and in 1973 (Sage 1973). The results of these two surveys are given in Appendix D, in which the Colne valley total for 1973 has been adjusted on the basis of data for Stockers Lake and Springwell GP given in Chesterman (1978). The appendix shows that the approximate total of breeding pairs was 201 in 1965 and 280 in 1973, an increase of 79 pairs or 39 per cent. However, it should be noted that Dyrham Park and Wrotham Park which held a total of three pairs in 1973, were in fact in Middlesex in 1965. Similarly, Greenhill Park (Barnet) and Hadley Wood lake, both of which held single pairs in 1965 were, by 1973, part of Greater London and not Hertfordshire. Additionally, the River Lea from Hertford Lock to Ware, Kings Meads (Hertford), Stanstead Abbots GP, the River Beane at Frogmore, Shafford Mill on the River Ver, and Bonningtons at Hunsdon, which together held a total of 24 pairs in 1973, had all been colonised since 1965. Ten sites which held a total of 15 pairs in 1973 were not covered in 1965, but almost certainly supported breeding pairs at that time.

Removing Greenhill Park and Hadley Wood lakes from the calculations, and assuming that the 10 sites (containing 15 pairs) covered in 1973 but not in 1965, had the same number of pairs in the latter year, would make the comparative totals 214 pairs in 1965, and 280 pairs in 1973, an increase of 66 pairs or 31 per cent. It must be pointed out, however, that 1973 was an atypical year in that the water levels at Hilfield Park and Tring Reservoirs were abnormally low resulting in fewer pairs nesting than would be the case in a normal year. The normal breeding population at Hilfield Park Reservoir would be about 18 pairs (as in 1972), and at Tring Reservoirs 20–30 pairs (Hayward 1968). Therefore, the true total for the reservoirs would be 38–48 pairs, giving a theoretical 1973 total of 311–321 pairs, an increase since 1965 of 97–107 pairs or 45–50 per cent.

According to Mead and Smith (1982), data collected from 1967–73 showed proof of breeding in 90 tetrads, and probable in five more. Examination of this data reveals records from about 28 sites additional to those listed in Sage (1973), although not all of these may have held breeding pairs every year. However, it seems reasonable to suggest that at that time the true total breeding population in the county may have been of the order of 330–350 pairs.

A study of Coot numbers at Tring Reservoirs was carried out from 1962–7 (Hayward 1968). He found that under normal conditions numbers were lowest at the beginning of the breeding season, rising rapidly during June and July owing to an influx of adult (and presumably) non–breeding birds. Numbers then remained high until the end of the year, with a gradual decrease towards the onset of the breeding season. Further studies at these reservoirs have been carried out by Peter Moles in recent years, and he has prepared Figure 6.8 showing his results, together with some of those from Hayward (op.cit.). The development of the breeding population of this species at Hilfield Park Reservoir from 1955–68 has been discussed in detail by Sage (1969). During this period the number of nesting pairs rose from one in 1957 to 18 in 1967, and 15 in 1968. The rise and fall in the numbers present at this reservoir follows a pattern similar to that at Tring Reservoirs. The maximum number of Coot ever recorded at Tring Reservoirs appears to be 1086 that were present in August 1982.

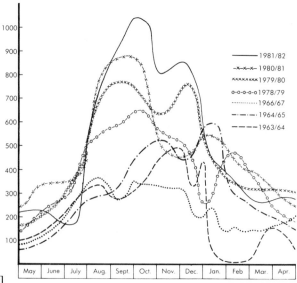

Figure 6.8 *Coot counts at Tring Reservoirs, 1963/64 to 1981/82*

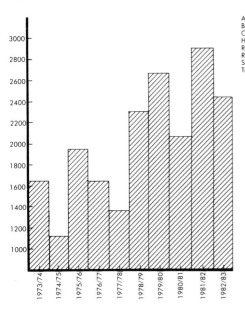

Figure 6.9   *Coot–Mean of November to February counts 1973/74 to 1982/83*

Substantial numbers of Coot are present in the county during the winter period from November–February inclusive. The major numbers at this time are found in the Lea valley below Hertford, the Colne valley below Rickmansworth, Hilfield Park Reservoir, and Tring Reservoirs. During the 25 years dealt with here the peak numbers at Hilfield Park Reservoir occurred from 1958–60 when the maxima were — 1150 on 25 January 1958 and 25 October 1959, 1200 on 8 November 1959 (this remains the highest count ever obtained in Hertfordshire), and 1126 on 2 October 1960. During the 10 years 1973–82 the maxima were 615 in November 1973, and 678 in December 1973. At Tring Reservoirs the maximum counts in the same 10-year period were 1038 in October and 970 in November 1981, 924 in September and 963 in December 1982. There have also been some high counts at the Rickmansworth GPs with maxima of 720 (at Troy Mill GP alone) in December 1975, 850 in January 1976, and 1057 in January 1982. Individual sites in the Lea valley below Hertford have produced some high counts, examples being — Rye Meads: 458 on 14 January 1965, 564 in December 1973, and 840 in January 1979; Broxbourne GP; 407 in November 1977, 460 in December 1979, and 556 in January 1980; Cheshunt GPs: 587 in January 1979, 592 in November and 680 in December 1981, and 705 in November and 685 in December 1982.

An attempt has been made to plot the total winter populations of this species at eight different sites for the winters 1973/74 to 1982/83, and the results are shown in Figure 6.9. However, the totals for some winters are too low due to a lack of counts on certain dates. This is particularly the case in respect of the Rickmansworth GPs where there were no counts at all for November and December of 1973 and 1974, December 1978, January and February 1974 and 1975, February 1977, and January 1978. A further problem with this locality is that even when counts have been made, not all of the pits may have been covered. In the case of Tring Reservoirs there were no counts for February of 1973–5 inclusive, January 1976, November 1975 and 1977, and December 1973–7 inclusive.

Great Bustard

Otis tarda

There has been no change in the status of this species since Sage (1959). It was known to frequent Royston (Therfield) Heath in the seventeenth century, and the last to be seen in the county was in that neighbourhood about 1808.

Oystercatcher

Haematopus ostralegus

An occasional but now regular visitor, most frequent in spring, and only a little less so in autumn and winter.

In Sage (1959) it was classed as an irregular passage migrant and winter visitor, and about 27 records were listed.

There has clearly been a change in the status of this species, since from 1958–82 (none were reported in 1971) there were a total of about 77 records, of which 27 refer to Tring Reservoirs, 27 to the Lea valley below Hertford, seven to Hilfield Park Reservoir, only five to the Colne valley, and 11 to miscellaneous localities. Analysis of the 77 records by month of occurrence gives the following result:

Jan.	Feb.	Mar.	April	May	June
6	7	13	11	4	3

July	Aug.	Sep.	Oct.	Nov.	Dec.
4	14	3	3	2	7

The June records comprise one at Tring Reservoirs on 4 June 1975, and 8 June 1976, and one at Rye Meads on 14 June 1981. The apparent scarceness of this species in the Colne valley is interesting, the only records being of single birds at Frogmore (Radlett) on 23 August 1959, at West Hyde GP on 11 March 1963 and again on 22 December 1969, Troy Mill GP on 15 March 1981, and at Stockers Lake on 6 December 1982.

There were only 11 records involving more than one bird, and very few of those were of five or more together — five at Tring Reservoirs on 18 May 1968, five at Rye Meads on 1 February 1970, five at Marshalswick on 31 July 1977, and 18 at Amwell GP on 2 January 1982.

Avocet

Recurvirostra avosetta

A very rare spring passage migrant, but with two June records. First added to the county list in 1973, there are currently seven records:

1973 A single bird was seen at Tring Reservoirs by several members of the staff of the British Trust for Ornithology on 28 June.

1974 Two present at Tring Reservoirs on 28 April.

1976 Two were seen at Hadley, near Barnet (Greater London) on 30 April, one of which flew off in the direction of Hilfield Park Reservoir where one was seen later that same day.

1978 Two seen over Rye Meads and Stanstead Abbots GP on 13 May flying NE.

1980 A solitary bird noted flying over Stanstead Abbots GP on 23 April.

1981 Two at Hilfield Park Reservoir on 2 June.

1982 Most recent record of no less than six seen at Hilfield Park Reservoir on 2 April.

Stone Curlew

Burhinus oedicnemus

A rare summer visitor breeding in the NE. of the county. Also a passage migrant and occasional winter visitor. This is esentially the same status as that given in Sage (1959).

Some historical information not given in Sage (op. cit.) is to be found in Nunn (1898). He states that in the 1840s the species was fairly common in all the open fields in the area of Royston, Therfield, Kelshall, and Sandon, but became scarcer as agriculture improved.

The Stone Curlew nests annually on arable farmland in the north of the county, although reports of this are not forthcoming every year. Indeed, in some years, such as 1959, 1962, 1963 and 1970, no observers report it at all. Taking the period 1958–66, we find very little definite evidence of breeding. In 1958 a pair were present at a site between Baldock and Royston (where breeding occurred in 1957) but no nest was found. In 1960 five were located near Royston, and four near Reed on 24 May, and about seven were calling in the Therfield area on 16 June, but no nests were found at any of these sites. A pair did, however, breed near Ashwell (just north of Arbury Banks) in 1964,

113

and there were two at Therfield on 28 June of that year. At least two pairs were present near Barley in the breeding season in 1965, but the only report in 1966 was of one on Therfield Heath on 14 August.

In Mead and Smith (1982) it is stated that during the period 1967–73 records were received from 12 tetrads, with breeding proved in six and probable in four more. Seven pairs were present and probably bred in the Royston area in 1973. Two nests were found between Baldock and Royston in 1971, and there were three reports of probable breeding in the Pirton area. The situation since 1973 is that a pair bred in the Ashwell area, and three pairs near Reed in 1974; in the Royston area one pair bred in 1977 and reared two young, and again in 1978 when there may also have been a second pair; in 1980 a pair probably bred at Royston; in 1981 a pair reared two young in the Royston area, and at least three were heard near Barley on 21 July; finally, in 1982, birds were first noted at a site in the Royston area in April, and three were seen there in May. Also in that year, a pair were seen at Cole Green on 24–25 April, with one still present on 4 May.

In the Barley–Reed–Royston area of north-east Hertfordshire, at least 11 pairs were present in 1975 and 12–14 pairs in 1976, but no definite proof of breeding was obtained in either year.

Records of migrants are not numerous and usually refer to one or two individuals, and most come from the north of the county. However, three flew south over Rye Meads on 12 July 1961; two were seen near the River Ash at Wareside from 1–7 April 1967; and there was one at Rye Meads on 1–2 May 1971.

Other records of interest concern a party of eight seen near Odsey in early November 1961, and the same number in one field at Reed on 2 August 1964. The former is only the fourth winter record for the county, the others being one near Clothall in December 1927; one at Box Wood, Stevenage, in February 1933 (Sage 1962); and a small flock near Kelshall on 15 November 1947.

Little Ringed Plover

Charadrius dubius

MAP 26 A scarce breeding species, primarily in the Colne and Lea valleys, but occasionally elsewhere. Also a passage migrant.

It was classed by Sage (1959) as a summer visitor, breeding locally, and a passage migrant.

Although most breeding pairs are found in gravel pits, exposed ground in the vicinity of sewage works has also been utilised from time to time. Attempts to tabulate the number of pairs present in Hertfordshire in the breeding season for the period 1958–82 has proved frustratingly difficult for several reasons, including obsessive secrecy regarding sites, conflicting details given in various local bird reports, and a general lack of published detail. However, data from various sources are shown in Table 6.12, but it

114

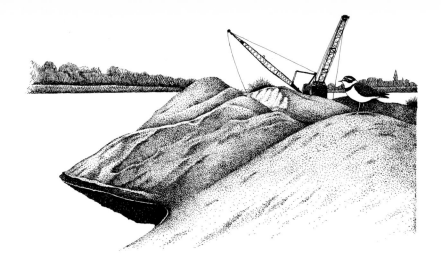

should be borne in mind that in addition to the problems already mentioned, coverage in some years was probably incomplete. Discrepancies between the figures in this Table and those in the published results of the various national surveys by Parrinder (1964), and Parrinder and Parrinder (1969 and 1975) are mentioned. It can be seen that during this 25-year period the maximum

TABLE 6.12   Population statistics of the Little Ringed Plover in Hertfordshire from 1958–82

Year	No. of pairs present	Number of sites in Colne valley	Lea valley	Others
1958	9[a]	1	2	1
1959	8	1	3	—
1960	8	1	4	—
1961	7[b]	2	5	—
1962	4	1	1	—
1963	3	1	1	—
1964	7	1	1	—
1965	13–14	6	3	—
1966	10–15	2	5	—
1967	8	2	3	—
1968	10	4	2	—
1969	data inadequate			
1970	11–14	5	1	1
1971	6	1	2	2
1972	11	2	2	—
1973	33	6	5	6
1974	6[c]	2	2	—
1975	7[d]	3	1	2
1976	13	3	2	2
1977	6	—	2	2
1978	9	3	—	5
1979	14	3	2+	5
1980	17	1	4	5
1981	19–21	1	4	6
1982	25	1	4	6

NOTES: (a) Parrinder (1964) gives seven pairs

(b) Parrinder (1964) gives six pairs

(c) The *London Bird Report* for this year says seven pairs at six sites

(d) This total includes a pair at Royston SF in July. The *London Bird Report* for this year says seven pairs at five sites

115

number of pairs present was 33 in 1973, 19–21 in 1981, and 25 in 1982. Over this period the species has nested in at least 30 different sites.

The maximum numbers are usually seen in July and August. Examples of maximum counts are 16 at Broxbourne SF from 23–29 July 1958, 40+ at Rye Meads on 29 July 1959, 12 at Maple Cross on 12 July 1963, about 20 at Tring Reservoirs on 3 September 1974, 10 at Rye Meads and Stanstead Abbots GP in July and August 1980, 24 at Rye Meads on 18 July 1981, and 29 near Cole Green on 27 June 1982. During migration odd birds have been reported from a variety of scattered localities which have included Ickleford SF, Letchworth SF, Nuthampstead, Tewinbury and Wareside.

Ringed Plover

Charadrius hiaticula

MAP 27 A rare and irregular breeding species. Also a common passage migrant and occasional winter visitor.

The first breeding record for the county was that of a pair at Rye Meads in 1957, as quoted by Sage (1959), who otherwise classed it as a common spring and autumn passage migrant.

There have been seven subsequent occasions when breeding was suspected, attempted but failed, or was successful. A pair was present at Rye Meads from 19 April to 11 May 1958, but their territory was flooded and no nesting took place. In 1959 up to three were present at this locality from April to July and, although no nest was found, a family party of four was seen on 1 July. The next instance of proved breeding was a pair at Amwell GP in 1976, and again in 1981. In 1977 a pair attempted to nest at Bowyers GP, Cheshunt. In 1982 a pair were present at Amwell GP from 5 March until June, but there was no proof of breeding. In that year a pair did, however, nest at Holwell Hyde near Welwyn Garden City. In order to avoid confusion it should be pointed out that the two instances of probable breeding of this species given in Mead and Smith (1982) in fact refer to two pairs that were present just over the Essex border at Nazeing GP in 1967.

Analysis of approximately 500 records for the period 1958–82 showed that the spring passage commences in March and reaches its peak in May. Some autumn migrants may appear in July, but the main movement is concentrated in August and September (normally involving far more birds than occur in the spring) and tapers off rapidly in October. The majority of the migrants pass along the valleys of the Lea and the Colne (uncommon), and through Tring Reservoirs. Occasionally, as in 1981 for example, there may be no records at all from Tring. A few migrants do, however, occur irregularly at other localities, as for example Hilfield Park Reservoir, and at Letchworth and Royston SFs.

Throughout the 25 years discussed here, groups in excess of five at any one time were not frequent. Examples were eight at Tring Reservoirs on 30 August 1958; 13 there on 8 October 1961; six at Hilfield Park Reservoir on 13

August 1963; up to six at Rye Meads in July and August 1964; eight at Maple Cross GP on 8–9 May 1965; eight at Tring Reservoirs on 17 September 1968; seven at Royston SF on 11 August 1971; 12 at Tring Reservoirs on 18 August and 30 on 14 September 1973 (the highest count for the period); in 1974 there were 11 at Stanstead Abbots GP in August and September, and at Tring Reservoirs 22 on 14 and 16 August, and 25 on the 29th. In 1976 there were up to 22 at Tring Reservoirs in May. Numbers at Tring have declined in recent years, partly as a result of increased autumn water levels.

There have been only eight winter records in the 25 years with which we are concerned – at Tring Reservoirs on 4 November 1970; one at Hilfield Park Reservoir on 24 January 1973; one at Tring Reservoirs in late February 1976; one at the reservoirs on 20 February, and four at the nearby sewage fields on 27 February 1977; one over Lower Wigginton on 4 November 1979; one at Rye Meads on 6 February, and another at Tring Reservoirs on 25 February 1982.

Kentish Plover

Charadrius alexandrinus

A very rare vagrant.

The first record of this species for the county was one at Startops End Reservoir, Tring, on 16 August 1964. In 1976 a pair were present at Tring Reservoirs from 22–24 April, and one on 25 April, and were seen by several observers. In the county bird report for that year (*Trans. Herts. Nat. Hist. Soc.* 28:28, 1979) it was stated that these were the second and third records for the county. However, since the bird seen on 25 April was almost certainly one of the two seen on the previous three days, it is best to regard the species as having only occurred twice.

Dotterel

Charadrius morinellus

A very rare spring passage migrant.

In Sage (1959) it was pointed out that it had formerly been a regular spring and autumn passage migrant, but had become extremely rare with the most recent record being in September 1913. Additional historical information is given by Nunn (1898) who states that it used to occur regularly on spring migration in the Royston–Therfield–Kelshall–Sandon area. He last saw it about 1877 when a flock of 60 or so appeared and stayed one day.

During the 25 years covered by this book there have been nine records:

1969   Two seen near Therfield on 15 May, 54 years since the previous record in the county.

1973   One reported at Pirton on 5 April (an abnormally early date), and five at Kelshall, near Royston, on 12 May.

1979   Eight at Ashwell on 27 to 28 April, followed by 39 on 11 May at Arbury Banks, near Ashwell, and 21 of these were still present on 12 May.

1981   One seen at Ashwell on 9 and 10 May, then nine at Newnham on 12 May with one still present on 13 May.

1982   A flock of 12 at Ashwell on 11 May flew off to the NW. in the early evening, and five were present near Barley from 12 to 16 May.

Golden Plover

Pluvialis apricaria

A common winter visitor and passage migrant, occasionally appearing also in summer. This is essentially the status accorded it in Sage (1959).

Although small numbers of this species may be seen during the winter months (November–February) at many scattered localities throughout the county, the larger flocks are normally restricted to certain favoured sites, although these may vary in location over a period of years. During the 25-year period with which we are concerned there have been five sites which have been of major importance for this species for varying periods, and a relatively small number of other localities where large numbers have been recorded on a few occasions. The main sites and their history are briefly summarised in Table 6.13. It has to be emphasised that the Table, and the histograms discussed later, are based on data available in the annual county bird reports and there will have been some years when coverage was incomplete.

TABLE 6.13   *Main Golden Plover wintering areas 1958–82*

Location	Period of use*	Max. No. Recorded	Min. No. Recorded
Shenleybury	1958–78	450	2
Symondshyde, Lemsford, Stanborough, Cromer Hyde	1965–82	700	10
Tewin, Datchworth, Bramfield, Woolmer Green, Burnham Green	1958–66	1000	60
Pirton area	1968–81	1000+	50
Ashwell area	1976–82	500	150

*Not necessarily used every winter during the years specified

The Shenleybury site reached its peak in the winter of 1961/62, and was not used at all from 1970-2 or from 1974-6. Maximum use of the Symondshyde site and adjacent areas was during the winters of 1967/68 (up to 600), 1968/69 (up to 600), and 1977/78 (up to 700). The population at Tewin and adjacent areas reached its peak in the winter of 1963/64 (up to 1000), and again in 1966/67 (up to 700). The Pirton area population was at its maximum in the winter of 1976/77 with 1000+ birds. The Ashwell area came into use relatively recently with a maximum population to date of 500 in the winter of 1982/83.

Other areas where high numbers have been noted include Peters Green, near Kimpton, with 250 in January 1961; Broxbourne with 200 in February 1961; Hamper Mill with 150 in December 1979 (this is not a common species in the lower Colne valley); the Harpenden area with 300 in December 1980, and 300 in January 1981; and in 1982: Stotfold with 400 in February, Gilston Park with 140 in February, and Redbourn with 300 in February; and Tring Reservoirs where 200 were seen in January 1980, 182 in February and 350 in December 1982.

Maximum numbers reported from all localities have been analysed in two groups (November–December and January–February) and the results are shown in the histograms Figures 6.10 and 6.11. Several points of interest emerge from this analysis. It can be seen that with two exceptions, all the peak numbers have occurred in the November–December periods, which suggests that many birds leave the county before the end of the year. An exception was the winter of 1976/77 when the total population was between 1440 and 1550 for the whole four-month period. The high of 1250 in January–February 1981 was a considerable increase over the 300 present during November–December 1980.

During the 22 winters from 1960/61 to 1981/82 there were only seven when the maximum populations for the four month periods were in excess of 1000, these winters being 1963/64, 1966/67, 1968/69, 1976/77, 1977/78,

Figure 6.10 *Golden Plover – November/December maxima at the main wintering sites, 1960–82*

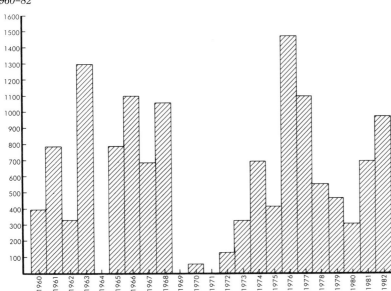

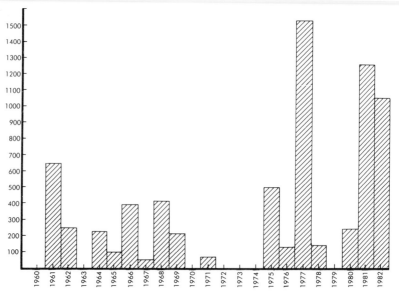

Figure 6.11   *Golden Plover – January/February maxima at the main wintering sites,*
1960–82

1980/81 and 1981/82. The weather conditions related to these peaks are summarised below:

1963/64   Brief period of severe frost in late November.
1966/67   Cold spell from mid-December until mid-January.
1968/69   Cold spell from late December until mid-January.
1976/77   Mainly mild, but with higher than average rainfall.
1977/78   Short cold spell in late November.
1980/81   Mild in January and February.
1981/82   Snow in December and early January.

It can be seen that the highest population level, that of 1550 from November 1976 through to February 1977, occurred in mild and wet conditions.

Generally speaking flocks decrease in size during January and February, to be followed by a marked increase during the spring passage in March and April. Some examples of the larger flocks noted were 370 at Codicote on 5 April, and 500 at Ayot St. Lawrence on 15 April 1967; 500 at Symondshyde on 15 March 1973; 400 in the Pirton area on 15 April 1974; 800 at Long Marston on 9 April 1975, and 400 there in late March 1976 and 1977; 600 near Sandon on 30 March, and 800 at Ashwell on 16 April 1977; c. 1000 at Ashwell from 29 March to 15 April, and 500 at Pirton on 21 April 1978; flocks of 1000 and 700 in the Ashwell area on 11 March 1979; near Pirton a flock of 1000 on 30 March had increased to 2000 by 12 April, and there were 1000 at Ashwell on 4 April 1980; the Sandon–Wallington area held a flock of 500 on 19 and 28 March 1981; and in 1982 there were 800 at Bygrave in April, and 1500 at Ashwell on 15 April. It is clear from the data that virtually all the large spring passage flocks occur on the low-lying clay–marl fields north of the Chiltern scarp.

Summer records during the 25 years reviewed here have been few. In 1967 there were two at Stevenage on 6 August, 27 at Therfield on 20 and 50 on 27

120

August. There were 15 at Wallington on 26 August 1976; 23 at Royston SF on 23 August 1977; and in 1979 there were up to five at Hunton Bridge from 28 June to 4 July, and one at Rabley Heath on 19 August.

Grey Plover

Pluvialis squatarola

A rare visitor, mostly in spring, but occasionally at other times.

In Sage (1959) it was classed as a rare winter visitor and passage migrant, and approximately 20 records were listed.

There are 18 records for the period under review with occurrences for 13 of the 25 years. There were eight spring, four autumn, and three winter records, and one each for the months of June, July and August. In chronological order these records are — Napsbury: one on 13 July 1959; Hilfield Park Reservoir: two on 21 February 1960; Old Parkbury: one on 30 December 1961; Maple Cross: three on 12 May 1963. In the county bird report for 1968 (*Trans. Herts. Nat. Hist. Soc.* 27:6, 1969) there was a remarkable record of a flock of 100 at Royston SF on 15 April. Subsequent evidence revealed that in fact only four of these birds were Grey Plovers, the remainder being Golden Plover. Tring Reservoirs: one on 18 and 20 October 1969; Hilfield Park Reservoir: one on 13 October 1973; at Tring Reservoirs in 1976 five different individuals were recorded — singles on 24–25, 28–29, and 29–30 May, and two from 6–8 June; there was one at the same locality on 17 September 1977; the first Lea valley record was one at Stanstead Abbots GP on 10 May 1979; Tring Reservoirs: one on 9 August 1980; in 1981 at Tring, one was heard at night on 15 April over the town, and there were two at the reservoirs on 17 December; the latest record was of one at Amwell GP on 13 May 1982.

Sociable Plover

Chettusia gregaria

A very rare vagrant.

There is only one record of this species for the county, and that is one seen at Wilstone Reservoir, Tring, on 29 October 1961 (Devlin, Jenkins and Lloyd-Evans 1962).

Lapwing

Vanellus vanellus

MAP 28 A common resident breeding species, passage migrant, and winter visitor. This is the same status accorded it by Sage (1959).

As a breeding species it is particularly associated with large arable fields, but some of the remaining areas of wet meadows in the county support quite high nesting populations, while somewhat lower densities are found in gravel pits and on permanent pastures. Mead and Smith (1982) record reports from 355 (70 per cent) of the 504 tetrads in the county, with breeding proved in 154 and probable in a further 75. It is thus widely distributed, but scarce or absent in the extreme south of the county. The data from the *Common Birds Census* plots in Hertfordshire indicate a marked decline in the breeding population from 1970 onwards. In central Hertfordshire, Gladwin (1983) indicates that the 1980 breeding population was less than 25 per cent of that which existed in 1956. In 1982 a survey of 42 wet grassland sites and 10 gravel pits (both active and reclaimed) was carried out and a total of 81 pairs of Lapwing were located (*see* Smith 1984). Of this total, 16 pairs were in the Colne valley, 19 pairs in both the Ver valley and the Lea valley above Ware, and seven pairs in the Stort valley. None at all were found on wet meadow sites in the valleys of the rivers Chess, Rib, Beane or Mimram.

There are some quite complex patterns of movement associated with this species in the county; there is evidence to suggest that immigrants from outside begin to arrive during the period of post-breeding flocking and dispersal, which usually takes place from July–September. During the months June–August, marked movements in a westerly direction are frequent. In many winters, cold weather movements (usually between SW. and NW.) are also commonplace.

Many of the post-breeding flocks contain fewer than 400 birds, but some examples of larger numbers are shown in Table 6.14. It may be noted that the flock of 4700 at Stanborough in September 1968 was the largest single flock ever recorded in the county up to that date. Very large numbers may appear in cereal growing areas after harvest. At Royston, for example, flocks of 'several thousand' were present from September–November 1967.

Flocks of 400 or more birds are frequently present at various localities during October and some examples of these are shown in Table 6.15. It can

TABLE 6.14   *Examples of concentrations of Lapwing during the post-breeding flocking and dispersal period from July to September, 1966–82*

Year	Location	Number	Date
1966	Shenleybury	500	16 August
1967	Lemsford and Stanborough	850	1 September
	Lemsford	690	17 September
1968	Stanborough	4700	12 September
1970	Pirton	400	30 August
1972	Hoddesdon area	500	14 July
1976	Pirton	1000+	date not recorded
	Tring Reservoirs	430	August
1978	Tring Reservoirs	645	August
	Graveley	800+	17 August
1979	Colney Heath area	800	12 August
	Ashwell area	800	24 August
1980	Kings Langley	400	16 July
	Maple Cross	400–500	14 September
	Tring Reservoirs	400	29 September
1981	Tring Reservoirs	800	31 July
	Amwell GP	650	23 August
	Ashwell area	1200	27 September
	Pirton	1000+	September
1982	Lemsford	950	7 September

be seen from this Table that with the exception of the flock of about 1000 at West Hyde GP in the Colne valley in October 1968, the largest October concentrations have consistently been in the Ashwell area, although a flock of 1000 was present at Pirton in October 1968.

TABLE 6.15   *Examples of October concentrations of Lapwing in Hertfordshire, 1966–82*

Year	Locality	Number	Date
1966	Weston area	400	15 October
1967	Norton	400	22 October
	Redbourn	400+	25 October
1968	West Hyde	1000	20 October
	Pirton	1000	27 October
1971	Royston SF	300–400	30 October
	Tring Reservoirs	450	31 October
1976	Ashwell area	1000	6 October
	Charlton	500	17 October
	Willian	500	31 October
1977	Ashwell area	1000+	7 October
	Sandridge area	500	29 October
1978	Ashwell area	1000	3 October
	Letchworth	500	5 October
	Stotfold	500	6 October
1979	New Ramerwick	500	13 October
1980	Graveley	400+	21 October
1981	Ashwell area	500	late October
1982	Ashwell area	1500	17 October

123

It is during the winter period from November–February that some of the most spectacular movements of this species are evident, and they are almost invariably associated with cold weather conditions. The hard winter of 1962/63 was a good example. During the last half of November at Ashridge, flocks were moving to the SW. almost daily; and at Rye Meads a flock of 1500 on 27 December had moved on by 29 December. It is of interest that a large-scale return movement to the NE. was noted at Ashridge from 6–9 March 1963. Some examples of large scale movements in subsequent years are given in Appendix E. As can be seen from the data in the Appendix, some of these cold weather movements are on a very large scale indeed.

During the winter period the species is widely distributed throughout the county in flocks which may vary greatly in size. The distribution and size of flocks of 500 birds or more for the years 1964–82 are shown in Appendix F. These data refer to flocks on the ground and are additional to those involved in the hard weather movements shown in Appendix E. It would appear that in those years when birds are not forced out by hard weather, that the peak population is reached in December and thereafter declines. Never the less, quite large flocks may still be seen in March, as for example, 500 near Baldock on 8 March 1976, 2000 at Ashwell (Northfield) on 11 March 1979, 800 at Ickleford SF on 1 March 1980, and c. 5000 at Graveley on 8 March and c.2000 near Wallington on 14 March 1982.

Knot

Calidris canutus

A rare passage migrant and winter visitor.

It was classed by Sage (1959) as a rare passage migrant and occasional winter visitor, and 27 records were listed.

There are a total of 18 records for 13 of the 25 years reviewed here, of which 12 refer to Tring Reservoirs. Eight of the records are for the winter months, six in the autumn, and four in spring.

At Tring Reservoirs there were four on 15 November 1959; singles on 18 November 1962; 23 January and 5 November 1964; and on 30 August, 27 September and 21 December 1969; 14 October 1970; 3–4 May 1973; two on 9 September 1975; one on 5 March 1976; and in 1978 there was a remarkable record of 45 flying low over the reservoirs on 7 September.

There are three records of single birds at Hilfield Park Reservoir — 11 November 1962, 18 August 1963, and 12 January 1969.

The remaining records are of two at Rye Meads on 19 April 1958; one at Amwell GP on 18 February 1979; and one at Hunsdon and Eastwick Meads on 10 March 1981.

Sanderling

Calidris alba

A scarce passage migrant and occasional winter visitor.

It was classed by Sage (1959) as a scarce passage migrant and all the records quoted were from Tring Reservoirs, except for one from Watford SF, three from Hilfield Park Reservoir, and two from the Lea valley.

The species occurred in 13 of the 25 years reviewed here, with a total of 28 records of which 16 refer to Tring Reservoirs. On a seasonal basis there were 17 spring, eight autumn, and three winter records. Five of the records refer to Hilfield Park Reservoir — one on 30 December 1970, two on 16 May and two on 24 November 1973, two on 8 May 1974, and one on 9 May 1978. The Lea valley provided five records — Rye Meads: one on 19 April 1958, two on 14 May 1959, one from 7–9 May 1964, and one on 17 April 1977; and one at Cheshunt GPs on 5 May 1963. The sole Colne valley record was one at Maple Cross on 5 May 1966, and the only record from the north of the county was one at Royston SF on 25 August 1959.

The maximum number recorded at any one time was seven at Tring Reservoirs on 13 May 1976. The third winter record (two were at Hilfield Park Reservoir as mentioned above) was one at Tring SF on 31 December 1968.

Little Stint

Calidris minuta

An occasional passage migrant, almost entirely in autumn, and not recorded every year.

In Sage (1959) it was classed as an irregular passage migrant, mainly during the autumn, so its status has not changed very much.

The species was recorded in 20 of the 25 years under review, with a total of about 85 records, of which some 60 per cent refer to Tring Reservoirs. Apart from six records from Old Parkbury GP, the only Colne valley records were one at Maple Cross on 10 September 1961, and two (probably the same birds) at Maple Cross on 5, 6 and 8 September 1964. The Lea valley produced 13 records and Royston SF 12 records. There were only three records from Hilfield Park Reservoir — five on 6 October 1960, one on 28 August 1963, and three on 29 September 1973. The maximum numbers recorded during the period under review was 12 at Tring Reservoirs on 23 September 1973, and 12 at Royston SF on 30 August 1975.

There are only two spring records both of single birds — at Tring Reservoirs on 27 April 1966, and again on 6 May 1967. All other records refer to the autumn migration period, commencing in August, reaching a peak in September (about 63 per cent of all the records), and with no records at all after October.

Temminck's Stint

Calidris temminckii

A very rare passage migrant.

Eight records were listed by Sage (1959) who classed it as a rare passage migrant. Most of these records were from Tring Reservoirs and all of single birds unless otherwise stated — 24 May 1939, 28–29 August 1943, 25 September 1949, 24 October–3 November 1950, and two on 14–15 September 1952. The only other records were of single birds at Rye Meads on 5 August, 8 September, and from 27–29 September 1957.

There have been just five subsequent records:

1976 One seen at Tring Reservoirs on the rather unusual date of 6 June.
1977 One at Tring Reservoirs on 23 and 24 May, one at Stanstead Abbots GP on 20 August and two probably of this species at Royston SF on 23 August.
1980 Lastly, three were present at Broxbourne GP on 11 May.

Pectoral Sandpiper

Calidris melanotos

A very rare vagrant.

Two records were given by Sage (1959). One was seen at Marsworth Reservoir, Tring, on 14 September 1949, and one at Rye Meads on 9 September 1957.

There have been three subsequent records:

1969 One made an extended stay at Tring Reservoirs from 19 October to 13 December.
1973 Another present at the same reservoirs from 3 September to 10 October.
1977 The latest record was one at Royston SF from 28 to 31 August.

Curlew Sandpiper

Calidris ferruginea

A scarce passage migrant, not recorded every year.

It was classed by Sage (1959) as an irregular passage migrant, mainly during the autumn, and with two winter records.

There were no records at all for nine of the 25 years covered by this book, and of the total of 29 records none refer to the winter. The species remains almost exclusively an autumn passage migrant, there being only three spring records — two at Rye Meads on 19 April 1958, one near Watford on 3 March 1963, and three at Stanstead Abbots GP on 30 May 1981. Of the total, 11 refer to Tring Reservoirs, seven to the Lea valley, six to Royston SF, two each to the Colne valley and Hilfield Park Reservoir, and one to the Knebworth area. The maximum number recorded at any one time was six at Broxbourne SF on 18 September 1959, and up to seven at Tring Reservoirs and sewage farm from 1–27 September 1969.

In addition to the Watford record mentioned above, the only other Colne valley record was one at Maple Cross on 24 July 1960. The two Hilfield Park Reservoir records, both of single birds, were 22 August 1963, and 30 August 1964. The Knebworth record refers to one at Mardleybury Pond on 24 August 1975.

Purple Sandpiper

Calidris maritima

A very rare vagrant with only three records:

1959　The first record for the county was one at Tring Reservoirs on 25 October.
1967　One seen on 10 August at Old Parkbury GP, Radlett.
1968　The latest record was one at Tring Reservoirs on 2 September.

Dunlin

Calidris alpina

A common passage migrant and winter visitor.

In Sage (1959) it was classed as a common passage migrant and occasional winter visitor.

A total of nearly 600 records for the period 1958–82 have been analysed. There would seem to have been a change in the winter status of this species in the county since Sage (op. cit.) as some 23 per cent of these records refer to the period November–February. In so far as migration is concerned only 20 per cent of the records fall within the period March–May, but 56 per cent refer to the July–October period, indicating that it is almost three times more abundant in autumn than in spring. In some years, however, the passage movements may be poor at both seasons. Based on the data for this 25-year period, the spring peak occurs in May and the autumn peak in August and September. There were only five June records, including the rather unusual one of a party of eight flying over Bramfield on 7 June 1964.

The numbers seen together at any one time are usually small. From 1958–69, for example, the maxima were 22 at Rye Meads on 27 July 1958, 20 at the same locality on 12 July 1959, 12 at Hilfield Park Reservoir on 16 October 1960, nine at Tring Reservoirs on 9 July 1961, and 10 at Hilfield Park Reservoir on 17 August 1963. In November 1970 quite unprecedented numbers appeared at Tring Reservoirs, varying from 25 to a peak of c. 100 on 8 November. The highest numbers noted in the county in subsequent years are all from Tring Reservoirs — 32 on 9 November 1973, up to 19 in September 1974, and in 1976: 18 on 2 February, up to 18 in March, and up to 17 in May. It may be noted that the highest numbers recorded by Sage (op. cit.) were 60 at Tring Reservoirs on 24 July 1948, and 45 at Rye Meads on 28 July 1957.

In terms of distribution within the county, it may be seen at any suitable habitat. However, it is of frequent occurrence at Tring and Hilfield Park Reservoirs, in the Lea valley, and also in the Colne valley but to a lesser extent.

Broad-billed Sandpiper

Limicola falcinellus

A very rare vagrant.

There have been no further records of this species since the two given by Sage (1959). These were one at Wilstone Reservoir on 6 October 1946; one at Rye Meads on 27 July was considered to be the same individual that was present at Broxbourne SF from 8–19 August 1958 (*London Bird Report* 1958:27–8, 1960).

Ruff

Philomachus pugnax

A common passage migrant and winter visitor.

It was classed by Sage (1959) as a more or less regular passage migrant and occasional winter visitor.

Almost 350 records for the period 1958–82 have been analysed, of which about 73 per cent refer to the months July to October, 14 per cent to the winter months (November–February), and 13 per cent to spring passage from March–May. There were only two June records within this 25-year period — in 1959 up to four were present at Rye Meads from 29 June until 29 July, and there was one at Tring Reservoirs on 3 June 1973. The species has been recorded annually during the period under review, usually in very small numbers at any one time, the vast majority of the records being from Tring Reservoirs, the Colne and Lea valleys, with a number also from Royston SF. There were only four records from Hilfield Park Reservoir — one on 30 August 1964, two on 20 November 1973, one on 13 September 1980, and one from 20–27 December 1981.

Some examples of the maximum number seen at any one time are — nine at Rye Meads on 18 August 1962; 10 at Royston SF on 2 September, 1963; 14 at Rye Meads on 26 April and 15 on 13 August 1964; 10 at Maple Cross on 11 May 1965; 14 at Tring SF on 26 September 1969; 12 with Golden Plovers on a field near Pirton on 26 March 1972; up to 12 roosting at Stockers Lake in February, and 30 (the largest flock ever recorded in Hertfordshire) at Marsworth Reservoir on 3 October 1976; and 10 in a field at Pirton on 25 February, 1982.

Jack Snipe

Lymnocryptes minimus

A widespread winter visitor in small numbers.

It was referred to by Sage (1959) as a fairly common winter visitor and passage migrant.

The earliest of the winter visitors usually arrive during the first half of

October and leave during April. However, individuals have been observed as early as 1 September and as late as mid-May. In most winters there will be records from anything up to 20 or more different sites, but there is considerable variation and in some years very few are seen. The species basically favours damp habitats ranging from the marginal vegetation of reservoirs and gravel pits, to sewage beds, watercress beds, riversides, ditches, and damp meadows.

Numbers in excess of five at any one time are infrequent, examples during the 25 years covered by this book being seven at Rye Meads on 25 December 1960; also at Rye Meads: 17 on 21 January and eight on 8 December 1962; up to seven on the watercress beds at Archers Green in the Mimram valley from January–March and October–December 1966; six at Broxbourne on 29 March 1968; in 1969, six (possibly more) at Marsworth Reservoir on 19 January, nine at Tewinbury in February, and six in Cassiobury Park on 9 February; six at Broxbourne GP on 21 February 1971; at Lemsford Springs: six on 31 December 1973, seven on 20 January and eight on 28 November 1974, and eight on 6 December 1975; 10 at Purwell Nine Springs on 15 February 1978; and 10 at Lemsford Springs on 16 January 1982.

Common Snipe

Gallinago gallinago

MAP 29 An uncommon resident breeding species, but very widespread and often abundant at some localities in the winter. This is basically the status given by Sage (1959).

In Mead and Smith (1982) there are records from 58 of the 504 tetrads in Hertfordshire, with breeding proved in 16 and probable in a further 17. Not surprisingly, most of the sites where it was found were in river valleys, particularly those of the Colne, Lea, Rib, Stort, and Ver, where wet-meadow habitat could still be found. Some of the records referred to gravel pits and to Tring Reservoirs. From 1974–81 breeding or suspected breeding was reported from Broxbourne GP, the Colne valley (various sites both above and below Rickmansworth), Hertford Meads, High Leigh (Hoddesdon), Ickleford Common, the Mimram valley (several sites), Purwell Nine Springs, Rye Meads, Sandon Green End, Sawbridgeworth Marsh, Stanstead Abbots GP, Tewinbury, Water End (Wheathampstead), and

TABLE 6.16 *Breeding distribution of the Common Snipe in 1982*

	No. of pairs
Colne valley	2
Ver valley	2
Upper Lea valley (above Ware)	2
Stort valley	5
Rib valley	5
Other sites	2
Total	18

Wateringplace Green. In 1982 a survey of waders breeding on damp grasslands was carried out in Hertfordshire as part of a national survey; the results are discussed by Smith (1984). A total of 18 pairs of snipe were located distributed as shown in Table 6.16.

This recent survey found that the species does not favour gravel pits or reclaimed gravel pits for breeding purposes. Many former traditional grassland sites appear to have been abandoned, and it seems that the breeding population has undoubtedly declined since 1973.

Outside the breeding season, peak numbers are normally attained during the winter months (although the build-up may commence in July); many localities may hold up to 40 birds at varying times. Maximum counts (of 50 or more) during the 10 years 1973–82 are shown in Table 6.17. Examples of high counts in earlier years are — 1958: flocks of 150 near Ware in January, and 100+ at Pole Hill Marsh on 27 November; 1959: Rye Meads 100+ on 14 March, and 100+ at Eastwick on 28 November; 1960: 200 at Rye Meads in March; 1962: up to 150 at Rye Meads in January–February, and 120 on 21 October; 1963: up to 100 at Rye Meads in March and 250 in December; 1964: 200 at Rye Meads on 15 February and 100 on 6 April; 1966: 50–60 at Tring Reservoirs and adjacent sewage fields on 25 September; 1968: Rye

TABLE 6.17 *Maximum counts of Common Snipe for the period 1973–82*

Year	Locality and numbers	Year	Locality and numbers
1973	Tring Reservoirs: 30 on 27 October Lemsford Springs: 53 in December Rye Meads: 100 in December	1978	Rye Meads: 50 in March Tring Reservoirs: 54 in October and 50 in November
1974	Lemsford Springs: 53 in January Tring Reservoirs: 60 in October Rye Meads: 200 in early December		Maple Cross: 70 on 10 December
		1979	Croxley Hall GP: 60–70 on 1 January Ickleford Common: 52 on 13 January
1975	Rye Meads: 200 from March-April, and 100 in October–November Royston SF: 60+ on 13 September		Cassiobury Park: 71 on 14 Jan., and 67 on 18 February Tring Reservoirs: 150 in February
1976	Cassiobury Park: 51 on 31 January Maple Cross: 50 on 29 February Tring Reservoirs: 110 in late Sept. and 80 in October Rye Meads: 200 in late December		Hamper Mill: 120 on 27 October Ver valley, St. Albans: 55 in December
		1980	Rye Meads: 100 on 6 January Hamper Mill: 60+ on 2 February
		1981	Moor Lane GP: 115 on 25 January Parndon Mill: 50+ on 28 January Tring Reservoirs: 50 on 12 December
1977	Rye Meads: 300 in late January Maple Cross: 122 on 22 October Tring Reservoirs: 65 in late October Moor Lane GP: 80 on 12 November	1982	Hertford Meads: 116 on 1 January Rye Meads: 75 on 13 February, and 112 on 30 December

Meads maximum 100 on 20 January, and 150 on 1 December, 120+ at Tring Reservoirs on 12 October, and 100 at Maple Cross on 28 December; 1970: 150 at Rye Meads on 24 January and 100 on 27 December, and up to 70 at Tring Reservoirs on 2 September; 1971: 250 at Rye Meads in February; in 1972: 60 at Rye Meads on 5 February; and 1982: at least 60 at Old Parkbury on 30 October.

Great Snipe

Gallinago media

A very rare vagrant.

Eight acceptable records were listed by Sage (1959). The earliest was one shot on Walsworth Common in January 1839. Another was shot at Ickleford Meadows in 1879, one at Oughtonhead Common in 1892, one near Royston on 30 August 1893, and one at Slip End (near Sandon) on 11 September 1897, and yet another at Stags End (near Great Gaddesden) on 11 October 1929. One was seen at Tring Reservoirs on 5 November 1941. The only spring record is that of one at Moor Mill, Radlett, on 22 March 1952.

There has been only one record during the period under review, and that was one at Rye Meads on 26 December 1959 (*British Birds* 53:418, 1960).

Long-billed Dowitcher

Limnodromus scolopaceus

A very rare vagrant.

This species, for which there is only one record, was added to the county list in 1977 when a juvenile was present at Tring Reservoirs from 22 October to 12 November (*British Birds* 71:503, 1978).

Woodcock

Scolopax rusticola

MAP 30 A fairly widespread, but possibly declining resident breeding species. Also a regular winter visitor.

It was classed by Sage (1959) as a scarce but regular breeding species, and a fairly common winter visitor.

Fieldwork carried out from 1967–73 and summarised in Mead and Smith (1982), resulted in records from 106 (21 per cent) of the total number of tetrads in Hertfordshire, with breeding proved in 12 and probable in 68 more. The records were mostly concentrated in localities with major areas of woodland in the west of the county (for example Ashridge and Frithsden) and in central Hertfordshire. During the period 1974–82 breeding was proved or suspected in approximately 35 different woodlands of which 14 were among the 60 most highly rated woodlands in the county (*see* Hinton

1980). Data for the years 1980–2 indicate breeding probable in about 25 different woodlands involving some 45 pairs. As before, these records are mostly from the larger woodlands, either entirely broad-leaved or with a proportion of conifers. These recent sites included Ashridge–Frithsden, Bramfield Park Wood, the Broxbourne Woods complex (including Wormley and Derry's Woods), Hitch Wood, the Knebworth estate woodlands, Northaw Great Wood, Symondshyde Great Wood, and St. Johns Wood (Walkern). Even allowing for incomplete coverage in these last three years, the evidence does suggest a decline in breeding status during the past 10 years. In discussing a breeding season survey carried out in 1981, Knightbridge (1984) reached the conclusion that there had been little if any decrease between 1967–73 and 1981. However, coverage in 1981 was very incomplete and the statistical analysis of the results is based on too small a sample to be acceptable.

Outside the breeding season the species is widely scattered with some records coming from sites where it is not known to breed. During the period 1980–2 the number of reports varied from 17 to 29. Most of these refer to single birds, but there were eight in Hitch Wood on 1 January 1980; up to six in Combs Wood (Watton-at-Stone) in January–March, and 11 shot at Gorhambury in November 1981; and nine in Hitch Wood on 3 December 1982.

Black-tailed Godwit

Limosa limosa

A rare passage migrant.

It was classed by Sage (1959) as an irregular passage migrant, and with two winter records.

There are a total of 24 records for 12 of the 25 years with which we are concerned, of which seven relate to the spring and 17 to the autumn. Twelve of the records are from Tring Reservoirs, three from the Lea valley, two each from the Colne valley and Hilfield Park Reservoir, and five from other localities.

The spring records are of two flying over Tring town at 2200 hours on 9 May 1967; one feeding in a field amongst cattle at Hatfield airfield on 23 May 1971; one at Cheshunt GPs on 26 April 1972; in 1976, two at Tring Reservoirs from 12–19 April, and three on 20 April, and up to four at Maple Cross from 24–30 April; and one at Amwell GP on 27 April 1980.

Autumn records from Tring Reservoirs comprise single birds on 10 and 18 September, and 1, 2 and 8 October 1961; 26 July to 11 August, two on 27 September, and one on 19 October 1974; and singles on 30 June and 4 July (both unusually early dates) 1976. The two Hilfield Park Reservoir records are of single birds on 24 August 1963, and 20–22 August 1975. There is only one Lea valley record for this season, and that was one at Rye Meads from 15–17 July 1962. There is also only one record for the Colne valley — four flying north over Maple Cross on 15 July 1965. The remaining autumn records are of two at Royston SF on 30 August, and one from 8–13 September 1975; and one in a stubble field at Ashwell on 15 October 1978.

Bar-tailed Godwit

Limosa lapponica

A rare passage migrant.

This is essentially the same status accorded it by Sage (1959) who listed 12 records, including two in winter.

There are approximately 19 subsequent records with about 10 in spring, eight in autumn, and one in winter. The spring records comprise two near Flaunden on 25 March 1968; singles at Tring Reservoirs on 7 May 1971 and 27 April 1973, and two on 13 May 1973; in 1976 there was a movement through Tring Reservoirs from 26 April to 2 May which may have involved up to 16 individuals, with a peak of 10 on 27 April; one was also seen at Stanstead Abbots GP on 1–2 May 1976; one was present at the same site on 17 April 1978; one was found at Welwyn Garden City on 19 May 1979; and a flock of 40 (the largest ever recorded in the county) flew north over Ware on 3 May 1980.

The autumn records consist of one at Frogmore GP, Radlett, on 23 August 1959; one at Hilfield Park Reservoir on 27–28 August, and a flock of 14 flying NE. over Rye Meads on 20 October 1963; two at Rye Meads on 12 September 1964; three at Tring Reservoirs on 21 August 1968; one at these reservoirs on 20 August, and another at Rye Meads on 4 September 1976; and one flying north over Amwell GP on 4 September 1981.

The only winter record is of one at Wilstone Reservoir, Tring, on 20 January 1964.

Whimbrel

Numenius phaeopus

A common passage migrant and very rare winter visitor.

It was classed by Sage (1959) as an irregular spring and autumn passage migrant. The largest flock recorded at that time was 11 over Harpenden on 11 May 1917.

During the 25 years reviewed here there were only two years (1964 and 1968) when there were apparently no records. In the great majority of cases the records refer to birds seen in flight, or heard passing over at night at widely separated localities throughout the county. In terms of individual records there is little difference between spring and autumn, but in fact the autumn passage almost certainly involves larger numbers. For example, ignoring flocks of less than 10 birds, there are ten records of flocks of 10 or more only two of which refer to the spring. Details of these records are as follows — 11 flying east over Tring Reservoirs on 21 May 1959; 15 flying north over Broxbourne GP on 4 May 1965; 20 flying SW. over Rye Meads on 13 August 1966; 24 passing SSW. over Baldock on 9 August 1967; 27 flying SSW. over Bramfield on 2 August, and 10 south over Ickleford on 3 August 1969; 16 flying south over Rabley Heath on 30 July 1978; 21 passing south over Broxbourne GP on 3 August, and 16 in the same direction over Tring Reservoirs on 20 August 1980; and 52 flying west over Tring Reservoirs on 4 August 1982.

The two winter records comprise one on a ploughed field at Shenleybury on 14 November 1965, and one at Hilfield Park Reservoir on 30 November 1971

Curlew

Numenius arquata

MAP 31 A very common passage migrant, rare summer visitor, and scarce winter visitor. There has been no definitive evidence of the breeding of this species in the county.

It was regarded by Sage (1959) as a common spring and autumn passage migrant, not infrequently occurring also in winter.

Despite the inclusion of this species in Mead and Smith (1982) there is no definite evidence whatsoever that it has ever nested in Hertfordshire, although it is certainly breeding in the Vale of Aylesbury not far from the county boundary. The pair present north of Datchworth in 1968 are known for certain not to have nested. In 1976 a pair holding a territory right on the Buckinghamshire–Hertfordshire border may possibly have bred, but no proof of this was obtained.

Analysis of nearly 240 records for the period 1958–82 shows that about 35 per cent refer to spring, 13 per cent to the summer (i.e. 13 June records), 43 per cent to autumn (July–October), and 16 per cent to winter (November–February). The peak spring movements occur in March and April, while autumn passage commences in July and peaks in August. As with the Whimbrel, many must pass at night and thus go unrecorded. In 1963 there was a very large scale movement over Ashridge througput the night of 19 July. There have been occasions when movements have lacked any particular pattern, with birds noted flying in various directions in the same season. There is evidence to suggest that a westerly movement commonly occurs from June to August.

The numbers seen together at any one time are usually small, and the only reports of flocks in excess of five birds are as follows — Tring Reservoirs: six flying west on 30 August 1964; in 1966, six flying west over Aldbury on 30 June, and 12 south over Weston on 7 August; about 25 passing SW. over Tring Reservoirs on 13 August 1969; 12 going west over Rye Meads on 18 August 1979; six at Royston SF on 11 August 1980; in 1981 there was a totally unprecedented record of of 56 on pastures at Allens Green, High Wych, on 23 August, and in the same year six flew west near Langley on 20 December. A flock of eight flew west over Bramfield Wood on 17 December 1981.

An unusual winter record is of two that remained at Hilfield Park Reservoir from 28 December 1963 until 9 February 1964.

Spotted Redshank

Tringa erythropus

An occasional passage migrant and very rare winter visitor.

There has been a change in status since Sage (1959) who classed it as a rare passage migrant, with one winter record.

During the 25 years reviewed here there were no records for 1971, 1972 or 1980, but a total of about 95 for the remaining 22 years. There is a very clear pattern to the movement of this species through Hertfordshire since about 93 per cent of the records refer to the autumn period. The only spring records were singles at Tring Reservoirs on 4 May 1968, 5 May 1974, and from 30 April to 2 May 1976. There is a single, out of context, record of one at Pirton on 15 June 1977. Over half of the autumn records are in August, with most of the remainder in September. An unusual record is of one that remained at Tring Reservoirs from 21 September to 21 December 1969. The only other winter occurrences were two flying south over Bramfield on 2 November 1969, one at Pirton SF on 28 January 1973, and one at Bourne End GP on 2 February 1976.

Virtually all the records refer to up to five birds at any one time, the only exception being 10 at Tring Reservoirs on 20 August, and six on 11 September 1976.

Approximately 45 per cent of the records refer to Tring Reservoirs, whilst North Hertfordshire accounts for 17 records, the Colne and Lea valleys for eight each, Hilfield Park Reservoir for one (on 21 August 1974), the remainder being from sundry other sites.

Redshank

Tringa totanus

A scarce and probably still declining breeding species, but a common **MAP 32** passage migrant and winter visitor. This is essentially the same status accorded it by Sage (1959), except that its breeding status has deteriorated due to the loss of wet meadows.

From 1958–66 (there were no breeding reports in 1964) most of the breeding records came from the Lea valley, but there were some exceptions. In the north of the county a pair bred on Ickleford Common in 1958, were present there in the breeding seasons of 1959 and 1961, and probably bred in 1963. Another regularly used locality was at Standon Lordship in the Rib valley where two pairs nested in 1958, were present in 1959, and definitely bred in 1960. In the breeding season of 1959 pairs were also present at Water End on the River Gade, and at Braughing watercress beds. A pair nested at the Water End site in 1960. The major breeding site in the Lea valley during this period was Rye Meads where there were five pairs in 1958, 12 pairs in 1959, seven in 1960, five in 1961, four in 1962, three in 1963, but only one pair in 1965 and 1966. Other sites held one or two breeding pairs and these included Kings Meads near Hertford, St. Margarets near Roydon, Broxbourne GP, Hoddesdon SF, one or two sites at Cheshunt, and at Waltham Abbey.

The period 1967–73 covered by Mead and Smith (1982) produced records from 23 tetrads with breeding proved in 10, and probable in seven more. With the exception of probable nesting at Tring Reservoirs (once a traditional locality), possible nesting at two gravel pits in the Colne valley below Rickmansworth, definite breeding near Kimpton, probable nesting in the Beane valley near Watton-at-Stone, and in the Mimram valley near Hertingfordbury, all the records referred to the Lea valley from Kings Meads, down to the vicinity of Waltham Abbey. The actual number of pairs involved was relatively small, the maximum for any one site being three pairs on Kings Meads.

Since 1973, even allowing for incomplete coverage in some years, the situation has probably deteriorated still further with most reports referring to one or two pairs at a handful of Lea valley sites. In 1975 a pair may have bred at Tring Reservoirs, and in 1976 a pair summered there but did not nest on the Hertfordshire side of the border. In 1978 pairs were present in the breeding season at Moor Mill and Frogmore, near Radlett, but nesting was not proved. The BTO/RSPB Wet Meadows Enquiry in 1982 resulted in the location of two pairs at Holwell Hyde near Welwyn Garden City (a new site); a pair at Broxbourne GP, four pairs in the Colne valley, and two pairs in the Ver valley.

On migration the species is of regular occurrence in small numbers at Tring Reservoirs, in the Colne and Lea valleys, and often at other suitable sites scattered around the county. It is more than twice as frequent in spring than in autumn. Numbers in excess of five at any one time are unusual and the highest counts for the 25 years reviewed here have nearly all been at Rye Meads — 19 on 30 March 1958; 14 on 1 April and 12 on 28 April 1962; up to nine in March, 10 on 5–6 April, 10 on 20 May, and 16 on 6 June 1964; six in April 1969 (and also six at Hertford Meads in April 1969); up to six at Rye Meads on 23 March and 5 April 1970. There were eight at Stockers Lake on 28 July 1973, and six at Fairlands Valley, Stevenage, on 27 March 1979.

In most winters one or two birds are reported from suitable localities around the county.

Marsh Sandpiper

Tringa stagnatilis

A very rare vagrant.

The only record remains that given by Sage (1959) of one shot at Tring Reservoirs in October 1887.

Greenshank

Tringa nebularia

A common and regular passage migrant, and rare winter visitor.

It was classed by Sage (1959) as a fairly common passage migrant, most frequent in the autumn.

Analysis of nearly 600 records reveals a very clear pattern to the movements of this species through the county, with only about nine per cent of the records falling within the spring period (the peak being in May), and no less than 89 per cent in the autumn. The latter movement begins as a trickle in July, peaks in August, then falls off rapidly during September. Records of more than five birds at any one time are rare, and for the period reviewed here were as follows — eight at Tring Reservoirs on four dates in September 1959; 14 over Rye Meads on 3 September 1961; six at Tring Reservoirs on 1 September, and eight at Hilfield Park Reservoir on 15 August 1963; six at Rye Meads on 9 August 1964; in 1965: six at Rye Meads on 28 August, seven at Tring Reservoirs on 12 September, and six at Hamper Mill on 19 September; eight at Royston SF on 12 September 1966; six at the same locality on 28 August 1967; seven there on 25 August 1968, and eight on 16 August 1969; seven at Tring Reservoirs on 23 August 1970; 11 at Rye Meads on 5 August 1972; nine at Tring Reservoirs on 19 and eight on 31 August 1974; seven at Royston SF on 24 and 27 August 1975; in 1977: nine at Royston SF on 23 August, 11 on 31 August, and six at Tring Reservoirs on 3 September; six at Royston SF on 14 August 1979; and lastly, six at St. Albans GP on 4 July 1980. The species is of regular occurrence at Tring Reservoirs, and in the Colne and Lea valleys, but may appear at any suitable site from time to time, including watercress beds.

A most unusual event took place at Tring Reservoirs in 1976 when nine were seen on 4 June, eight on 5 June, and one on 7 June. Records in this particular month are completely at variance with the normal pattern.

The winter records comprise four at Tring SF on 22 November 1969; two at Tring Reservoirs on three dates in November 1970; one at West Hyde GP on 9 November and 22 December 1973; in 1974: one at West Hyde GP on 10 January, one by the River Chess near Latimer on 12 January, and one at Stockers Lake on 24 February; in 1976: one at Stockers Lake on 21 February, one at Croxley Hall watercress beds on 29 February, and one at Ickleford on 30 December.

Lesser Yellowlegs

Tringa flavipes

A very rare vagrant.

There is still only one definite record of this species in the county, and that is the one given by Sage (1959) of a single bird at Wilstone Reservoir from 18-23 September 1953. What may have been one of this species was present at Little Tring Reservoir on 18 September 1955, but was not confirmed (ibid.).

Solitary Sandpiper

Tringa solitaria

A very rare vagrant.

This species was added to the county list in 1967 when one that was present at Rye Meads from 24 September to 9 October was trapped and ringed (*British Birds* 61:341, 1968).

Green Sandpiper

Tringa ochropus

A very common passage migrant, particularly in autumn, and a widespread but not numerous winter visitor.

In Sage (1959) it was classed as a fairly numerous passage migrant and winter visitor.

There is now rarely a month in which at least one or two of this species are not present in the county. Both on passage and in winter it is liable to be encountered wherever there is suitable damp habitat. There is hardly a river valley in the county (particularly where there are or have been watercress beds) where it has not been recorded at one time or another, and the same comment applies to gravel pits, sewage farms, and reservoirs. Small numbers now overwinter at widely scattered localities, particularly at watercress beds and sewage farms, and it is now probably more abundant from November–March than it is on spring migration. The first spring migrants appear in March, but the peak movement comes in April, dropping off very sharply during May. It is about twice as numerous on the autumn passage, with the earliest arrivals appearing in June, building up steadily in

140

Figure 6.12   *Green Sandpiper at Lemsford Springs, an important British site for this species.*   *Photo: © Barry Trevis*

July to reach a peak in August, then falling off again in September and October, at which time some remain to be joined by others in the winter.

Totals of 10 or more at any one time are uncommon. From 1958–72 the only records in this category were 17 at Broxbourne SF on 12 August 1960, 16 at Hitchin on 16 July 1961, and 11 at Tring Reservoirs on 18 August 1971. There are more records for the 10 years from 1973–82, all of which except for one spring and five winter reports, are for the autumn passage period, and all except five refer to Lemsford Springs or Tring Reservoirs. The exceptions are 12 at High Leigh, Hoddesdon, on 28 August 1974; 10 at Maple Cross on 9 July, 15 at Royston SF on 9 August 1977; 10 at Stanstead Abbots GP on 18 August 1978; 11 at Cole Green on 10–11 August 1982. The remaining maximum counts are summarised in Table 6.18.

TABLE 6.18   *Maximum numbers of Green Sandpipers recorded from 1973–82*

Year	Lemsford Springs	Tring Reservoirs
1973	11 in November–December	—
1974	14 on 21 September	16 in August
		24 in September
1975	14 from 1–9 August	12 on 16 July
	17 on 26 August	
1976	—	12 in August
1977	—	11 on 16 August
	—	16 in Autumn
1978	—	14 on 10 and 24 August
1979	10 in January	10 in July
	11 on 4 March	
	12 on 18 October	
1980	10 in January	—
	10 on 9 October	
	10 in November	
1981	14 in September	—
	20 in October	
1982	12 in January	—
	10 in September	
	10 in October	
	10 in November	

Wood Sandpiper

Tringa glareola

An occasional passage migrant, almost exclusively in autumn, and not recorded at all in some years.

The status of this species has not changed greatly since Sage (1959) who classed it as a somewhat irregular passage migrant, mainly in the autumn.

During the 25 years reviewed here there were no reports of this sandpiper at all for the years 1978, 1979, or 1981. This species is even rarer on spring passage than the Green Sandpiper since over 90 per cent of the records refer to the autumn period. There are only three April records — single birds at Rye Meads on 5 April 1959, at Tring Reservoirs on 25 April 1971, and at Hillfield Park Reservoir on 22 April 1980. There are nine May records, and in 1964 there was one at Rye Meads on 9 and 11 June. The autumn passage commences in July, reaches a peak in August, and declines rapidly during September. The latest records are of single birds at Broxbourne SF on 3 October 1959, Hoddesdon watercress beds on 11 October 1960, and at Aldenham Reservoir on 10 October 1964. Virtually all the records refer to just one or two birds at any one time, and the highest counts in this 25-year period were seven at Rye Meads on 8 July 1959, and five at West Hyde GP on 24 July 1980.

This species is also much less widespread than the Green Sandpiper, with most records coming from the Colne and Lea valleys, and Tring Reservoirs. Other sites include Hilfield Park Reservoir, and the sewage farms at Codicote, Kimpton and Royston, before these were modernised.

Common Sandpiper

Actitis hypoleucos

MAP 33 A very rare breeding species, common passage migrant and occasional winter visitor. This is basically the same status accorded it by Sage (1959), who quoted seven definite instances of nesting.

The subsequent breeding history of this species is as follows. In 1958 a pair summered at King's Meads, near Hertford, but there was no evidence that they bred. However, a pair with young were seen at Hertford SF on 16 June that year. A pair did breed successfully at King's Meads in 1961, and may have done so again in 1969. In 1967, in the Colne valley, a pair nested at Maple Cross but were apparently unsuccessful. What may have been a second pair almost certainly bred at West Hyde GP, as a pair with two young were seen there in July and August. A pair were present at Hamper Mill GP during the summer of 1968 but there was no evidence of breeding.

One or two birds are occasionally present in winter at sundry localities, but in some years none are seen at all as was the case in 1982. From 1958–72 there were a number of years when no spring migrants were recorded, but during the years 1973–82 it was recorded annually in April and May, although the actual numbers involved were relatively small. The spring migration commences in earnest during April, rises to a peak in May and then drops off sharply, there being very few June records. Based on an analysis of records for the 10-year period mentioned above, the autumn migration is approximately three times the volume of the spring migration. The majority of records refer to up to 10 birds at any one time, and numbers in excess of this figure are almost invariably in the autumn and are restricted to a very few localities. The only spring records in this category are 15 at Rye Meads on 5 May 1958, and 14 at Tring Reservoirs on 26 May 1977. The autumn passage begins in July, peaks in August, and declines quite sharply during September. Maximum autumn counts for the period 1958–82 are summarised in Table 6.19.

In terms of the geographical distribution of records, this species, like the Green Sandpiper, may be seen wherever there is suitable habitat in the form of gravel pits, reservoirs, rivers, sewage works, or watercress beds.

TABLE 6.19 *Maximum autumn counts of Common Sandpipers for the period 1958–82*

Year	Rye Meads	Tring Reservoirs	Other Sites
1959	29 on 29 July	—	—
1960	—	25–30 on 30 August	—
1962	14 on 18–19 August	—	—
1964	15 on 23 July	—	Maple Cross: 13 on 21 August
1965	11 on 22 July	14 on 15 August	Broxbourne GP: 15 on 16 August
1966	11+ on 10 September	20+ on 26 August	—
1967	25+ on 12 August	12 on 13 August	—
1968	15 on 9–10 August	10 on 17 August and 7 September	—
1969	27 on 9 August	15 in August	—
1970	20 on 23 August	20 on 10 August and 3 October	—
1971	—	12 on 29 August	Royston SF: 10–12 on 19 August
1972	11 on 5 August	—	—
1973	12+ on 12 August	13 on 1 September	Broxbourne GP: 15 on 31 August Maple Cross: 15 on 22 September
1974	25 in August	25 in August and 37 in September	Maple Cross: 15 on 22 August
1975	—	—	Hilfield Park Res: 20 on 20 August
1976	—	12 on 20 August	—
1977	20 on 21 and 25 August	—	Royston SF: 15 on 9 and 20 August
1978	15 on 12 August	—	Royston SF: 15 on 6 August
1979	19 on 4 August	—	Stanstead Abbots GP: 12 on 6 and 8 August
1980	21 on 1 August	—	Stanstead Abbots GP: 15 on 27 July Amwell GP: 12 on 31 August
1981	15 in August	—	—
1982	12 on 15 August	—	Stanstead Abbots GP: 15 on 7 August

Spotted Sandpiper

Actitis macularia

A very rare vagrant.

The sole record is that of an adult in summer plumage seen at Hilfield Park Reservoir on 2 September 1956, at which time it was regarded as a race of the Common Sandpiper. This record has been accepted retrospectively by the *British Birds* Rarities Committee (*see London Bird Report* 1980:45, 1981).

Turnstone

Arenaria interpres

A scarce passage migrant, and very rare winter visitor.

It was classed by Sage (1959) as a rare passage migrant.
There were a total of 34 records during the 25 years reviewed here, of which 22 refer to Tring Reservoirs, six to Hilfield Park Reservoir, four to the Lea valley, and two to other localities. It is primarily a spring passage migrant with 25 of the records referable to this period, and only eight to the autumn. With two exceptions all the records refer to three or less individuals at any one time. The exceptions being 12 flying over Rothamsted on 11 May 1960, and six at Hilfield Park Reservoir on 3 May 1978. The four Lea valley records are of single birds at Rye Meads on 12 May, and at Stanstead Abbots GP from 12–14 May 1976; at Amwell GP on 3 May 1980; at Stanstead Abbots GP on 26 December 1981, an unusual date and the first winter record for the county. There are no records for the Colne valley, and the only record from the north of the county was one at Royston SF on 17 August 1969.

Red-necked Phalarope

Phalaropus lobatus

A very rare vagrant.

This is the same status accorded it by Sage (1959) who was able to quote only two records. The first was one shot at Tring Reservoirs in October 1885, and the other a female in full breeding plumage that was present at these reservoirs from 2-7 June 1948.

There have been three subsequent records. One was present at Rye Meads from 18-27 October 1959; one was seen at Tring Reservoirs on 25 August 1966, and another from 2-9 May 1982.

Grey Phalarope

Phalaropus fulicarius

A very rare vagrant.

There would appear to have been a change in status since Sage (1959) classed it as a rare autumn passage migrant and winter visitor, and listed about 16 records.

There have been only six subsequent records — in 1959 single birds were seen at Kings Langley GP on 11 October, at Rye Meads on 27 and 31 October, and 1 November (presumably the same bird in all three cases), and at Hilfield Park Reservoir on 1 November; one at Rye Meads from 4-10 October 1960; one at Tring Reservoirs from 17-19 September 1961; and lastly, one at the same locality on 11-12 November 1982.

Pomarine Skua

Stercorarius pomarinus

A very rare vagrant.

The only records remain the two listed by Sage (1959). An immature shot at Gosmore, near Hitchin, on 19 December 1914, and an adult seen at Tring Reservoirs on 22 November 1928.

Arctic Skua

Stercorarius parasiticus

A very rare vagrant.

Eight records were given by Sage (1959). One was picked up dead near Offley on 2 September 1829. One was shot at Stevenage on 5 November 1881, and another at Langleybury in 1882. Four birds, of which at least one was of this species, were seen at an unspecified locality on 24 September 1927. In 1946 there were no less than three records — single birds at Stockers Lake on 11 May, at Tring Reservoirs on 12 May, and at a gravel pit in the Lea valley on 28 May. An adult flew north over Old Parkbury GP, Radlett, on 10 June 1956.

There are just two subsequent records. An immature was found alive at Wheathampstead on 30 September 1978, and one flew NW. over Potters Bar on 27 September 1981.

Long-tailed Skua

Stercorarius longicaudus

A very rare vagrant.

The only records are the two given by Sage (1959). One was present and photographed at Tring Reservoirs from 27–30 August 1919. However, some features of this individual fitted the Arctic Skua, so there is an element of doubt as to which species was involved. A female seen at Easneye, near Ware, in late September 1937, was later found dead.

Great Skua

Stercorarius skua

A very rare vagrant.

Only one record was listed by Sage (1959), and that was of one killed at Braughing on 24 September 1867.

The only additional record is of one seen at Tring Reservoirs on 24 October 1962.

Mediterranean Gull

Larus melanocephalus

A very rare vagrant.

The only record is one at Stanstead Abbots GP on 1 January 1982.

Little Gull

Larus minutus

A scarce but regular spring and autumn migrant and rare winter visitor.

Sage (1959) listed six records up to 1957 as follows. One shot at Tring Reservoirs on 16 September 1927. At Wilstone Reservoir, Tring: one seen on 3 May 1936, another on 16 November 1941, three on 9 May 1946, and one on 14 and 18 October 1952. At Hilfield Park Reservoir one was seen on 22, 23 and 30 October 1955.

Since then Little Gulls have been observed with increasing frequency in 22 of the 25 years from 1958–82, the exceptions being 1963, 1964 and 1965.

The records for the spring and autumn passage periods are summarised in Tables 6.20 and 6.21. As can be seen, most records are from Tring Reservoirs which appears to be an important inland feeding stage for this species. Five

TABLE 6.20   *Total number of Little Gulls observed in Hertfordshire during the spring passage periods, 1958–82*

Location	European standard five day period						
	17 22–26 March	18 27–31 March	19 1–5 April	20 6–10 April	21 11–15 April	22 16–20 April	23 21–25 April
Tring Reservoirs	1	11	1	8	21	7	12
Elsewhere	—	—	2	2	2	5	4
Total:	1	11	3	10	23	12	16
	24 26–30 April	25 1–5 May	26 6–10 May	27 11–15 May	28 16–20 May	29 21–25 May	30 26–30 May
Tring Reservoirs	17	30	11	6	1	—	1
Elsewhere	13	3	3	1	—	—	—
Total:	30	33	14	7	1	—	1

spring records which refer to birds 'passing over' quote directions of flight as east (four) and north-east (one). There is a tendency for birds to stay at reservoir sites for a few days. Birds which stayed and were thus observed at a site in more than one of the five day periods in Table 6.20 are included in the

TABLE 6.21   *Total number of Little Gulls observed in Hertfordshire during the autumn passage periods*, 1958–82*

Location	July	August	September	October	November
Tring Reservoirs	1	12	14	3	3
Elsewhere	1	4	4	5	1
Total:	2	16	18	8	4

*The records cover the period 18 July to 15 November

147

totals for each of the periods in which they were seen. It is none the less impossible to calculate the precise number of different birds involved as birds of the same age seen on successive dates may be the same or different individuals.

Numbers exceeding three have been recorded on seven occasions as follows: in 1974, a maximum of 15 on 11 April and 15 to 18 birds on 5 May at Tring Reservoirs. In 1978, ten were at Tring Reservoirs on 29 April. In 1980, seven at Tring Reservoirs on 29 March and four at Hilfield Park Reservoir on 29 and 30 April. In 1981, five at Tring Reservoirs on 13 April, and four at Troy Mill on 26 April.

There are two summer records of single birds, at Tring Reservoirs on 30 June 1959, and at Amwell GP on 6 June 1982.

The three winter records are of single birds at Tring Reservoirs on 1 February 1959, Troy Mill GP on 10 December 1967, and at Cheshunt GP (an oiled adult) on 22 December 1979.

As can be seen from Tables 6.20 and 6.21 Little Gulls occur most frequently in spring. The majority of birds seen in spring are adults but first and second summer birds are seen in most years. The autumn passage includes juveniles as well as older birds.

Black-headed Gull

Larus ridibundus

An abundant passage migrant and winter visitor that has bred.

Black-headed Gulls have bred, or attempted to do so, in the county on at least five occasions. The first was in 1950 when a pair laid eggs which were taken at Watford SF. In 1961 breeding took place for the first time at Maple Cross SF when 11 young were fledged from six nests. Four pairs nested there again in 1962 and 1963. In 1964 a single nest was found to be occupied on 14 June but not subsequently. There has been no subsequent evidence of breeding although six pairs were present in May 1965.

The numbers of Black-headed Gulls visiting Hertfordshire have increased substantially since Sage (1959) described it as a very common winter visitor and passage migrant. It continues to be recorded in all months of the year.

Black-headed Gulls start returning to the county in late June. At first the birds, mostly adults, feed almost entirely at waste tips where household and other putrescible rubbish is dumped. In 1982, T. W. Gladwin carried out an intensive study of gull populations feeding at two such sites in central Hertfordshire. The numbers of Black-headed Gulls present at the tips at Cole Green and Foxholes, near Hertford, between late June and the end of October are tabulated in Appendix J. As can be seen, the birds virtually deserted these sites throughout August and September although there was no change in the frequency, material content, or other practises of the tipping activity during that time. The fact is that Black-headed Gulls prefer

Figure 6.13 *Gulls feeding at Cole Green household waste tip in October 1982.*

Photo: © *Tom Gladwin*

to feed on invertebrate soil animals. However, there are few habitats where these are available to the birds until cereal crops are harvested. The disappearance from waste tips coincides with the onset of harvest when most Black-headed Gulls are found feeding on recently burnt stubble or fields being, or recently, ploughed. Gladwin's study found that 23 per cent of the expected winter population had returned by mid-August and 41 per cent by mid-September. About a third of Black-headed Gulls feed on agricultural land throughout the winter.

Throughout September and October passage increases and many birds pass through and arrive from Scandinavia, the Baltic and Low Countries. As can be seen from Appendix I numbers roosting in the county reach a maximum in January. Numbers have progressively increased since 1953 and by January 1983 some 40 000 Black-headed Gulls were roosting on Hertfordshire's reservoirs: 25 000 on Hilfield Park and 15 000 at Tring (*see* Appendices G and H). At the same time the Lea valley reservoir roosts held 55 000 birds: 35 000 on the William Girling and 20 000 on the King George V. Although outside the county a large proportion of these birds spread out each day to feed in that part of the county west of the river Lea from Hatfield to Wheathampstead and Harpenden, others extend north to Royston, east to Bishops Stortford and Sawbridgeworth, and even into the counties beyond.

In the winter of 1982/83 about 82 per cent of Black-headed Gulls roosting on Hilfield Park Reservoir fed in the area of Hertfordshire which approximates to the catchment areas of the Ver, Gade, Chess and Colne, extending north to St. Albans and Harpenden, north-west to Berkhamsted and west to Rickmansworth. On most afternoons small parties of Black-headed Gulls leave Hilfield Park heading towards Staines and the Lea valley and numbers are observed arriving from the same direction. In November 1982 T. W. Gladwin followed these movements on successive days and found that there is a considerable interchange of birds between the roosts at these three sets of reservoirs. Sage (1959) and Siva-Jothy (1982) described similar observations at Hilfield Park Reservoir.

149

Most Black-headed Gulls roosting at Tring fly out to feed in Buckinghamshire.

As can be seen from Appendix I the main departure and spring passage takes place in late February and March, although small numbers continue to pass through in April.

The movement of Black-headed Gulls through the county is usually on a broad front although, as described by Sage (1959), most birds concentrate along four linear landscape features namely the Chiltern Hills, the Colne valley northwards to the Hitchin Gap, the Lea valley northwards also to the Hitchin Gap, and the Stort valley, across Cambridgeshire through the Gog Magog hills. The majority of birds follow these routes between the Thames valley, Hertfordshire and the Wash.

Common Gull

Larus canus

A common winter visitor and abundant spring migrant.

The status of the Common Gull seems to have changed little since Sage (1959) described it as a regular but not numerous winter visitor. It is common, often abundant, on spring migration but remains scarce in the autumn.

Common Gulls are mainly grassland feeders and, with so few preferred habitats, it is not surprising that only relatively small numbers winter in the county. Further, as can be seen from Appendices G and H, numbers vary considerably from year to year. In an intensive study of gulls at the two household waste tips at Cole Green and Foxholes, Hertford, carried out between June 1982 and April 1983, Gladwin found that only a relatively small proportion (less than 8 per cent) of wintering Common Gulls are normally found at or near tips containing household and other putrescible material. Exceptionally there were 1000 at the Panshanger rubbish tip on 25 February 1981.

As can be seen from Appendix I the wintering Common Gull population largely arrives between late October and early December. Observed movements suggest these birds arrive from both the Wash and the Thames estuary. Maximum winter numbers are reached in mid-January. Only a very small roost is found at Tring Reservoirs where the exceptional number of 1201 were counted in January 1980 (*see* Appendix H). However, the only other roost site at Hilfield Park Reservoir, normally holds between 2000 and 3000 birds (*see* Appendix G), 2750 being counted there in January 1983. Larger numbers roost on the reservoirs in the southern section of the Lea valley outside the county. In January 1983 these roosts held 12 100 birds of which 12 000 were on the William Girling reservoir. In recent years only a small proportion of these birds have been flying out to feed in Hertfordshire, the majority apparently spreading out in the easterly quadrant across central Essex.

The winter population of Common Gulls leaves Hertfordshire in late February and early March when a huge migration of these birds through the county develops. The characteristics of this spring migration, which continues at a high level into early April and sometimes extends into early May, have changed little since described by Sage (1959). During March numbers at the reservoir roosts regularly exceed the winter numbers. This is evident from Table 6.22 which shows the monthly maxima at Tring Reservoirs between January and April 1978–82.

TABLE 6.22   *Maximum number of Common Gulls roosting at Tring Reservoirs in the months January to April, 1978–82*

Year	January	February	March	April
1978	50	500	600	100
1979	352	600	600	141
1980	1201	nc	nc	200
1981	93	10	500	300
1982	296	5	300	20

nc = Not counted

Even higher numbers have been counted at Tring in spring, the highest being 1000 on 26 March 1964.

A similar pattern occurs at Hilfield Park Reservoir except that the numbers involved are much larger. Thus in 1982/83 the winter maximum of 2753 reached on 23 January 1983 was exceeded on 11 March when 3000 were present. Two days later, on 13 March, numbers had fallen to 130 demonstrating how quickly the birds move on. A month later on 13 April, 891 were present. Common Gulls migrating through Hertfordshire in spring follow much the same routes as Black-headed Gulls to the Wash before crossing the North Sea bound for the Baltic and Scandinavia. During the passage period small flocks are to be seen resting on fields in all parts of the county.

Common Gulls are rarely seen in the county during the summer and there is no evidence of any autumn passage other than that due to the arrival of the over-wintering population.

Lesser Black-backed Gull

Larus fuscus

An abundant autumn visitor and spring and autumn passage migrant, common winter and scarce but regular summer visitor.

Sage (1959) described this species as a regular passage migrant but also noted that it had begun to appear frequently during the winter. Since then, as can be seen from Appendix G and Table 6.23, there has been a great increase in the numbers occurring at all seasons.

TABLE 6.23 *Maximum numbers of Lesser Black-backed Gulls roosting at*
Hilfield Park Reservoir in each month from June to January
1955/56 and 1982/83

Years	June	July	Aug.	Sept.	Oct.	Nov.	Dec.	Jan.
1955/56	14	57	169	608	223	45	—	—
1982/83	106	nc	960	2244	2200	650	142	106

nc = No count

The figures for 1955/56 were quoted by Sage (1959) and those for 1982/83 obtained by Gladwin as part of an intensive study into the roosting and feeding habits of gulls in Hertfordshire. The mid-January 1983 count of 106 compares with 1000 in 1973 and 1975, and 1300 in 1980 (*see* Appendix G). It remains to be seen if the January 1983 figure was exceptional or part of a new downward trend. By comparison, as can be seen from Appendix H, Lesser Black-backed Gulls are scarce winter visitors to the county's other major reservoirs at Tring. The species is also largely absent in winter from the reservoirs in the southern part of the Lea valley beyond the county boundary. Thus Hertfordshire's wintering population is almost entirely to be found roosting on Hilfield Park Reservoir. Lesser Black-backed Gulls visiting the county feed almost entirely at household waste tips. During the autumn and winter of 1982/83 Gladwin found that 86 per cent of the birds roosting at Hilfield Park Reservoir were feeding on Hertfordshire waste tips. The remaining 14 per cent flew daily into the London area to feed. After feeding the birds are usually to be seen loafing on adjacent fields and open spaces.

The spring and autumn migrations of the Lesser Black-backed Gull through the county are complex, apparently involving three or more populations. From late February through to mid-April moderate numbers pass northwards on a broad front towards the Wash. This northerly movement includes small numbers of 'dark' birds of the Scandinavian race *L. f. fuscus* although most birds are of the paler British race *L. f. graelsii.* There is a simultaneous but more concentrated movement of birds passing from south-west to north-east along the Chilterns. However, the largest phase of the spring passage has developed rapidly since being first reported in 1972. Probably reflecting the substantial northward shift in its winter range, it comprises a large westward and north-westward broad-front movement of adults of the British race and lasts from late March to mid-May. These are presumably returning to breeding colonies along the western seaboard of Britain. Spring migrants tend to pass straight through the county although small resting flocks are occasionally seen on fields and similar open spaces. An example of the numbers involved was obtained by Gladwin during his study of this species at the household waste tips at Cole Green and Foxholes in 1982. On 1 May 1982 there were 286 Lesser Black-backed Gulls on the tip at Cole Green, all but two of which were of the Scandinavian race. In a two-hour watch at that site 122 birds of the British race passed west. The following day only 16 birds were present on the tip but adults of the British race were passing west at the rate of between 80 and 100 per hour throughout the day. The same passage was observed in Cambridgeshire, North Essex and Central Suffolk.

Lesser Black-backed Gulls now occur regularly in Hertfordshire in every month of the year and small numbers, i.e. less than 100, of first and second summer birds have been over-summering since 1979. These birds are usually seen feeding at household waste tips.

The autumn passage is a mirror image of the spring movements but with three major differences. Starting in late July the movements of birds south from the Wash and south-west along the Chilterns now contain a good proportion (10–20 per cent) of birds of the Scandinavian race, whilst the easterly movements, presumably from breeding colonies along the west coast of Britain, include many juvenile birds. Flocks of up to 300 or 400 birds are regularly reported resting in fields along the Chilterns and less frequently in other parts of the county during this period. The third difference from the behaviour of spring migrants is that, whilst most juveniles tend to pass straight through, many older birds and adults remain throughout the autumn, roosting on Hilfield Park and Tring Reservoirs and flying out daily to feed at household waste tips. As can be seen from Appendix I and Table 6.23, the roosting population at Hilfield Park Reservoir reaches its maximum in September and October. The same is also true at Tring Reservoirs where the reported maxima in recent years have been 670 in October 1978, 413 in October 1979, 300 in August 1980, 168 in October 1981, and 180 in October 1982. A large autumn roost also exists on the Lea valley reservoirs which are outside the county. Many of the birds roosting there also fly out daily to feed at suitable waste tips in Hertfordshire.

It is difficult to quantify the different movements and, in view of recent changes, a new study of this species movements through the county is needed.

Lesser Black-backed *x* Herring Gull

Larus fuscus x *L. argentatus*

A hybrid Lesser Black-backed Gull *x* Herring Gull was reported from Tring Reservoirs on 11 March 1979 (*Trans. Herts. Nat. Hist. Soc. 28. Part 5. 13*).

Herring Gull

Larus argentatus

A common winter visitor and passage migrant.

Prior to 1930 the Herring Gull was a rare bird in Hertfordshire. Occurrences and numbers increased and by 1957 it had become a common winter visitor and passage migrant (Sage 1959). Numbers continued to increase and, as evidenced from counts of roosting birds at Hilfield Park Reservoir (*see* Appendix G), reached a peak sometime around 1968 or 1969 when 7250 were present on 11 January. Since then numbers have declined and in January 1983 only 98 birds were present in the roost. At Tring, as can be seen from Appendix H, the Herring Gull is a regular visitor but only in very small numbers, i.e. less than 30 (Holdsworth *et al.*, 1978). Exceptionally, the largest number ever recorded there were 139 in February 1979. The great majority of Herring Gulls visiting the county are rubbish tip feeders; at Hilfield Park Reservoir the decline may be partly due to the closure of 'nearby' waste tips and changes in waste disposal practises. These have seriously reduced such feeding opportunities in the area which includes Rickmansworth, Watford, St. Albans, Radlett and Borehamwood. However, numbers roosting on the William Girling and King George V reservoirs in the southern part of the Lea valley beyond Hertfordshire have also decreased. Here numbers have fallen by about 69 per cent since 1969 to 5000 in January 1983. Most birds seen at waste tips east of Hatfield are from the Lea valley roosts. After feeding, and indeed sometimes whilst on passage, Herring Gulls rest on fields apart from other species. The largest such flock observed seems to have been one of 400 at Bramfield on 17 January 1981.

Small numbers of Herring Gulls pass through the county on both spring and autumn migration. Recently, there have been some significant changes in certain aspects of these movements. Larger numbers are seen in spring than in autumn, although even then flocks of more than 50 birds are rare. Most spring migrants pass up the Colne and Lea valleys heading for the Wash. This phase of passage lasts from late February to early April. In recent years, small numbers of adults have also been noted passing west in April and early May.

In the 1950s the autumn passage, as described by Sage (1959), lasted from mid-June to late October. However, as can be seen from Appendices I and J, Herring Gulls are now rare in the county before the end of September. By the early 1980s autumn passage had become typically very light and mainly confined to the period from early October to mid-November. Most passage is observed in the Colne and Lea valleys. In contrast, very few Herring Gulls pass through Tring or along the Chilterns in spring or autumn.

The true identity and relative status of the sub-species of Herring Gull occurring in Hertfordshire urgently need close attention. In recent years 'large' Herring Gulls, some little smaller than Great Black-backed Gulls, have become a regular feature at domestic waste tips. Whilst these are probably of the nominate race *L. a. argentatus* from Scandinavia and the Low Countries, the only record to have specifically referred to this form was of one at Ashwell on 26 and 29 September, and 18 October 1981. In 1982 Gladwin carried out an intensive study of gulls feeding at two large household waste tips at Cole Green and Foxholes, Hertford. During his study he failed to find any Herring Gulls of 'yellow-legged' forms and it can therefore be assumed that these are rare in the county. The only record of a 'yellow-legged' bird is of one with the characteristics of the southern form *L. a. cachinnans* seen at Tring Reservoirs on 17 December 1981 and during January 1982.

Iceland Gull

Larus glaucoides

A very rare winter visitor.

There are two Hertfordshire records as follows:

1963   A second-winter bird in the Panshanger on 17 February.
1965   One in near-adult plumage at Holwell Hyde rubbish tip, Cole Green, on 12 February.

Glaucous Gull

Larus hyperboreus

A very rare winter visitor.

Sage (1959) lists six occurrences since when there have been a further nine records in the period 1958 to 1982. The records are as follows:

1941   One at a rubbish tip near Tring in November and at Wilstone Reservoir on (6 March 1942) (*British Birds* 25:277).
1942   One near West Hyde, Rickmansworth, on 1 and 15 March (*British Birds* 25:271).
1943   An immature at Watford SF on 23 January (McCulloch 1943).
1956   At Hilfield Park Reservoir an adult on 8 January, an adult and immature on 22 and 24 January, and an immature on 23 January. It is assumed these observations refer to no more than two birds.
1957   An immature at Bishops Stortford rubbish tip on 5 and 6 January.
1966   Two adults at Hamper Mill on 18 and 19 December.
1974   One at Wheathampstead rubbish tip on 12 February.
1976   One over Bramfield Forest on 28 March.
1977   One at Tring Reservoirs on 31 December.
1979   One at Wigginton on 27 January.
1980   At Stanstead Abbots GP, a first winter bird from 13 to 19 January, an adult on 18 and 19 October, and another first winter bird on 30 November.
       One at Hilfield Park Reservoir on 28 October.

Iceland or Glaucous Gull

Larus glaucoides or *L. hyperboreus*

An immature bird of one or other of these species was seen at Lodge Hollow refuse tip, Hoddesdon, on 5 December 1959, and 1 January 1960.

Great Black-backed Gull

Larus marinus

A regular winter visitor and passage migrant in small numbers.

Once rare, Sage (1959) described the Great Black-backed Gull as occurring regularly but by no means exceptionally numerous. Since then numbers wintering in Hertfordshire increased to reach a peak in 1969 or thereabouts, and substantially decreased thereafter.

As can be seen in Appendix I, the majority of birds seen in the county arrive in October and depart in February and early March. Like most 'large' gulls, the wintering population feeds at tips where domestic and other putrescible waste is dumped. Great Black-backed Gulls are scarce if not rare at Tring Reservoirs (*see* Appendix H) and most Hertfordshire birds roost on Hilfield Park Reservoir, and on the William Girling and King George V reservoirs in the southern part of the Lea valley outside Hertfordshire. In January 1969, 52 were counted roosting in the Lea valley and 2750 at Hilfield Park Reservoir. As can be seen from Appendix G, numbers then declined and in January 1983, whilst the Lea valley roost contained 250 birds, only 90 were present at Hilfield Park.

Away from the reservoirs, flocks of 100 or more birds are exceptional and occur mainly at rubbish tips or rest areas on nearby fields. The largest such flock on record was of 450 at Holwell Hyde rubbish tip on 19 November 1967.

Small numbers pass through the county on both spring and autumn passage. There are few summer records.

Kittiwake

Rissa tridactyla

A rare winter visitor and passage migrant.

The frequency and seasonal pattern of occurrences has not changed significantly since Sage (1959) described it as an irregular winter visitor and passage migrant. There have been a further 25 occurrences in the period 1958–82 as follows:

1959 One at Broxbourne on 1 January.

Eleven, including seven immatures, over Ware on 11 January.

1960 An immature at Startops End Reservoir, Tring, on 7 July.

1968 Single immatures at Tring Reservoirs on 3 and 10 August and 8 September.

1970 Single immatures at Tring Reservoirs on 25 and 26 April and 26 May.

1971 An adult at Tring Reservoirs on 17 May.

1972 One at Hilfield Park Reservoir on 19 and 21 February.

1977 A first summer bird at Tring Reservoirs on 24 May and one at Stockers Lake on 25 November.

1978 An adult found dead at Rye Meads on 18 March and an adult at Tring Reservoirs on 12 May.

1979 Singles at Cheshunt GP on 12 February, Stansted Abbots GP on 23 March (adult), and Troy Mill GP on 28 April (adult).

1980 Three (an adult and two immatures) at Maple Cross SF on 18 April, and three (all adults) at Hilfield Park Reservoir on 20 and 22 April.

1981 One at Tring Reservoirs from 30 April to 6 May with a second bird present on 4 May.

At Hilfield Park Reservoir there was one on 27 and 29 April and two on 28 and 30 April and 1 May.

1982 An immature at Cheshunt GP on 10 January.

Two adults and an immature at Hilfield Park Reservoir on 13 and 14 April were found dead on 15 and 17 April.

One at Tring Reservoirs on 16 December.

Sandwich Tern

Sterna sandvicensis

A scarce passage migrant.

In Sage (1959) it was classed as a rather rare passage migrant.

It occurred in 16 of the 25 years reviewed here, with a total of 30 records. Of this total, 10 refer to the spring (April and May), and 18 to the autumn. There were two records for June — three at Stockers Lake on 28 June 1971, and one at Amwell GP on 6 June 1981. The latest autumn date is 25 September. Generally the records refer to between one and three birds at any one time, but exceptions have been 14 flying south over Rye Meads on 1 May 1965, 13 at Tring Reservoirs on 24 September 1972, 47 (the largest flock ever recorded in the county) flying over Broxbourne GP on 10 September 1973, and nine at Tring Reservoirs on 21 September 1980.

Tring Reservoirs account for 13 of the records, the Lea valley for eight, the

Colne valley for four, and Hilfield Park Reservoir for three. The only reports from elsewhere being two flying south over Rabley Heath on 15 August 1978, and one at Stevenage on 17 September 1980.

Roseate Tern

Sterna dougallii

A very rare vagrant.

The only record is of one seen at Tring Reservoirs on 18 May 1969.

Common Tern

Sterna hirundo

MAP 34 A regular breeding species, common passage migrant, and very rare winter visitor.

This represents a change in status since Sage (1959) at which time it was known only as a regular passage migrant.

The history of the breeding of this tern in Hertfordshire began in the Lea valley, which remains the only regular nesting area. In 1962, three adults were present in the Cheshunt–Rye Meads area from May onwards, but there was no evidence of nesting. In 1963 a pair bred at Cheshunt GP. Nothing happened in 1964, but in 1965 a pair were present at Broxbourne GP from 2 May to 30 August (with up to six birds in June and July), but there was no proof of breeding. The situation changed in 1966 when at least three pairs were present in June and July of which at least two pairs bred, and the third pair may have done so. The subsequent history of this site was as follows — 1967, four pairs nested on shingle islands; 1968, six pairs bred but only seven young reached the flying stage, and up to 17 birds were present in June; 1969, nine pairs were present in June together with three nests, but only five young fledged; 1970, 18 birds were present by 23 May and seven pairs subsequently nested, but all failed due to rising water levels resulting from infilling with domestic refuse; 1971, three pairs bred but only raised one young, and 20 birds were present on 31 July; three pairs bred in 1972 and fledged five young; in 1973 four pairs attempted to breed but the nests were flooded; in 1974 two pairs were again flooded out, but one pair did manage to fledge two young in 1975. There were no subsequent instances of breeding at this gravel pit.

In the early 1970s floating rafts were placed in position on a lagoon at Rye Meads in order to provide breeding sites for birds displaced from Broxbourne GP, and the first pair nested in 1972. The subsequent history at Rye Meads is shown in Table 6.24. Elsewhere in the Lea valley a pair bred at Stanstead Abbots GP in 1971, two pairs in 1972, and single pairs in 1973 and 1979. A pair nested at Hoddesdon GP in 1972, but not subsequently. At Amwell GP a pair bred in 1979 and 1980, and three pairs in 1981. At

TABLE 6.24   *Data on Common Terns nesting at Rye Meads, 1973–82*

Year	No. of pairs	No. of young ringed	
1973	6	16	
1974	18	29	c. 50 present on 11 August
1975	18	35	45 adults present on 18 May
1976	18	44	
1977	c. 25	43	
1978	25–30	60	80 present on 25 June
1979	38	83	Up to 50 present in May and 80 in June
1980	37	88	Up to 50 present in July
1981	35–40	85	
1982	c. 35	73	62 present at Broxbourne GPs on 14 July

NOTE: Six Common Terns ringed as pulli at Rye Meads have been recovered abroad in Ghana (one), Senegal (three), Togo (one) and Mauretania (one). The great majority of the young that are ringed at Rye Meads fledge successfully.

Cheshunt GPs one pair bred in 1973, two pairs in 1976, and one pair in 1980.

In the Colne valley a pair reared three young at Stockers Lake in 1976, and attempted to nest again in 1977 but failed. A pair were present at Royal Oak GP in June 1980, but there was no evidence that they nested. In 1981 pairs were present at several sites in the Colne valley, at Park Street GP by the River Ver, and at Tring Reservoirs, but in no case was there any suggestion of breeding.

This tern passes through Tring Reservoirs, and the Colne and Lea valleys regularly on both spring and autumn migration, and also appears occasionally at other localities such as Hilfield Park Reservoir and Stevenage, but is rarely seen in the north of the county. It is most numerous on the spring migration but flocks in excess of 10 birds are not frequent, although the total numbers passing through may be quite high (*see* comments under Common/Arctic Terns). Some examples of maximum numbers during the period under review, excluding gatherings in the Lea valley breeding area, are 21 at Hilfield Park Reservoir on 22 August 1964; 33

at Tring Reservoirs on 26 May and 47 on 27 May 1977; in 1981, 22 at Tring Reservoirs on 9 May and 19 on 11 May, 17 at Troy Mill GP on 11 May, and 15 at Maple Cross on 4 October; and 40, considered to be this species, at Tring Reservoirs on 6 September 1982. The spring movement takes place mainly in April and May, with occasional records in March, and the autumn movement from July to September with the occasional October record.

The only winter record is of one seen at Hilfield Park Reservoir on 14 November 1970.

Arctic Tern

Sterna paradisea

A regular and probably common passage migrant, although the fact that many are not distinguished from Common Terns tends to obscure the picture. This is basically the same status accorded it by Sage (1959).

There is no doubt that the Arctic Tern is much more numerous on the spring migration than in the autumn. In fact the number of records specifically assigned to this species from 1958–82 is quite small. The vast majority of the records refer to Tring Reservoirs, with less than 20 from Hilfield Park Reservoir, six from the Lea valley, and five from the Colne valley. On the basis of the available records there were some years when very few passed through, and others when apparently exceptional numbers were reported. In the county bird report for 1976 it was stated that there had been the usual large spring passage, there being a total of eight records with a maximum of 18 at Tring Reservoirs on 28 April. However, in 1978, possibly as a result of greater observer activity, it was found that during the spring passage at Tring Reservoirs from 16 April to 13 May, a minimum of 179 passed through, with peaks of 20 on 1 May, 41 on 2 May, 24 on 6 May, and 22 on 7 May. A similar situation occurred again in 1980 when at least 188 passed through Tring Reservoirs between 22 April and 24 May, with peaks of 102 on 22 April, and 46 on 23 April; at least 81 passed through Hilfield Park Reservoir in the same period, with peaks of 17 on 22 April, and 14 on 26 April and 6 May. In 1981 at Hilfield Park Reservoir it was reported from 15 April to 6 May, with no less than 88 on 29 April.

The few Colne valley records comprise at least two at Helicon GP on 29 April, and up to four at Troy Mill on 6 May 1973; one at Troy Mill GP on 27 April 1979; one flying NNW. at Stockers Lake on 29 May 1980, and again at Troy Mill GP, two on 24 April and seven on 26 April 1981, and one on 29 April 1982.

In the Lea valley there were singles at Cheshunt GPs on 27 July 1963, Broxbourne GP on 1 May 1965, Cheshunt GPs on 17 April 1974, three at Broxbourne GP on 18 May 1975; one near Ware on 23 June 1977 (an unusual date), six flying north at Stanstead Abbots GP on 26 April 1980, and one at Amwell GP on 26 April 1982.

Common or Arctic Tern

Sterna hirundo/paradisea

As mentioned earlier, there are occasions when terns are seen but cannot be specifically assigned to one or other of these two species. As with the Arctic Tern, the majority of these records occur in the spring period, as for example, 14 at Tring Reservoirs on 24 April and the same number at Broxbourne GP on 12 May 1960, 35 at Tring Reservoirs on 4 June 1963, 12 at Tring Reservoirs on 19 May 1964, 25 there on 25 April 1971 and, in 1978, a minimum of 82 passing through with maxima of 40 on 1 May and 15 on 8 May. The unassigned autumn records include 12 flying SW. over Ware on 5 July 1959, 10 at Tring Reservoirs on 17 August and 14 on 3 September 1962, and *c.* 40 at Tring Reservoirs on 6 September 1982 which were believed to be Common Terns.

A very late record is of one at Tring Reservoirs on 2 November 1959.

Little Tern

Sterna albifrons

A scarce passage migrant.

In Sage (1959) it was classed as an irregular passage migrant.

During the 25 years dealt with here there were no records of this species for 1960, 1961, 1963, or 1973, and a total of 41 records for the other years. Of this total, 26 are for the spring migration period, 12 for the autumn, and three for the month of June — single birds at Tring Reservoirs on 21 June 1964, 6–7 June 1965, and two on 27 June 1967. The records primarily refer to between one and three birds at any one time, the exceptions being nine (probably this species) at Hilfield Park Reservoir on 13 September 1974, four at Tring Reservoirs on 27 April 1976, and four at Amwell GP on 9 May 1981.

In terms of distribution of the records within the county, 25 are from Tring Reservoirs, eight from the Lea valley, three from Hilfield Park Reservoir, one from the Colne valley (one at Troy Mill GP from 28–30 April 1981), and two isolated records of three at Stevenage on 5 May 1977, and one at Bishops Stortford on 27 April 1981.

Black Tern

Chlidonias niger

A regular spring and autumn passage migrant, usually but not always more abundant in spring. This is the same status accorded it by Sage (1959).

There is little doubt that the main passage route is through Tring Reservoirs, and numbers elsewhere are usually small, as in the Colne and Lea valleys. Spring passage may commence in April, with the maximum numbers appearing in May, and a few occasionally moving through in June. The autumn passage begins in July, the main movement takes place in August and September, and late birds occasionally appear in October.

During the 25 years reviewed here the maximum numbers seen at Tring Reservoirs in spring have varied considerably, and in some years very few have been seen. During the first 10 years some high numbers were recorded — 100+ on 2 May 1958, 75 on 23 May 1959, and 100-105 on 31 May 1966. From 1968-82 numbers were apparently much lower with maximum counts of 30 on 5 May 1971, 31 on 26 May 1977, 30 on 12 and 22 on 13 May 1980. In the Lea valley the highest count was 100+ on 23 May 1959, and no subsequent records have come anywhere near this figure, the maxima being 14 at Rye Meads on 2 June 1963, eight at Stanstead Abbots GP on 4 May 1970, 17 at Rye Meads on 5 May 1974, up to six there from 18-25 May 1975, and six at Cheshunt GPs on 9 May and six at Rye Meads on 13 May 1981. In the Colne valley there have been some years when it was not seen at all in spring, and when it did appear only one or two birds were involved. The highest counts were six at Maple Cross on 10 May 1970, and 18 at Troy Mill GP on 15 May and nine on 2 June 1977. A similar comment applies to Hilfield Park Reservoir, and the maximum seen was seven on 16 May 1973.

During the period 1958-67 the maximum autumn counts at Tring Reservoirs were 40-50 on 20 and 22 August 1962, 60+ on 31 August and 30+ on 1 September 1963, 21 on 14 July 1964, 23 on 24 September 1965, and 15+ on 9 August 1967. Subsequent years produced some counts on a similar scale with 53 on 4 and 46 on 5 August 1969, 55 on 3 August 1971, 55 on 16 September 1974, 12 on 25 August 1977, 17 on 20 August 1978, 12 on 18 August 1979, 13 on 19 September 1980, and 17 on 12 September 1982.

Autumn counts elsewhere have been relatively insignificant compared to those at Tring Reservoirs. In the Lea valley the maxima were 12 at Rye Meads on 15 August 1962, and 49 at the same locality on 15 September 1974. As in the spring, numbers in the Colne valley (on those occasions when the species is seen at all) are small, and the highest counts were six at Troy Mill GP on 26 September 1965, seven near Rickmansworth on 14 August 1975, and seven at Troy Mill GP on 13 September 1981. At Hilfield Park Reservoir the maximum recorded during this 25-year period was 18 on 23 September 1980.

White-winged Black Tern

Chlidonias leucopterus

A very rare vagrant.

The only record given by Sage (1959) was that of an adult and an immature at Tring Reservoirs on 7 October 1929.

The only subsequent record is of two seen at Hilfield Park Reservoir on 19–22 September 1970 (*British Birds* 64:354, 1971).

Guillemot

Uria aalge

A very rare vagrant for which there have been no further records since those given in Sage (1959) — one shot at Aldenham Reservoir in November 1882, and another at Hertford Meads on 5 April 1888.

In James and Sawford (1979) mention is made of a specimen obtained in the Baldock area. None of the references quoted by these authors give any more detail, the lack of which dictates that this cannot be accepted as a definitive county record.

Razorbill

Alca torda

A very rare vagrant, the only record being that given by Sage (1959) of an adult found dead at Easneye, near Ware, on 23 October 1934.

The three specimens mentioned by James and Sawford (1979) are unacceptable due to the complete lack of supporting data, although two are listed in the museum records as having been obtained at Hitchin.

Little Auk

Alle alle

A very rare vagrant.

It was classed as a rare visitor by Sage (1959), and in Sage (1962) the date of the record of one found alive near Redbourn in 1950 was corrected from 10 April to 10 February.

There are two subsequent records. One was seen at Tring Reservoirs on 4 November 1965, and another found dead at Reed, near Barkway, on 31 October 1967.

Puffin

Fratercula arctica

A very rare vagrant.

It was classed as a rare visitor by Sage (1959) who listed a dozen records. There have been five subsequent records:

1958　One found exhausted near Hitchin on 18 October after a westerly gale, and on 21 October another was found at Rickmansworth.
1961　One seen at Tring Reservoirs on 18 September.
1969　An immature was found at Radlett on 2 October.
1979　Lastly, one was found alive at Westmill, near Buntingford, on 15 February.

Pallas's Sandgrouse

Syrrhaptes paradoxus

A very rare vagrant.

This species reached Hertfordshire during the irruptions of 1863 and 1888. The records of its occurrence therefore remain as listed by Sage (1959) as follows:

1863　Nine females were shot on Therfield Heath in June.

1888   Two were picked up near Royston in mid-May.
       Two of a flock of 40 were shot at Jepps Farm, Hoddesdon on 20
       May.
       Seven were seen near Batch Wood, St. Albans, on 22 May.
       One seen at Wheathampstead in late May.
       One shot at Bennington on 4 June.
       One shot at Letchworth (date unknown).
       Several seen around Baldock (date unknown).

(Feral) Rock Dove

Columba livia

An abundant resident.

The flocks of variably plumaged pigeons which are a common feature of
towns and larger villages are recent descendants of dovecote pigeons,
escapes from fanciers collections and stray racing pigeons. All have the Rock
Dove as their original common ancestor.

Feral Rock Doves form flocks in which the membership bond is
particularly strong. Thus it is rare for a bird to leave one flock and join
another. Each flock holds a distinct territory and flock size depends on
available food, like bread, mostly provided deliberately or accidentally by
people. Breeding, at least by some individuals, may occur throughout the
year.

The high nuisance and health risk due to their droppings soiling buildings
and public facilities is well known. Some types of bricks and building stone
can be seriously damaged by droppings; cleaning and restoration can be very
expensive. It is surprising that there have been no serious population studies
of this species in Hertfordshire. In view of the birds flocking behaviour
enumeration of the population should be relatively easy.

Stock Dove

Columba oenas

A common resident.   **MAP 35**

At the beginning of the 19th century the Stock Dove was to be found in SE.
England only. Since then it has increased and spread throughout the whole
of Britain.

In Hertfordshire it was described by Sage (1959) as a plentiful and well-
distributed species that had increased since 1930. However, between 1956

and 1961 the population suffered massive losses. In the springs of 1957, 1958, 1959 and 1961, 117 dead Stock Doves were found on fields around Bramfield and there were probably many more that died undiscovered. The cause of death appeared to be the result of ingesting organo-chlorine insecticide seed dressings which were then being widely used (Gladwin 1983). The species remained quite common in parkland and woodland habitats around Welwyn Garden City and Digswell but breeding success was much reduced. At Digswell Place there were two cases of egg breakages in 1959, a typical symptom of shell-thinning caused by organo-chlorine substances. It seems reasonable to assume that populations were similarly affected wherever these toxic compounds were in use. Numbers started to increase again in 1963 following the controls placed upon the use of such chemicals.

The fieldwork for the *Breeding Bird Atlas* conducted between 1967 and 1973 found the Stock Dove to have increased and to be once again widely distributed throughout the county in agricultural as well as parkland, woodland and semi-urban habitats (Mead and Smith 1982). Birds were found in 68 per cent of all tetrads and were proved to have bred in 24 per cent of them. Nests have been found in buildings such as churches, and water towers at Hunsdon.

The rapid increase has continued to the present day (1984) and has not been noticeably arrested by the loss of nest sites caused by Dutch elm disease. None the less Stock Doves are far less numerous than Woodpigeons.

From late July to May Stock Doves form small flocks. In spring they are mostly found on newly ploughed or recently sown fields and from late summer on cereal fields. Sage (1959) quotes two records of flocks of 100 or more. Over 100 were seen near Aldenham on 18 March 1934, and 100 at Bayfordbury in November 1952. Apart from 100 near Hitchin on 3 December 1961, no flocks of more than 20 birds were reported until 1969. Since then flocks of between 50 and 100 birds have been increasingly observed and can now be said to be commonplace. The largest recent flocks reported were of 2–300 near Sandridge on 3 November 1971, 150 at Woodhall Park on 27 March 1976, 150+ at Philipshill Wood on the Hertfordshire–Buckinghamshire border near Chorleywood on 27 January 1979, and 200 at Datchworth on 1 March 1979. The largest flock reported in May was of 62 at Cole Green on 26 May 1982.

Woodpigeon

Columba palumbus

MAP 36 An abundant resident.

There is no evidence to suggest that the Woodpigeon has been other than abundant for at least the last two hundred years. Sage (1959) described it as an exceedingly numerous resident and winter visitor and quoted instances of huge flocks. 'Thousands were observed passing over Watford from north to south on 9 December 1907. They took eight minutes to pass, flying high and darkening the sky. Another huge invasion occurred in 1929, and it is said that on 28 December hordes of these birds practically covered 12 hectares of land on a farm near St. Albans.' There are several recent records that could be described in similar terms.

Woodpigeons breed abundantly in all parts of the county; in hedgerows throughout the agricultural areas, copses, woodlands, and urban and semi-urban habitats. Large winter flocks, usually in brassica crops, particularly oilseed rape, or at roosts, are a common feature. Flocks of up to 2000 are not uncommon. The largest flocks seen in recent years include 4–5000 flying south over Hilfield Park Reservoir on 6 December 1964, 6000 flying east over Stanstead Abbots GP on 16 November 1980, and 5000 at Pirton in December 1981. Analysis of records quoting flock sizes from 1969 to 1981 suggests that there has been an increase in the number of winter flocks, a general increase in flock size, and an extension of flock survival as late as the end of April and into May (*Trans. Herts. Nat. Hist. Soc.* 29:44). Gladwin (1983) found the breeding population in central Hertfordshire to be increasing but was unable to quantify the change. However, the great increase in the cultivation of oilseed rape means a greater availability of a favoured food during the critical winter months and significant increases in population might therefore be expected.

In the past the sight of large late-autumn and winter flocks has given rise to the hypothesis that many of the birds are possibly of continental origin. This is not supported by ringing results, although few Woodpigeons are ringed in the county, and it seems probable that the large majority of birds observed originate from within this and adjacent counties. However, large immigrations, apparently from the continent, are occasionally observed on the east coast, the inland penetration of these birds to or through Hertfordshire has yet to be proven.

Collared Dove

Streptopelia decaocto

A common resident.

MAP 37

This species is widely distributed throughout the county. It breeds commonly in all areas except in the arable farmlands of the north-east where small numbers only are found in and around some villages and farmsteads. It is most numerous close to and around the larger villages and less densely developed areas of the older towns. In early autumn large flocks form in some areas as many, but not all, birds disperse, some over quite long distances.

Figure 6.14   *Collared Dove, a common species which first bred in Hertfordshire in 1958.*
Photo: © Tom Gladwin

Flocks are regularly observed from early autumn through to spring particularly around mills and grain stores. There is strong evidence of movements in late April and May but whether these are due to the dispersal of winter flocks or migration in the true sense has yet to be determined.

Collared Doves were first observed in Hertfordshire in 1957. Between 22 July and 3 September a single adult was seen on several dates at Rye Meads where two, both adults, were present on 4 August.

Breeding was confirmed for the first time in 1958. A pair was discovered by a small chicken unit at Westmill Farm, between Tonwell and Ware, on 15 June and on 6 July a nest containing two nearly fledged young was found in an adjacent pine tree.

None were seen in the county again until 1961 when pairs were present at Digswell and Ware, and three at Hitchin throughout the spring and summer. Birds were also seen at Odsey in August. One at Hitchin was the only bird seen during the ensuing winter. In 1962 there were two pairs at Hitchin and Ware during the spring and summer with large numbers at Hitchin through the autumn and winter reaching a maximum of 52 on 30 November.

Two pairs bred at Harmergreen, Digswell, in 1963, and five adults and 11 juveniles were present at Westmill Farm, which site had not been visited since 1961. Fourteen were present at French's Mill, Ware, on 12 April and the winter flock at Hitchin reached a maximum of 105 in November and December. Birds were seen for the first time at Cuffley — an adult on 5 September, and Northaw — a juvenile on 5 October.

The colonisation continued rapidly. In 1964 breeding occurred in several new locations including Long Marston, near Tring (five pairs), and Bramfield (nine pairs). There were increases at Harmergreen (four pairs) and Westmill Farm, Tonwell, where there was a flock of 37 on 22 August. Flocks of 20 or more were otherwise observed in seven widely separated districts, the largest being of 78 at Ware Lock in December. By 1966–7 the species was breeding in most parts of the county. Numbers continued to increase rapidly and present population levels were reached by about 1978, since when numbers in central Hertfordshire and probably in the county generally have been stable (Gladwin 1983). The rate of increase is well illustrated by *Common Bird Census* data graphically illustrated in Mead and Smith (1982).

Autumn and winter flocks of between 100 and 200 birds are regularly observed. The largest flocks recorded were of 3–400 at Almshoe Bury during November and December 1972, and 350 at Ashwell on 7 January 1978.

Turtle Dove

Streptopelia turtur

A common summer visitor and passage migrant.   **MAP 38**

This species was described by Sage (1959) as a common summer visitor breeding throughout the county. It breeds commonly in the hedgerows and copses of the agricultural areas, and in both deciduous and coniferous woodlands. Numbers have increased rapidly during the past 25 years. During the fieldwork for the *Hertfordshire Breeding Bird Atlas* carried out between 1967 and 1973, Turtle Doves were found in 88 per cent of all tetrads (Mead and Smith 1982). The species is mainly absent from the urban and semi-urban areas. Gladwin (1983) found the species to have increased in central Hertfordshire and Mead and Smith (1982) demonstrated that the 'local population seems to be increasing faster than the national one'. The evidence being that the *Common Birds Census* index for Hertfordshire from 1964 to 1980 shows double the rate of increase (150 per cent) than the national one.

The main arrival occurs in May although some birds are seen in the last few days of April in most years. The earliest record appears to be of a single bird at Cheshunt on 14 April 1974. Turtle Doves are diurnal migrants and both spring and autumn passages are evident to observers. Flocks of up to 20 birds are common in spring and of up to 50 in late July and August when the main departure occurs. Late summer flocks are particularly common among the Chilterns especially in fields on the chalk around places such as Ashwell, Kelshall and Royston. Flocks exceeding 100 are unusual but have been recorded on at least seventeen occasions between 1952 and 1982; by far the largest being of 350+ at Royston SF on 2 August 1970.

169

Small numbers, usually ones and twos, are seen in September in most years; there are eleven October records, eight since 1968, involving one to three birds on dates up to the 18th of that month.

Two very unusual records are of six at New Mill End on 6 November 1954, and one in Prae Wood, St. Albans, on 29 January 1976.

Ring-necked Parakeet

Psittacula krameri

A rare visitor of feral origin.

This species, introduced from South Asia as a cage bird, has now established a self-maintaining population in southern England and has therefore been assigned to category C in the list of British and Irish Birds maintained by the British Ornithologists' Union. There are 12 Hertfordshire records as follows:

    1974   One at Bragbury End from 10 February to 14 March.
           One at Kimpton Mill from 21 December 1974, to (19 March 1975).
    1975   One at Gilston Park on 22 November.
    1976   Seven at Widford on 21 November.
    1977   One at Digswell Lake on 13 February remained in the area until
           July.
           One flew east over Tring Reservoirs on 22 October.
    1979   A male seen regularly at St. Albans from 17 March.
           One at Tring Reservoirs on 13 October and one at Walkern on 21
           October.
    1981   One at Panshanger on 4 April.
           One at Batlers Green, Aldenham, on 15 November.
    1982   One at West Hyde, Rickmansworth, on 19 June, and at Maple
           Cross on 4 July (presumed to be the same bird).

It is perhaps worth noting that five of the records are in October and November.

Cuckoo

Cuculus canorus

MAP 39   A common summer visitor.

The Cuckoo is a common summer visitor to most parts of the county except the urban areas. Following a sudden decline in the early 1960s

170

populations have steadily increased and are now probably higher than when Sage (1959) also described it as a common and well distributed summer visitor. Mead and Smith (1982) similarly found the species to be well distributed between 1967 and 1973 and, apart from the urban areas, to be scarcest in the 'prairie-like' farmlands in the north-east. Gladwin (1983) found evidence of a small increase in central Hertfordshire between 1956 and 1980. Analysis of the county records however, suggests that an increase of between 30 per cent and 50 per cent has occurred in farmlands in the central and western areas of the county in the 25 years up to 1982. This is still less than the increase of over 100 per cent suggested by the local *Common Birds Census Index* (Mead & Smith 1982). Dunnocks are evidently the majority foster species in the county. Locally, Reed Warblers are also important hosts.

The main arrival of Cuckoos takes place in the second half of April and early May with departure in the second half of July and early August. The earliest validated record is of one calling at Odsey on 30 March 1958. Twenty eight birds have been seen in September, the latest at Stanborough Reedmarsh on 16 September 1968.

Barn Owl

Tyto alba

A very rare resident.   **MAP 40**

In 1877 the Barn Owl was described as common in almost all districts of Hertfordshire. By the beginning of the 20th century a decrease was evident and in 1962 it was stated to be getting increasingly rare. By 1922 it was said to have become scarce in the vicinity of Hertford and in 1934 Dr A. H. Foster described it as diminished in North Hertfordshire. It had become virtually extinct in the Elstree area by 1944, was decreasing around Baldock and Bishops Stortford and no doubt elsewhere. Sage (1959) described it as 'now rather local' and its remaining strongholds as being around Tring, Ashridge, Berkhamsted, Chipperfield and Chorleywood in the west; Bishops Stortford in the east; and in the area south of Royston to Barley, Barkway, Buntingford and Braughing. Since then it has declined almost to the point of extinction and is now a very rare bird indeed.

Analysis of data from all available sources for the years 1958 to 1961 shows that birds were seen at 79 discrete locations, mostly in the area of the 'remaining strongholds' described by Sage (1959). There are two useful censuses of breeding numbers. Eleven pairs bred in the Broxbourne, Brickendon and Ware areas in 1959. Seven of these successfully reared young and one pair were shot. In 1961 twelve breeding pairs were found in the Digswell, Tewin and Bramfield area including seven previously undiscovered nest sites. Young fledged from seven of these nests, one pair were shot, and one pair and one other adult found dead at or near their nest sites. Thereafter the decline accelerated. The *Breeding Bird Atlas* (Mead and Smith 1982), for which fieldwork was carried out between 1967 and 1973 found the species to be breeding in 33 tetrads and possibly in 26 more. Most birds were however recorded in the early years of this work. In 1969 pairs bred at Codicote, Hemel Hempstead and at a long established nest site in railway buildings at Ware. There were only five other records. The Ware birds were subsequently killed on local roads. A similar fate also befell pairs at Digswell, Bragbury End and Staines Green, near Hertford. In 1970 pairs bred at Hatfield where young were found in a nest, and near St. Albans where at least two birds fledged. Breeding was not recorded again until an incubating female was found in East Herts in May 1981. However, in 1980 a pair may have nested in the Kimpton–Ayot St. Lawrence area and pairs were seen near Hitchin in June, and Stevenage in May. At that time Barrett (1980) thought it possible that a few unrecorded pairs of these easily overlooked species were still breeding in the east of the county, and this is now known to be so (A. J. Harris, pers. com.). None the less, in the ten years 1973 to 1982 no more than 11 Barn Owls were reported in any one year. Outside the breeding season Barn Owls are known to wander widely and it is possible that most of these birds originated from outside the county.

The causes of the decline are several but the relative impact of each is difficult to assess. It is reasonably proven that the huge decrease in the early 1960s was due to the accumulation of toxic insecticides such as Aldrin, Dieldrin and Heptachlor. It is also known that as grasslands disappeared, many birds were forced to hunt increasingly along roadside and railway lineside verges. As a result there were also a significant number of traffic deaths in the 1960s. The decline however, started at the beginning of the 20th century, long before either of these causes existed. Barn Owls are known to suffer high mortality in unusually cold winters. Further, there has been a continuing reduction in nest sites with the felling of old trees on farmlands and removal or modification of suitable buildings. Neither of these factors seems likely to be the underlying cause of the long-term element in the decline. If Barn Owls are to be assisted to become re-established in the county it may be necessary to provide nestboxes in areas with high populations of small mammals in short grassland, and away from major roads and railways.

Little Owl

Athene noctua

MAP 41 A widely distributed resident.

The Little Owl was first recorded in Hertfordshire in 1877 and was proved to breed for the first time in 1897. Within the next 25 years it had become common in most if not all of the county. In the 1930s numbers decreased throughout the county but recovered again from the mid-1940s onwards. Sage (1959) described it as quite common in the county as a whole. By 1965 numbers had fallen considerably, probably due to the use of toxic

insecticides. Since then numbers have increased again. Between 1967 and 1973 breeding was proved in 85 tetrads and probably occurred in 104 others (Mead and Smith 1982). Since then the slow increase reported by Gladwin (1983) has continued throughout the county but numbers are still significantly below the peak levels of the mid-1950s. None the less Little Owls are once again present in most parklands and areas of farmland with some mature trees. There is some evidence that it may even be the commonest owl in the Ashwell area and other more 'open' districts (T. J. James, pers. com.).

Tawny Owl

Strix aluco

A common resident.   **MAP 42**

Sage (1959) described the Tawny Owl as an abundant resident breeding throughout the county not only in woods and copses but also in parks and large gardens in urban areas. The use of toxic insecticides in the late 1950s and early 1960s and the cold winter of 1962/63 resulted in a massive decrease in the population in most of the county. Since then numbers have steadily increased. Mead and Smith (1982) found the species to be widely distributed throughout the county during the period 1967–73. Gladwin (1983) found the population in central Hertfordshire to be less in 1980 than in 1956 but still increasing. In recent years it has reappeared at a number of former urban sites in Hertford, Potters Bar, St. Albans and Welwyn Garden City. It is again the most numerous of the owls in the county, with an overall population in 1982 little different from that of 1958. As a result of successful occupation in a variety of sites, the provision of nestboxes in some urban parklands, woodlands and on farmlands with mature hedgerow trees is to be encouraged. In the meantime there is some evidence of increased scarcity in the open areas of North and East Hertfordshire due to a reduction in the number of nest and roost sites.

Long-eared Owl

Asio otus

MAP 43 A scarce winter visitor and rare resident.

Sage (1959) described the Long-eared Owl as breeding fairly commonly in the fir plantations and spinneys in the north of the county but considered it less common than it had been some fifty years earlier. In the rest of the county, as the quoted records show, it had long been a rare breeding bird. Only one winter record is given, that of one at Tring Reservoirs in December 1886.

The *Hertfordshire Breeding Bird Atlas* (Mead and Smith 1982) shows that Long-eared Owls were found in 27 tetrads within the present county boundary. Breeding occurred in four tetrads and probably in 15 others. It would seem that the species has benefited from coniferous reafforestation for most birds were found in the belt of such woodlands and copses across the centre of the county. Few were located in its former stronghold in the north of the county.

Since few observers make nocturnal excursions in search of this species its current status is difficult to assess. In the spring of 1984, Gladwin, seeking to check its presence, found birds in two traditional sites near Bramfield (probably two pairs) and in Broxbourne Woods. Nests with young had previously been found at Bramfield in 1967, when seven individual adults were present in the spring, and again in 1972, and at Broxbourne in 1977. Birds have been seen at the Bramfield sites in most years since 1961. In addition to the birds at Bramfield, the product of intensive field work for the *Breeding Bird Atlas* in 1967 was the discovery of other birds in Crackendell and Warren Woods (Ayot St. Peter); Scratch Wood (Flamstead); Hall Wood, Hog Wood and Pightle Dell (Kimpton); Panshanger (two pairs); Tewin Wood; and by Welwyn Garden City golf course. Other summer records, i.e. May to August inclusive, in the period 1958–82 are from Hitch Wood (1960), Elstree (1962), Cuffley (1963), Buntingford (1974), St. Albans (1978), Reed (1979), Symondsyde (1981), Bennington (1981), and Oughton Head (1982). It would therefore seem that the breeding population of this rare resident is under-recorded.

In addition to the resident breeding birds, small numbers have recently started to winter in the county. All such records for the months September to April from 1958–82 are as follows:

1963 One in Mimms Woods on 21 March.
1966 Three in Dowdells Wood, Ayot St. Peter, on 5 March.
1973 One at Essendon on 20 and 28 February.
1974 Two (not *one* as in *Trans. Herts. Nat. Hist. Soc.* 28:18) at Oughtonhead Common on 3 and one on 17 October.
1975 Two at Nomansland Common, Sandridge, on 6 December.
      One at Rye Meads on 6 and 7 December.
1977 At least one in Bloodhounds Wood in April.
      One in Wain Wood on 14 October.
      One at Rye Meads on 15 October.
      One at Oughtonhead Common on 5 November.

1978   One at Rye Meads on 1 April.
        One at Hemel Hempstead on 19 September.
1979   Two to four at Cheshunt GP from 14 January to 10 March, and
        one thereafter to 28 April.
        One to two at Rye Meads from 17 March to 28 April were known to
        be additional to the birds seen at Cheshunt GP.
        One at Graveley on 24 January.
        One at Cheshunt GP on 24 November.
1980   Five roosting in a holly bush at Wheathampstead on 1 January.
        One at Cheshunt GP from 17 February to 23 March.
        Two at Stanstead Abbots GP on 2, and one on 21 March.
1981   One at Stanstead Abbots GP on 20 March.
        One in Tingley Wood on 12 April.
1982   One, caught and ringed, at Bennington on 24 January.
        One at Stocking Pelham on 27 February.
        Five roosting near Stevenage in March with one remaining from 4
        to 13 April.
        One at Rye Meads on 31 October.
        One at Wallington on 3 December.

It is possible that the few birds seen in woodlands in March and April were breeding. The majority of the above records, however, clearly refer to winter visitors. A large influx along the east coast from Northumberland to Kent took place between October and December 1978 (Davenport 1982) and it can be assumed that the unprecedented numbers seen in the county in the early months of 1979 were a product of that movement.

Short-eared Owl

Asio flammeus

A regular autumn and winter visitor.

The status of this species remains unchanged since Sage (1959) described it as a regular autumn and winter visitor which is most frequently seen in the north of the county.

Short-eared Owls have occurred in 23 of the 25 winters between 1958/59

175

and 1982/83 inclusive, the exceptions being 1958/59 and 1960/61. Most of the birds, as can be seen from Table 6 . 25, continue to be seen in North Hertfordshire where the regular sites include Ashwell, Royston, Graveley and Pirton, and along the county boundary at Pegsdon Hills, Pitstone and near Stotfold.

The majority of records are from late October to mid-April with extreme dates of 25 September and 10 May. The only record outside this period is of one seen at Royston on 1 July 1973.

In the autumn of 1978 there was an unusually large influx of Short-eared Owls into Britain (Davenport 1982), and the winter of 1978/79 produced 20 per cent of all the birds seen in the 25-year period 1958 to 1982. Possibly

TABLE 6.25 *Minimum number and distribution of Short-eared Owls seen in Hertfordshire, 1958–82*

Winters	North Herts.	Lea valley*	Elsewhere	Total
1958/59 to 1977/78	47	4	12	63
1978/79	15	4	8	27
1979/80 to 1981/82	12	5	8	25
Autumn 1982	2	8	7	17
Total:	76	21	35	132
% of Total	58	16	26	

*Amwell to Cheshunt

more significant, the last five years, 1978 to 1982, produced a minimum of 75 different birds or 57 per cent of the 25-year total.

White (1982) analysed the contents of 29 pellets from five Short-eared Owls present in the Lea valley in April 1980, and from 1 February to 1 April 1981. Fifteen of the pellets contained the remains of birds, including Skylark, thrushes, finches, and buntings. The pellets also contained the remains of seven species of small mammals.

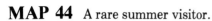

Nightjar

Caprimulgus europaeus

MAP 44 A rare summer visitor.

Sage (1959) described the Nightjar as a fairly common summer visitor that had deserted a number of former breeding localities.

Since then, as shown by Table 6.26, numbers have continued to decrease and only a few pairs have been present in the county in recent years (Smith 1982). Young conifer plantations have been the preferred habitat in the 25-

176

Year	Woodland Group				All other Sites	Total
	Bramfield Forest and Park Wood	Harmergreen and Puttockhill Woods & Mardley Heath	Broxbourne and Hoddesdon Woods	Symondshyde Great Wood		
1958	1	—	8	—	6	15
1959	1	—	8	—	2	11
1960	2	—	10	—	4	16
1961	6	—	11	—	1	18
1962	9	—	13	—	3	25
1963	9	3	14	—	9	35
1964	14	2	6*	—	3	25
1965	11	7	8	—	—	26
1966	4	nc	2	—	—	6
1967	9	6	6	—	1	22
1968	9	5	5	—	—	19
1969	2	1	3	—	1	7
1970	3	—	2	—	1	6
1971	1	—	4	—	—	5
1972	3	—	1	—	—	4
1973	1	—	1	2	—	4
1974	—	—	3	1	—	4
1975	—	—	1	1	—	2
1976	—	—	2	3	—	5
1977	—	—	2	2	—	4
1978	—	—	3	1	—	4
1979	—	—	3	—	—	3
1980	—	—	9	1	—	10
1981	—	—	3	2	1	6
1982	—	—	2	1	—	3

*Count only covered part of the woodlands   nc = Birds present but not counted

177

year period 1958 to 1982 during which time all former traditional habitats have been deserted. This is apparent from a study of Table 6.26. The disappearance from traditional long-established heathland and open woodland habitats is evident from Column 6 which includes the last breeding populations from Ashridge (1959, 1960, 1962), Berkhamsted and Northchurch Commons (1958, 1960, 1963, 1964, 1969), Frithsden Beeches (1964), Gaddesden (1959, 1967), Gustardwood (1963), Hexton (1958) and Hitch Wood (1958 to 1963). In contrast the numbers in Columns 2 and 3 show the typical colonisation of young conifer plantations in the Bramfield and Harmergreen complexes and their subsequent decline as the plantations begin to mature. Young conifer plantations are similarly the principal habitat in the woodlands around Broxbourne and Hoddesdon, and in Symondshyde Great Wood.

Swift

Apus apus

MAP 45 A common summer visitor and passage migrant.

Swifts breed commonly in most parts of the county, nesting behind tiles and in the roof spaces and towers of older cottages, houses, churches and in suitable industrial and public buildings. In the last twenty-five years there has been a large reduction in the number of available nest sites caused by redevelopment in some towns and villages. The breeding population has fallen accordingly. In recent years small numbers have started nesting behind the fascia boarding of modern houses and in custom-built nestboxes.

The first Swifts are usually seen in the last few days of April. Apart from an unsubstantiated but published record of 300 at Tring Reservoirs on 8 April 1967 (*Trans. Herts. Nat. Hist. Soc.* 26:243), the earliest appears to have been three at Rye Meads on 19 April 1962.

The main arrival and peak in the spring passage occurs in May but may extend into June in the event of unfavourable weather. Huge numbers are often observed passing in spring. Over 10 000 passed north over Bramfield on 11 May 1969. This passage continued all day with some 1200 birds passing per hour. Similar observations have been made in the Colne and Lea valleys, at Hitchin, Royston, Tring Reservoirs and Wheathampstead.

In cold weather large concentrations seeking insects may be seen flying low over large open bodies of water such as gravel pits and reservoirs. Numbers of 1000 or more occur regularly in such conditions at sites such as Hilfield Park Reservoir, Troy Mill and West Hyde. Larger concentrations noted elsewhere were 4–5000 at Rye Meads on 12 May 1963, and 5000 at Tring Reservoirs on 25 May 1976. Ringing studies have shown that the majority of birds in these huge hunting concentrations are from local breeding populations, i.e. from generally no more than 10 km away and nearly all from within a radius of 25 km.

As a result of the lack of flying insects Swift lose weight rapidly during cold weather and in a prolonged period of such conditions some mortality is known to occur (Gladwin and Nau 1964).

In a normal season when arrival and the start of breeding have not been delayed or extended by the weather, local birds depart suddenly in the first ten days of August. Small numbers continue to be seen into early September. Thereafter 'stragglers', possibly from Scandinavia, continue to be observed in most years, even as late as early October. The latest records are of eight at Much Hadham on 14 October 1972, singles at Rye Meads on 17 and 23 October 1976, and five at Oughton Head on 5 November 1977.

There are multiple recoveries of birds ringed in the county in Spain, Morocco, Congo, Mali, and Malawi.

Alpine Swift

Apus melba

A very rare vagrant.

The species has been observed on three occasions but probably involving only two different individuals.

One was present at Troy Mill GP, West Hyde, on 26 September 1965 (*British Birds* 59:292). It must be considered probable that it was the same individual that was seen at St. Albans four days later on 30 September 1965 (*British Birds* 60:334). Another was seen over the golf courses at Hartsbourne, Bushey Heath, on 14 May 1977 (*British Birds* 71:510).

Kingfisher

Alcedo atthis

A fairly common resident.

MAP 46

The population and distribution of this species has not shown any detectable overall change since Sage (1959) also described it as a fairly common resident. The *Hertfordshire Breeding Bird Atlas* (Mead and Smith 1982) shows it as breeding along all of the major river valleys and at a few

179

sites beside the Grand Union Canal. Breeding occurs regularly at most major groups of gravel pits, lakes and reservoirs. A few pairs continue to breed in the north of the county, particularly around Hitchin. There are several instances of pairs breeding in dry gravel pits up to a mile from the nearest significant water. Gladwin (1983) found it had increased overall in central Hertfordshire between 1956 and 1980. This local increase was due to more breeding pairs along the Mimram, where Sage (1959) described it as local, and the Lea between Essendon and Welwyn Garden City.

The population tends to suffer huge losses in cold winters but usually recovers in two or sometimes three years. However, in the severe winter of 1962/63 it was thought that the breeding population within sixty miles of London, which includes the whole of the county, had been virtually exterminated. Its recovery over some seven years is documented by Meadows (1972) who pointed out that it must have involved recruitment of immigrants from outside the area.

The peak breeding population in the county is probably between 70 and 90 pairs.

Two of the three foreign recoveries of British ringed birds were from Rye Meads, one in France and one in Guernsey.

Bee-eater

Merops apiaster

A very rare vagrant.

There have been four recorded occurrences of this species in the county as follows:

c.1882   One at Sherrards Wood (otherwise Sherrardspark Wood), Welwyn (Sage 1959).
1905   Four were seen at Hitchin of which one was apparently caught alive.
1955   One at Old Parkbury, Radlett, on 12 July.
1973   One, possibly two, were seen at Stevenage on 29 June (*British Birds* 67:329).

Roller

Coracias garrulus

A very rare vagrant.

The Hertfordshire records of this species remain the two given by Sage (1959) as follows:

1852   An adult female shot at Callipers Hall, Chipperfield Common, on 20 September.

1932   One seen at Sandon on 6 February (Stone 1932).

Hoopoe

Upupa epops

A rare vagrant.

Excluding a record from Totteridge, which was then in the county, Sage (1959) describes 16 occurrences of Hoopoes in Hertfordshire in the history up to 1957. Since then there have been a further 22 records.

Two of the records listed by Sage (1959) lack precise dates of observation. The remaining 14 records are from the months of April (six), May (three), June (one), July (two), August (one) and September (one). Six of the records are from the years 1950 to 1953 and include both of the autumn occurrences.

The 22 records between 1958 and 1982, all of single birds, are as follows:

1958   Berkhamsted on 6 and 7 August.

1959   Bishops Stortford from 20 to 30 June.

1960   Barley on 28 April.

1962   Boxmoor on 16 October.

1964   Walkern on 9 April.

1967   Childwick Green on 17 April.
           Frithsden Beeches on 20 May.

1970   Near Steps Hill (Bucks) but in Hertfordshire on 27 April.
           Bramfield Forest on 30 April and 1 May.

1971   Potten End from 16 to 18 May.

1973   Hilfield Park Reservoir on 5 May.

1975   Stanstead Abbots on 20 April.

1976   Berkhamsted Common on 13 May.

1977   Ashridge on 12 May and from 4 to 17 June.

1978   Harpenden on 13 March; the earliest Hertfordshire record.
           Hitchin on 11 April (long dead).
           Wheathampstead from 11 to 13 May.
           Harpenden on 12 and 15 June and into July.

1980   Rye Meads on 13 and Broxbourne GP on 14 and 15 April; considered to be the same bird.
           Hemel Hempstead on 12 October.

1982   Potters Bar from 20 to 22 May.
           Smallford GP, Hatfield, on 10 November; the latest Hertfordshire record.

The apparent increase in the observations of this conspicuous species may be due, at least in part, to increased observer activity and coverage.

Wryneck

Jynx torquilla

A rare spring and occasional autumn migrant that has bred.

Once a common, even abundant summer visitor, the population declined rapidly in the early part of the present century such that by 1935 or thereabouts, it had become a very scarce bird (Peal 1968). Sage (1959) described it as local in the exteme if not extinct except as a migrant, and gave the last known breeding as being at St. Albans in 1951. It was subsequently revealed that a few pairs had continued to breed in the area between Hertford, Hertford Heath, Goose Green, Brickendon and Bayford until at least 1958. Regular breeding sites included old woodpecker holes in two oak trees in a garden at Bayford, and old orchards adjacent to Broad Riding Wood, and at the junction of Elbow Lane and The Roundings, Hertford Heath (*Trans. Herts. Nat. Hist. Soc.* 27:221). Since then pairs have been observed in the breeding season as follows:

1963	A pair in Mimms Woods on 21 April stayed for two weeks.
1966–9	A pair present in April in Northaw Great Wood in each year but breeding not suspected.
1971	A pair were present in a garden at Water End, Hemel Hempstead, until mid-May.
1972–3	A pair nested successfully in an old orchard at Dunkirks Farm, Hertford, in both years. Most of the orchard was felled during the 1973/74 winter.
1977	A pair bred successfully at Ringshall. The birds arrived on 16 May and nested in a decaying oak trunk. At least three young fledged from a nest that contained seven eggs on 12 June and five young on 30 June. The birds were last seen on 16 August. An adult was also seen feeding a juvenile in the Stevenage area in July.

Single birds have also been seen in spring in Northaw Great Wood on 18 July 1961, 12 April 1963, 10 and 22 April 1965 and during early April 1970. There are 15 other spring records (10 in May) in the 25-year period 1958–82 of which four are also from the Bayford, Broxbourne and Cuffley areas. These include two March records of single birds at Ashlyns, Berkhamsted, on 29 March 1958, and at Cuffley on 24 March 1967.

In the 25-year period 1958–82, increasing numbers have been observed on

TABLE 6.27   *Total numbers of Wrynecks observed in Hertfordshire in autumn, 1958–82*

	European standard five day period					
	45	*46*	*47*	*48*	*49*	*50*
Period	*9–13 Aug.*	*14–18 Aug.*	*19–23 Aug.*	*24–28 Aug.*	*29 Aug.– 2 Sept.*	*3–7 Sept.*
1958–62	—	1	—	—	1	1
1963–67	—	—	—	1	1	2
1968–72	—	1	—	2	2	1
1973–77	1	1	3	—	1	2
1978–82	—	—	—	—	3	4
Total:	1	3	3	3	8	10

	51	*52*	*53*	*54*	*55*	*Number of different birds observed*
	8–12 Sept.	*13–17 Sept.*	*18–22 Sept.*	*23–27 Sept.*	*28 Sept. –2 Oct.*	
1958–62	—	—	—	—	—	2
1963–67	—	—	—	—	—	3
1968–72	1	5	7	2	1	20
1973–77	6	3	1	2	5	24
1978–82	5	4	1	1	1	15
Total:	12	12	9	5	7	64

NOTE: Birds which stayed for a few days and were observed in more than one of the five day periods, are included in the figures for each of the periods in which they were seen. Because of this the number of different birds observed (64) is less than the total of all five day period observations.

autumn passage. As shown in Table 6.27 most of these birds, thought to be of continental origin, occur in September.

Green Woodpecker

Picus viridis

A fairly scarce resident.   **MAP 47**

Sage (1959) described this species as a very common resident throughout the county being least numerous in the extreme north.

Mead and Smith (1982) found it to be a rare bird in the north-east of the county and 'patchily' distributed elsewhere. T. J. James (pers. com.) found four or five pairs in Northaw Great Wood in 1964, none in 1970, and only a single bird in 1974. Gladwin (1983) found there had been a large decrease in central Hertfordshire between 1956 and 1980 but that numbers had been reasonably stable since 1970. The loss of long established grassland feeding sites may be a major cause of the decline, although this species also suffers large losses in cold winters. Analysis of county records indicates the present Hertfordshire population to be between 100 and 120 pairs, most of which are located in the southern, central, and western woodlands and parklands.

Great Spotted Woodpecker

Dendrocopos major

MAP 48   A fairly common resident.

Twenty-five years ago the Great Spotted Woodpecker was considered to be a little less numerous than the Green Woodpecker (Sage 1959). By reason of the latter's decline the Great Spotted Woodpecker is now the most numerous and most widely distributed of the three species of Woodpecker found in the county. Mead and Smith (1982) found it to be a common resident in most large areas of woodland, broad-leaved and coniferous, but relatively scarce in the cereal belt in the north and north-east of the county where it is possibly seriously under-recorded. Gladwin (1983) could find no detectable change in the overall population in central Hertfordshire between 1956 and 1980. Populations are however very variable. T. J. James found 27 or 28 pairs in Northaw Great Wood in 1964, five to seven pairs in 1970, and 12 pairs in 1974. Unlike the Lesser Spotted Woodpecker, Dutch elm disease does not appear to have provided the population with any significant temporary benefits. Great Spotted Woodpeckers, also unlike the other species, are frequent beneficiaries at the greatly increased number of garden feeding stations in winter.

The resident population are of the British race *D. m. anglicus.* In November 1968, a bird ringed and photographed in Bramfield Forest by the Mimram valley Ringing Group was referred to the Scandinavian race *D. m. major.* The same bird was retrapped where ringed on 6 January 1969.

Lesser Spotted Woodpecker

Dendrocopos minor

MAP 49   A common resident.

At one time the scarcest of the three species of woodpecker occurring in the county (Sage 1959) it is now relatively common, and although not as widespread, is not much less numerous than the Great Spotted Woodpecker. It is probably overlooked by many observers, a possibility considered both by Sage (1959) and Mead and Smith (1982). Sage (1959) described it as a rather local resident. This it evidently was for each of the seven years 1958 to 1964 only produced between four and seven records. In 1965 it was reported from Northaw Great Wood for the first time and from 13 other widespread localities and in 1967 there were many more records from 22 areas. In 1968, the first full year of fieldwork for the *Breeding Bird Atlas*, it was found in 49 tetrads and, significantly, several observers expressed surprise at finding it in their home areas. The increase has continued assisted, it seems, by the effects of Dutch elm disease for there are many records of pairs breeding in dead elms since 1969. Populations vary greatly between some years and seem to be particularly vulnerable during hard winters. None the less the Lesser Spotted Woodpecker is now to be found in all parts of the county where copses and woodlands contain a good proportion of old trees.

White-winged Lark

Melanocorypha leucoptera

A very rare vagrant.

There is one record for the county, as follows: in 1955 an adult female at Hilfield Park Reservoir from 12 to 17 August (Sage and Jenkins 1956).

Woodlark

Lullula arborea

A very rare visitor that has bred.

MAP 50

Sage (1959) found this to be a very local breeding species and occasional passage migrant and winter visitor. At best it has always been a scarce bird in the county. Prior to 1958 there were only five proven instances of breeding. Otherwise breeding season records, most between 1950 and 1957, are of a few instances of singing birds from Ashridge, Elstree, Ridge, Ridgehill, Bushey Heath, Bushey Park, Mimms Woods, Hertford Heath, Cuffley and along the Hertfordshire–Buckinghamshire border near Chorleywood.

Since 1957 the species has been reported as follows:

1958   Three pairs probably bred along Elbow Lane by Highfield and Box Woods, Hoddesdon.
One at Broxbourne on 1 November.
A nest with three eggs, possibly of this species, was found at Cuffley (T. J. James, pers. com.).

1959	Single birds singing at Elbow Lane by Box Wood, and at Harmer Green Wood, Digswell, and a male in Cassiobury Park on 17 May.
1960	Singles over Rye Meads on 10 September and 2 October.
1964	One by Northaw Great Wood on 12 July.
1965	One at Broxbourne GP on 27 February.
1968	One at Aston on 6 January.
1968–73	During the fieldwork for the *Breeding Bird Atlas* pairs bred at two sites near Kings Langley in 1968 and possibly at a third (per C. J. Mead). Another pair was located in Nyn Park. The breeding pairs shown in the *Breeding Bird Atlas* (Mead and Smith 1982) in three tetrads around Ashridge were in the area of Beechwood Park School (per C. J. Mead).
1973	Singles at Oughtonhead Common on 8 November, Balls Wood on 10 November, and Cuffley on 23 November.
1974	One in Balls Wood, Hertford, on 7 April.
1977	One at Royston SF on 17 September.

Skylark

Alauda arvensis

MAP 51 An abundant resident, passage migrant and winter visitor.

Skylarks are abundant in all agricultural and grassland areas throughout the year, and there is no reason to suppose its status has ever been otherwise. Sage (1959) also found it to be a very common resident and passage migrant. However, a temporary setback occurred in the late 1950s and early 1960s when populations suffered massive mortality as a result of the use of the persistent organo-chlorine insecticides. In the springs from 1957 to 1959 and in 1961 large numbers of dead Skylarks were found around Bramfield where farmers had been using seed dressed with Aldrin and Dieldrin. It seems reasonable to assume that similar mortality occurred wherever these substances were used. The effect of the cold winter of 1962/63 was to reduce populations further. Recovery was rapid, and between 1967 and 1973 it was found to be present during the breeding season in 98 per cent of all tetrads (Mead and Smith 1982). Gladwin (1983) found little change in the population in central Hertfordshire between 1956 and 1980, and it seems that the species has recovered from the effects of the toxic chemical period.

Outside the breeding season Skylarks form into flocks, mostly of less than 100 birds. Flocks of between 100 and 300 birds are seen occasionally, but larger flocks appear to be rare. The largest numbers seen together on the ground are 500 at Rye Meads on 16 February 1963, 500 with finches at Chorleywood on 30 December 1970, 1350 at Chorleywood on 5 January 1971, 1000 at Wallington on 4 January 1979, and 1000 at Troy Mill and West

Hyde on 28 January 1979. All of these exceptional flocks coincided with movements due to cold weather.

A broad-front diurnal westward to north-westward passage of Skylarks is observed annually between mid-October and late November. On peak days several thousands of these birds may be seen passing over chosen observation points almost anywhere in the county. The largest movements however, are undoubtedly those due to the onset of cold weather. Unlike the autumn movements these tend to follow a south-westerly direction. One such movement to the SW. started on 31 December 1978 when over 1500 passed over Baldock in 20 minutes and 1000+ were seen over Rickmansworth. On the following day, 1 January 1979, 1570 passed SW. over Tring in 40 minutes, 1000 SW. over Baldock, 1000+ S. over Croxley Common Moor, and 800 W. at St. Ippollytts.

One of several Skylarks trapped and ringed at Rye Meads on 3 February 1963, during the severe winter of 1962/63, exhibited characteristics of one of the Eastern races. Colour photographs in the possession of Gladwin and a detailed description of this distinctive bird were compared with a series of skins in the British Museum (Natural History). Due to plumage variations within races, precise subspecific determination was not possible. However the bird appeared to be closest to *A. a. dulcivox* of Western Siberia and Turkestan.

Sand Martin

Riparia riparia

Common spring and autumn migrant and local, sometimes scarce, summer visitor.

MAP 52

Sand Martin populations have substantially declined since Sage (1959) described it as a fairly common summer visitor.

The first birds are normally seen in the last few days of March. Earliest records being of two at Tring Reservoirs from 11 to 13 March 1977, and of single birds at Hilfield Park Reservoir on 14 March 1972, Royston on 14 March 1977, and Ickleford on 14 March 1981. Although one or two hundreds may occasionally be seen feeding over open water at gravel pits and reservoirs in the first half of April, the main arrival usually occurs in the second half of that month extending, in some years, into May. During the period of peak passage numbers of between 300 and 400 are typically recorded in the Colne and Lea valleys and at the main reservoirs.

The breeding population is largely dependent on the availability of sand or gravel faces. These have increased in the last 25 years as a result of expansion by extractive industries. Thus there appears to be no lack of potential nest sites. Indeed, a significant number of former regular breeding faces that are still extant remain deserted. Despite this, the breeding

187

population in Hertfordshire has suffered a huge decline largely, it seems, due to the drought in the Sahel. In 1965 members of the Mimram Valley Ringing Group, participating in the British Trust for Ornithology's Sand Martin enquiry, counted 1041 burrows at sites in or adjacent to the whole of the Beane, Colne, Lea and Mimram valleys. Of these, 711 burrows were within the area surveyed by the London Natural History Society in 1960 when 602 burrows were counted (Nau 1961). However, in 1980 and 1981 the total breeding population of the whole county was probably only 200 to 250 pairs (186 and 153 pairs were reported), and in 1982 about 300 pairs (294 pairs reported). Since the great majority of breeding sites are in the area covered by the 1965 survey the decline in the 18 years to 1982 may be reasonably estimated to be between 80 and 85 per cent. The decline in the numbers of Sand Martins compared with other hirundines is evident from Table 6.28 which shows the numbers ringed at Rye Meads between 1960 and 1982.

Small numbers occasionally nest in drainage holes in the stone faced bank

TABLE 6.28   *Number and relative percentages of hirundines ringed at Rye Meads, 1960–82*

Species	Number ringed				Total ringed	Number ringed as percentage of total of all hirundines			
	1960–67	*1968–72*	*1973–77*	*1978–82*		*1960–67*	*1968–72*	*1973–77*	*1978–82*
Sand Martin	3338	910	320	1047	5615	73	56	22	29
Swallow	987	447	562	965	2961	22	28	40	26
House Martin	214	257	536	1640	2647	5	16	38	45
Total:	4539	1614	1418	3652	11223				

of the Grand Union Canal at West Hyde and Tring, and in a similar habitat by the River Lea at Rye House.

The autumn passage starts in July with peaks occurring through August, sometimes earlier, to mid-September. During this period large numbers occasionally exceeding 1000 are seen over open water habitats and at reed-bed roosts. Examples of high numbers include 3000 passing Broxbourne on 23 July 1960, and between 1000 and 1500 mostly at Rye Meads and Tring Reservoirs on many dates in August and early September between 1961 and 1968. Since then assemblies of 1000 or more have been noted on only four occasions; at Cheshunt on 22 August 1973, Stockers Lake on 6 August 1977, and Troy Mill on 6 September 1977 and 4 September 1980. Consistent with the decline and in complete contrast to the situation that was observed in the early 1960s, there were few reports of autumn flocks or gatherings of between 250 and 500 birds in the five-year period 1978 to 1982.

The autumn passage through the county is primarily from NNW. to SSE. (Mead and Harrison 1979). Analysis of over 300 ringing recoveries shows that most birds come from or are recovered within the area of Britain east of a line from Cumbria to Sussex. Foreign recoveries of Sand Martins ringed in Hertfordshire are from France (at least 10) and Spain (5).

Small numbers are very occasionally seen into early October. The only reported November occurrences are of a single, presumably the same, bird at Tring Reservoirs on 4 and 6 November 1982. More remarkably one was seen at Chorleywood on 6 December 1956.

Swallow

Hirundo rustica

Common, often abundant, spring and autumn migrant and summer visitor. **MAP 53**

There appears to have been no significant change in the status of this often abundant species since Sage (1959) described it as a very common summer visitor and passage migrant.

The first Swallows usually arrive in the first ten days of April. However, the bulk of the spring passage occurs in late April and the first half of May. In some recent years the spring passage has extended into early June. There are four March records of one at Kings Langley and two at Rye Meads on 30 March 1958, one at Tring Reservoirs on 29 and 30 March 1979, and three at Maple Cross on 29 March 1981. Swallows are diurnal migrants and movements involving large numbers, i.e. more than 500 birds, are regularly observed in spring. In cold weather similar numbers of these aerial feeders may congregate, searching for winged insects, over large bodies of open water, e.g. lakes and reservoirs, and along suitable waterways. Numbers exceeding 1000 were observed at Hamper Mill (1000+) on 20 April 1966, and at Kimpton (1500) on 13 May 1978.

As found by Mead and Smith (1982) Swallows breed commonly in all parts of the county, nesting on a wide variety of structures, e.g. under bridges, in farm and industrial buildings, outhouses, garages, etc.

The autumn passage, often visible and involving many thousands of birds, occurs from August to early October with a very distinct peak throughout September. Large roosts may occur at any suitable reed-bed and gatherings of up to 1000 are regularly recorded. The highest numbers were an estimated 10 000 at Stanborough Reedmarsh and in two reed-beds at Smallford in August and September 1968. At Tring Reservoirs the maximum numbers roosting in recent years were 3500 on 14 September 1977, 4000+ on 20 September 1978, with 2250 still present on 2 and 3 October, 3000 on 4 September 1980, and 2000 on 18 September 1981.

Elsewhere there were 2500 at Rye Meads on 17 September 1961, 6500 in a total of 8000+ hirundines at Hilfield Park Reservoir on 22 September 1979, 2000+ at Park Street on 26 September 1979, and 8000 at Maple Cross on 16 September 1980. Smaller autumn roosts or gatherings of between 500 and 1000 birds are regularly observed. The reported directions of the autumn passage are from SW. to SSE. but predominantly S.

Small numbers continue to be seen into early November in most years. The latest records are of single birds at Stevenage on 28 November 1978, and Rye Meads on 28 November 1982.

There are three recoveries of Hertfordshire ringed Swallows in South Africa. A particularly interesting recovery concerns a bird ringed in Italy on 26 April 1963 and controlled by Rye Meads on 5 September 1964.

Red-rumped Swallow

Hirundo daurica

A very rare vagrant.

Single birds of this species have been recorded in the county on four occasions as follows:

1949   At Aldbury, near Tring, on 11 June (Gaskell 1950).
1966   At Hilfield Park Reservoir on 1 October (*British Birds* 60:323).
1981   At Wilstone Reservoir, Tring, on 17 May (*British Birds* 75:513).
1982   At Hilfield Park Reservoir on 18 May (*British Birds* 76:505).

House Martin

Delichon urbica

MAP 54   A common often abundant, spring and autumn migrant and summer visitor.

This very common species, similarly described by Sage (1959), is widely distributed throughout the county, breeding on buildings in rural as well as urban situations. The rapid colonisation of certain types of new residential estates in new towns has been a feature since the early 1960s. In 1966, for example, a survey found 397 occupied nests in Stevenage New Town. There is some evidence that such colonisation is, at least in part, achieved by a shift of population from rural villages.

The first House Martins usually arrive in the first ten days of April. There are only two March records of single birds at Stockers Lake on 31 March 1970, and at Cheshunt on 29 March 1981. However, the main spring passage and arrival normally occurs in late April and the first half of May and, sometimes, may even extend into June. Large gatherings in spring are unusual, but large northward movements are regularly observed. There is an urgency about the spring passage and birds with destinations beyond Hertfordshire pass rapidly through the county.

During adverse weather large numbers may congregate to search for winged insects over open water. For example, there were 500 at Troy Mill GP on 26 May 1979, 600 at Maple Cross on 31 May 1980, and 1200 at Mill Green, Hatfield, on 27 May 1982.

The breeding population of the House Martin is now the largest of the three hirundine species that breed in the county. Gladwin (1983) found that the population in central Hertfordshire had increased by at least 30 per cent between 1956 and 1982. In recent years the numbers ringed at Rye Meads, where more House Martins are ringed than anywhere else in Britain, have exceeded those for both Sand Martin and Swallow (*see* Table 6.28).

Some House Martins continue breeding until well into the autumn and there are several records of young still being fed in the nest in mid-October. At Digswell a pair were still feeding well developed young in the nest on 26 October 1975.

The autumn passage starts in August but the main passage generally reaches a distinctive peak between mid-September and early October. There are many records of autumn movements quoting directions between SSE. and W., but predominately between S. and SW. It is difficult to assess the relative numbers involved because unlike other hirundines, House Martins do not form large communal roosts in reed-beds or other situations in which they can be readily counted. Migratory or pre-migratory flocks of up to 250 are common, and there are many records of flocks of between 250 and 500 birds. There are three autumn records of 1000 birds or more. Over 1000 were seen moving S. over Bramfield on 28 September 1969, 1500 at Maple Cross on 2 October 1975, and 1200 feeding over playing fields at County Hall, Hertford, following a storm on 21 September 1982.

Small numbers are occasionally seen in early November. The latest records are of one at Maple Cross on 23 November 1980, up to four at Theobalds Park from 20 November to 1 December 1982, three at Lemsford Springs on 29 November and five on 1 December 1974, and three near Hertford on 3 December 1873.

Tree Pipit

Anthus trivialis

A local summer visitor.   **MAP 55**

As described by Sage (1959) the Tree Pipit was until quite recently a common and widely distributed summer visitor. However, in the 25-year period to 1982 the breeding population has substantially declined. During the period 1967 to 1973 breeding occurred, or probably occurred, in 122 tetrads. In 1967 there were at least 70 singing males in the woodlands at Aldbury Common, Berkhamsted Common and Ashridge Park, and in 1969 69 singing males were located in 14 tetrads in the 10 km Ordnance Survey Square TL21 (*Ornithological Atlas of Hertfordshire* survey data). Analysis of all available records shows that the breeding population of Hertfordshire between 1967 and 1973 was at least 250 pairs and probably about 300 pairs. It was therefore described as still common in most major woodland areas in the central, southern and western areas of the county (Mead and Smith 1982).

In 1979 a minimum of 30 pairs were still present in the Aldbury Common and Ashridge area but less than ten were reported in the three following years. The number of singing males found in TL21 has been less than ten in every year since 1977. Analysis of all records from 1979 to 1982 suggests the total county population in that period was probably between 40 and 60 pairs although the populations in the southern part of the county are probably under-recorded.

The British Trust for Ornithology's *Common Birds Census Index* only evidences a relatively small decline in the national population. In Hertfordshire the much larger fall is probably due to habitat changes. During the 1960s a large part of the Tree Pipit population was found in young conifer plantations where the retention of some tall trees provided essential song posts. Such woodland, as for example existed for a short period at Bramfield, Broxbourne, Harmergreen, and Symondshyde, rapidly becomes unsuitable as the conifers begin to mature. The closure of the canopy has also reduced the suitability of some deciduous woodlands. In the Northaw area Tree Pipits have disappeared from the open country where they were once widespread.

In spring the first birds have usually arrived by the middle of April and the earliest record appears to be of one singing at Aldbury on 29 March 1973. There is a lack of information about the autumn departure and any migration through the county. Breeding populations appear to depart in August. There are a few September records, the latest being of one at Hilfield Park Reservoir on 28 September 1973.

Meadow Pipit

Anthus pratensis

MAP 56 A common, sometimes abundant, spring and autumn migrant and winter visitor, and scarce breeding species.

The status of the Meadow Pipit has largely remained unchanged since Sage (1959) described it as a local resident breeding species, but numerous and widespread in winter and on passage. As shown by Mead and Smith (1982) small numbers breed regularly on the established grassland habitats along the chalk hills from Tring to Hitchin, and around Royston and Therfield. Small numbers also breed regularly in the Lea valley at Hertford Meads and Rye Meads, and on small remnant grasslands at Stanstead Abbotts and St. Margarets. In the west of the county occasional breeding is noted at a number of sites including, more recently, Croxley Moor and Maple Cross. Elsewhere breeding is even more erratic. There are some 20 to 25 widely scattered sites where one or two pairs of Meadow Pipits have probably attempted to breed on one or perhaps two occasions in the years 1958 to 1982.

A large spring passage through Hertfordshire occurs between mid-March and mid-April. Flocks of up to 50 are commonly seen in most parts of the county and flocks of up to 100 are not uncommon. The largest numbers on record are of 160 at Hilfield Park Reservoir on 27 March 1960, 250 at Rye Meads on 1 April 1962, 200+ at Gorhambury on 25 March 1967, 200 roosting in young conifers at Bramfield on 8 April 1970, and 200 at Bowyers Lake, Cheshunt, on 15 and 16 March 1981.

In autumn small numbers appear from mid-August onwards. However, the largest numbers pass between mid-September and the end of October, sometimes extending into early November. Flock sizes are much as in spring. The largest numbers reported being 200 at Rye Meads on 24 October 1963, 200+ at Batlers Green on 29 September 1976, and 400 at Rye Meads on 8 October 1960.

Although common in winter, numbers vary considerably from year to year. In 1972, for example, there was only one report of a flock of more than eight birds. In most years however, feeding concentrations and roosts of up to 50 are observed at most suitable sites, and larger numbers up to 150 are occasionally seen at Hertford Meads and Rye Meads, and other sites in the Lea and Colne valleys.

Meadow Pipits depart rapidly at the onset of unusually cold winter weather. Thus, for example, 180 were counted moving SW. at Stockers Lake on 1 January 1979, and 240 moving W. at Maple Cross on 12 December 1981.

At Rye Meads a number of birds have been retrapped in winters subsequent to those in which they were ringed.

Meadow Pipits seen in the county vary considerably both in the general colour of plumage and in the extent of streaking on the underparts. Occasionally particularly 'yellow' birds are seen which are more typical of the form that occurs along the Atlantic coasts of Britain during the passage periods, and which are considered to belong to the form *A. p. theresae.* Several such birds have been noted at Rye Meads, both in spring and autumn, whilst two to three seen at Maple Cross on 24 March 1968 were specifically attributed to this form.

Rock Pipit

Anthus spinoletta

Regular but scarce autumn and spring migrant and winter visitor.

The first Rock Pipit to be reported in Hertfordshire was observed at Aldenham Reservoir on 28 October 1923 (*London Naturalist* 1923:17). By 1957 there were records of 13 Rock Pipits having been seen in the county. One of these, seen at Wilstone Reservoir, Tring, on 16 October 1952, was the first Water Pipit *A. s. spinoletta* to be reported in the county. The other 12 were originally attributed to the British race *A. s. petrosus* (Sage 1959). Eight of these 12 birds were seen in the months of October and November, one at Hamper Mill, Watford, on 20 August 1935, and at Hilfield Park Reservoir there was one on 1 February 1956 and two on 3 March 1957. Thus Sage (1959) described the Rock Pipit *A. s. petrosus* as a rare mainly autumn visitor and the Water Pipit *A. s. spinoletta* as a very rare vagrant. Significantly nine of the thirteen birds listed by Sage (1959), including the sole record of a Water Pipit, were observed between 1950 and 1957, and five in the years 1955 to 1957. All were observed around the perimeter of open bodies of water, 11 at reservoirs.

It is now known that Rock Pipits occurring in Hertfordshire may refer to three different forms, namely:

Water Pipit *A. s. spinoletta*
Scandinavian Rock Pipit *A. s. littoralis.*
British Rock Pipit *A. s. petrosus*

However, the present limits of knowledge are such that separation of these forms in the field presents difficult problems at different seasons and may at times be impossible. In particular *A. s. littoralis* and *A. s. petrosus* appear to be inseparable in the field in autumn and winter plumage and thus none of the records listed by Sage (1959) can be satisfactorily attributed to the latter. They must now be treated as simply referring to the species *A. spinoletta.*

The Scandinavian Rock Pipit regularly winters around the east, south, south-west and west coasts of Britain. The evidence for this includes a number of ringing recoveries of birds ringed in Scandinavia. In 1963 a small westerly passage of Rock Pipits, mainly single birds, was noted at Tring Reservoirs from 20 to 23 October (*Trans. Herts. Nat. Hist. Soc.* 26:26). The other three autumn records in which the directions of flight are noted refer to birds moving SW. (2) and W. (1). Thus on the available evidence it seems reasonable to hypothesise that Rock Pipits, which are not Water Pipits, seen in Hertfordshire in autumn probably include westward moving Scandinavian Rock Pipits. British Rock Pipits certainly occur in spring when they are separable from the other two forms, and there is no reason to suppose they do not do so in autumn. None the less more evidence is needed before any satisfactory conclusions or statements can be made about the relative status of British and Scandinavian Rock Pipits at that season.

By careful observation Water Pipits can be satisfactorily separated from the other two forms in autumn and winter. However, another problem of identification occurs with the onset of the spring moult. In breeding plumage Water Pipits are very similar to Scandinavian Rock Pipits and both are then very easily distinguishable from the British Rock Pipit. Thus it is possible that some spring birds reported as Water Pipits could have been returning Scandinavian Rock Pipits. This particularly as few observers have until recently given close attention to such birds. A bird studied closely at Rye Meads on 18 March 1963 and for which a very detailed description was made was reported by the observers as having the characteristics of the Scandinavian race. This record which would have been the first for *A. s. littoralis* in the county was not unreservedly accepted 'in view of the considerable variation in all races of this species' (*Trans. Herts. Nat. Hist. Soc.* 26:26). A reassessment of this record in the light of subsequent studies (Williamson 1965, Osborne 1971, Brackenridge and Hogg 1982, and Koning 1982) suggests the original identification should now be confirmed.

On the available information the status of the different forms of the Rock Pipit is best sought from a seasonal analysis in which distinct differences in preferred habitats also become apparent.

(a) *Autumn*
In most years small numbers of Rock Pipits pass westwards through the county between late September and mid-November. These probably include birds of both Scandinavian and British forms. Most of these birds are seen at reservoirs and a few along sparsely vegetated margins of flooded gravel pits and other large open bodies of water.

(b) *Winter*
Small populations of Water Pipits regularly winter on watercress beds and sewage lagoons, particularly in the Colne and Lea valleys. Most of these

birds arrive in late November and early December and leave in mid-March, sometimes a little later in early April. Rock Pipits of unknown race have also been seen very occasionally in winter (*see* Table 6.19).

(c) *Spring*

Birds of all three forms are recorded in small numbers in spring. As in autumn, most spring birds are observed along the banks of reservoirs and similar situations. British Rock Pipits and Water Pipits make up the majority of records but the Scandinavian Rock Pipit is beginning to be reported and probably occurs more frequently than the records suggest. The latter because until recently few observers seemed to be aware of its existence as an identifiable form in the county.

Rock Pipits (*A. s. littoralis* and *A. s. petrosus*) were recorded in all years from 1958 to 1982 except 1971 and 1977. The records are summarised in Table 6.29 below. Increases in numbers during the autumn and spring passage periods are clearly evident.

Birds which stayed for a period and were thus observed in more than one month are included in the figures for each of the months in which they were

TABLE 6.29   *The number of Rock Pipits* (A. s. littoralis *and*
A. s. petrosus) *recorded in Hertfordshire in each calendar month
from September to April, 1958–82*

Sept.	*Oct.*	*Nov.*	*Dec.*	*Jan.*	*Feb.*	*March.*	*April*
5	27	8	9	8	3	16	8

seen. The total for January includes a record of six present at Tring Reservoirs from 2 to 18 January 1970.

There are two records of British Rock Pipits outside the period covered by the table. Single birds were present at Broxbourne GP on 13 May 1967, and at Rye Meads on 18 July 1981.

Only the second Water Pipit to be recorded in Hertfordshire was present at Rye Meads from 11 to 19 April 1959. Since then small numbers have been seen in most years during the spring and autumn passage periods.

In the winter of 1962/63 a single Water Pipit was discovered on watercress beds at West Hyde (Johnson 1966). During the following winter of 1963/64 and in December 1964 at least two different birds were present at Springwell and West Hyde. In January and February 1965 newly alerted observers discovered Water Pipits at various sites, mostly watercress beds, in the Chess and Colne valleys. A maximum of 13 different birds were present in those valleys on 7 February 1965. In 1965/66 the population again reached a maximum of 13, this time on 16 January 1966. One found on watercress beds by the River Mimram at Archers Green on 18 December 1966 was the first bird to be seen in winter away from the Chess and Colne valleys. Since then small numbers have wintered annually in the county mostly on watercress beds and sewage lagoons. The majority of observations continue to be made on watercress beds in the Colne valley and also on sewage lagoons at Rye Meads. Since the first wintering birds were identified in 1962/63 a number of watercress beds and open irrigation sewage farms have closed and in recent years the numbers observed have been fewer. Osborne (1971) examined the Water Pipit phenomenon in the London area and found there had been no increase in passage birds at reservoirs to explain or corroborate any sudden increase in birds wintering. He suggested that it seems reasonable to conclude that increases in winter records are more closely connected with improvements in standards of identification, than with any change in status. None the less his analysis does not take account of different habitat preferences or of the fact that wintering Water Pipits arrive in late November, ie after the October peak at reservoirs.

Yellow Wagtail

Motacilla flava

The following three sub-species, separately described in the sub-sections that follow, are referred to by the Hertfordshire records:

(*a*) Blue-headed Wagtail *M. f. flava*
(*b*) Yellow Wagtail *M. f. flavissima*
(*c*) Syke's Wagtail *M. f. beema*

(*a*) Blue-headed Wagtail

Motacilla flava flava

An occasional spring and rare autumn migrant.

Sage (1959) classified the Blue-headed Wagtail as a rare passage migrant and listed eight spring and two autumn records although viewing one of the latter with scepticism. Blue-headed Wagtails have since occurred in 17 of the 25 years from 1958 to·1982. During this period there were 50 spring records between 3 April and 31 May involving at least 65 different birds, and several summer and three autumn records. Occurrences in spring are summarised in Table 6.30.

The maximum numbers in the period covered by Table 6.30 were at Hilfield Park Reservoir where there were three on 29 April 1981 and four on

TABLE 6.30   *The number of Blue-headed Wagtails observed in Hertfordshire during the spring passage periods, 1958–82*

European standard five day period								
19	20	21	22	23	24	25	26	27
1–5	*6–10*	*11–15*	*16–20*	*21–25*	*26–30*	*1–5*	*6–10*	*11–15*
April	*April*	*April*	*April*	*April*	*April*	*May*	*May*	*May*
2	1	1	4	5	22	8	13	3

30 April 1982. Other records were of five at Rye Meads on 28 May 1964 and singles at Maple Cross on 23 and 24 May 1981, and at Tring Reservoirs on 31 May 1981. Since 1958 there has been an upward trend in the numbers of Blue-headed Wagtails seen in spring.

In summer, a male was seen repeatedly collecting and flying off carrying food at Tring Reservoirs on 15 June 1967, and another was seen feeding a juvenile at Maple Cross on 14 June 1981. Single birds were also seen at West Hyde on 15 June 1968, Royal Oak GP on 6 June 1973, and Maple Cross on 20 July 1976.

In autumn single birds were seen at Rye Meads on 4 to 10 October 1960, and at St. Albans GP on 23 August 1981. Variant wagtails are frequently seen in the autumn and a number of these are almost certainly *M. f. flava*. An unusual number of variants occurred at Rye Meads in the autumn of 1961.

The majority of Blue-headed Wagtail records are from the Colne and Lea valleys and from Hilfield Park and Tring Reservoirs.

(b) Yellow Wagtail

Motacilla flava flavissima

A common spring and autumn migrant and local summer visitor. **MAP 57**

As stated by Sage (1959) the Yellow Wagtail was said to be a scarce bird in the county in 1878. Subsequently between 1900 and 1930 it colonised the Colne and Lea valleys and several other areas, mostly in the southern half of the county. By 1957 it was sufficiently numerous for Sage (1959) to describe it as a common but locally distributed summer visitor, and tolerably numerous breeding bird in the Colne and Lea valleys.

During the late 1950s and 1960s population levels were apparently maintained. In the Lea valley, the stronghold of the species in Hertfordshire, examples of breeding numbers include 21 pairs at Rye Meads, 13 pairs between Ware and St. Margarets, and 14 pairs on Hertford Meads, in 1958; and 23 pairs in 40 ha (100 acres) at Broxbourne Meads in 1959. Small numbers were also known to be breeding at Wormley and Cheshunt. Thus the population in the Lower Lea valley between 1958 and 1960 was probably of the order of 80 to 100 pairs. In or adjacent to the Colne valley two to three pairs were known to be breeding at Batchworth, Chorleywood, Colney Heath, Maple Cross, Radlett (Old Parkbury), Stockers Lake, Tolpits and West Hyde. The breeding population of the county in the years 1958 to 1960 can therefore be confidently stated as being between 100 and 125 pairs. Some ten years later, in 1969, numbers were still relatively high. Thirteen pairs nested on Hertford Meads (T. W. Gladwin) and 13 to 14 pairs at Rye Meads (B. S. Nau). Elsewhere breeding occurred at Broxbourne, Cheshunt, Frogmore (2–3 pairs), Maple Cross GP, Maple Lodge Sewage Works (2–3 pairs), Tring Reservoirs and West Hyde.

During the survey work for the *Hertfordshire Breeding Bird Atlas* (Mead and Smith 1982) carried out between 1967 and 1973, a few previously undiscovered pairs were found breeding in the Beane valley, at a number of gravel pits, and on the gault clay north of Tring. Overall, as shown by Mead and Smith (1982), breeding was proven or probably occurred in 42 tetrads.

Since 1970 numbers have decreased rapidly. By 1981 the county's breeding population was probably about 25 to 30 pairs. In that year only 11 pairs were located in the Hertfordshire part of the Lower Lea valley, three pairs on Hertford Meads (T. W. Gladwin) and eight pairs south of Ware (Lee Valley Project Group per G. White). There were six pairs at Marshcroft Farm, Tring, two pairs at Maple Cross, Batlers Green and Rickmansworth, and single pairs at Letchmore Heath and Moor Mill. One or two pairs also breed at Tring Reservoirs in most years. Although many wet meadows, the preferred habitat of this species in Hertfordshire, have been lost or are no longer suitable, the decline cannot be entirely blamed on habitat losses. Hertford Meads, consistently grazed for at least 45 years, seems little changed yet numbers have declined from 14 pairs in 1958 to 3 pairs in 1981.

Unusually, single pairs nested in a cereal field at Chorleywood in 1964 and 1965, a potato field at Mill End in 1977, and in a bean field at Walkern in 1980.

In spring the first birds are usually seen towards the end of the first decade in April although there are several March records, the earliest being of one at Amwell GP on March 27 1982. The spring passage period is a long one, extending well into May. Flocks of up to 40 or 50 are usually seen at some time in each spring in the Colne and Lea valleys and at Tring Reservoirs.

Post breeding flocks start to form in early July and the main passage lasts from early August to the third week in September. The peak period is late August and early September when numbers at principle sites like Hertford Meads, Maple Cross, Rye Meads and Tring Reservoirs may occasionally reach 100 or more. The largest flocks on record were at Rye Meads where there were 300 on 12 August 1961, 150 on 31 August and 5 September 1963, and at Hatfield where there were over 200 on the British Aerospace airfield on 12 September 1981. Numbers observed on autumn passage have declined in recent years; since 1970 maximum numbers exceeding 50 at any one site have been less frequent.

There are numerous records for October and three for November. Fourteen were still present at Broxbourne on 9 November 1958, an injured bird at Stanstead Abbots GP from 7 to 14 November 1982, and one at Tring Reservoirs on 19 November 1967.

Yellow Wagtails ringed in Hertfordshire have been recovered in Portugal (three) and Morocco (two).

[(c) Syke's Wagtail]
[*Motacilla flava beema*]

A rare vagrant.

Birds having characteristics of Syke's Wagtail were seen at Tring Reservoirs on 13 April 1979 and 4 May 1982, and at St. Albans GP from 21 April to 4 May 1982. As a result of the problems of identification none of these birds can be referred to the sub-species *M. f. beema* with sufficient confidence for it to be categorically stated that *M. f. beema* has occurred in Hertfordshire.

Grey Wagtail

Motacilla cinerea

A local resident.

MAP 58

This species is largely as described by Sage (1959), a local resident which is widespread in winter and on passage. In Hertfordshire Grey Wagtails nest beside the relatively fast flowing upper parts of the chalk streams and by weirs, particularly along the slow flowing lowland rivers, i.e. the lower reaches of the Colne and Lea. Small populations along the Grand Union Canal and River Stort favour locks.

Mead and Smith (1982) found that between 1967 and 1973 it bred or probably bred in 46 tetrads, mostly by the rivers Beane, Chess, Colne, Gade, Lea and Mimram and in a few places beside the Grand Union Canal. In 1970 populations were at a peak having probably doubled in the previous decade (*Trans. Herts. Nat. Hist. Soc.* 27:106). The Rivers Survey carried out by Nature Conservancy Council in 1977 also found it to be widely distributed along most streams and rivers. However, populations have since declined, probably as a result of a sequence of cold winters, and the breeding population in 1982 was probably between 30 and 50 pairs.

Ringing studies have shown that local birds may roam widely along the water-courses during the winter and it is difficult to know to what extent birds from the continent or other regions of Britain reach the county. Concentrations of more than ten birds have been recorded on only two occasions. Both records are from Rye Meads where there were 19 on 15 October 1960 and 11 on 10 December 1972.

Pied and White Wagtail

Motacilla alba

The following two sub-species, separately described in the sub-sections that follow, occur in Hertfordshire:

> *(a)* White Wagtail *M. a. alba*
> *(b)* Pied Wagtail *M. a. yarrelli*

(a) White Wagtail

Motacilla alba alba

Regular spring and scarce autumn passage migrant.

The status of this sub-species appears to be unchanged since Sage (1959) described it as a regular spring passage migrant which probably also occurred during the autumn passage when identification is difficult.

Between 1958 and 1982 this form was observed in every year except 1974 and 1975. The majority of the occurrences, set out in Table 6.31, are during the spring passage period from late March to early May.

TABLE 6.31   *The number of White Wagtails observed in Hertfordshire during the spring passage periods, 1958–82*

European standard five day period									
16	*17*	*18*	*19*	*20*	*21*	*22*	*23*	*24*	*25*
17–21 March	*22–26 March*	*27–31 March*	*1–5 April*	*6–10 April*	*11–15 April*	*16–20 April*	*21–25 April*	*26–30 April*	*1–5 May*
1	17	18	6	21	20	21	29	17	10

Also in spring there are four records of single birds between 4 and 13 March and five records involving nine different birds between 7 and 18 May.

Sage (1959) gives no summer records. However, between 1958 and 1982 single birds were observed on eight occasions in June and July.

The evident autumn passage is probably understated as a result of problems with identification at that season. In 1961 special attention was given to Pied and White Wagtails passing through Rye Meads. The result was that White Wagtails were seen regularly from 29 July to 11 October during which period there were exceptional maxima of 25 on 8 September and 15 on 9 September. Apart from eight on 19 August, seven on 20 August and 4 October, and five on 11 October, numbers were less than five. Otherwise between 1958 and 1982 there are records of fifteen White Wagtails seen between 20 August and 23 October.

In winter single birds were present at Wilstone Reservoir, Tring, on 9 November 1969, Hilfied Park Reservoir from 20 January to 22 March 1973, Lemsford Springs NR on 4 February 1973, and Ashwell on 8 January 1977.

The large majority of records are from Rye Meads, gravel pits in the Colne and Lea valleys and Hilfield Park and Tring Reservoirs.

(b) Pied Wagtail

Motacilla alba yarrelli

MAP 59   A common resident and passage migrant.

The status and distribution of the Pied Wagtail remains much as described by Sage (1959), although it has become less numerous in some

200

areas. Huge losses, described as disastrous by Mead and Smith (1982), occurred in the winter of 1962/63. As shown by the *Common Bird Census* index for the county, recovery was much slower than nationally and Mead and Smith (1982) found it to be widely but patchily distributed between 1967 and 1973. Its relative scarcity in the north and north-east of the county may be due to the dryness of those areas. Mead and Smith (1982) also pointed to gaps in its distribution in central and southern districts. Gladwin (1983) found that although numbers in central Hertfordshire were about the same in 1980 as in 1956, suggesting a full recovery since the winter of 1962/63, these gaps in distribution were still apparent and there is no evidence that the situation has ever been otherwise.

Outside the breeding season Pied Wagtails form large communal roosts in reed-beds and shrubberies, often in man-made structures. From 1971 to at least 1976 up to 480 roosted in shrubs in the quadrangle of Dacorum District Council Offices. Since 1975 up to 400 have roosted at the Lister Hospital, Stevenage. As described by Boswall (1966) small numbers have from time to time attempted to establish roosts in greenhouses, particularly in the Lea valley. Such attempts have been short lived as owners are usually quick to take discouraging or preventive action. Other roost sites have included sewage machinery at Rye Meads and boiler houses in large industrial buildings. The largest and best studies roost in the county occupied the boiler house of Rye House power station from the winter of 1963/64 to March 1982 when the station closed (Barratt 1980). In the early years, occupation was from November to May, but the period gradually extended and from 1974 birds were present in every month of the year. Peak numbers were generally reached between the end of November and early January. The maximum numbers counted in each autumn to spring period were as follows.

1964/65	72	1970/71	438	1976/77	790
1965/66	103	1971/72	451	1977/78	946
1966/67	188	1972/73	751	1978/79	1018
1967/68	214	1973/74	759	1979/80	863
1968/69	264	1974/75	571	1980/81	1109
1969/70	301	1975/76	826	1981/82	901

The figures quoted have been extracted from the *Annual Reports on Birds Observed in Hertfordshire.* The figures for 1974/75 and 1975/76 differ from those given in Barratt (1980) which are subject to transcription errors.

Other large numbers of Pied Wagtails counted at a Hertfordshire roost were 1800 at Maple Cross SF on 27 October 1978, and 1000 in reeds at the same site on 27 October 1979. Analysis of the monthly counts of the Rye House power station roost shows three distinct peaks in October/November, mid-winter and March/April. There is an evident passage of Pied Wagtails through the county in autumn and spring when many birds, particularly from northern Britain, are migrating to and from wintering areas in France, Spain and Portugal. None the less ringing recoveries show that a very high proportion of birds occurring at communal roosts are of relatively local origin, i.e. less than 20km.

Waxwing

Bombycilla garrulus

An occasional winter visitor.

Waxwings have never been regular or numerous visitors to Hertfordshire. Further, there has been little or no change in their frequency of occurrence in the county in the present century. The species was observed in the county during 13 of the 25 winters from 1957/58 to 1981/82. The records for this period are summarised in Table 6.32, which includes previously unpublished records of five in January 1959 and one in January 1960 at Cuffley.

As can be seen from Table 6.32 there was a large irruption of this species in the autumn of 1965 (Cornwallis and Townsend 1968). In the county the

TABLE 6.32   *Summary of records of Waxwings observed in Hertfordshire in the winters from 1957/58 to 1981/82*

Winter	Period covered by observations	Number of locations at which birds were seen	Total of maximum numbers of birds at each site
1957/58	24/11–22/12	1	1
1958/59	17/1–22/1	3	10
1959/60	23/12–26/2	3	24
1961/62	8/12	1	2
1962/63	23/12	1	10–12
1963/64	24/1–26/1	3	3
1965/66	25/10–29/4	26	132
1970/71	24/10–27/3	10	80
1971/72	4/12–25/2	2	2
1974/75	27/11–26/1	2	8
1975/76	18/11–23/11	4	8
1978/79	23/1	1	1
1981/82	1/1–14/1	2	2

irruption had three distinct phases. The main arrival from the continent occurred between 10 November and 19 December, when 26 birds were variously present at 13 locations. During January and February 1966, only small numbers were seen irregularly in seven areas. Thereafter, between 1 March and 28 April a maximum of 99 birds were seen at 10 locations, probably reflecting the return passage to the continent.

Flocks of more than 15 birds have been observed in the county on only seven occasions as follows:

c. 60 at Watford on 19 February 1947
19 at Harpenden on 23 December 1959.
c. 30 at Chorleywood on 16 and 17 March 1966.
23 at Hemel Hempstead on 7 April 1966.
19 at Welyn Garden City from 25 December 1970, to 19 January 1971.
19 at Goffs Oak on 14 January 1971.
22 or more in Broad Riding Wood, Broxbourne, on 19 February 1971.

Dipper

Cinclus cinclus

A very rare winter visitor.

Dippers have been observed in Hertfordshire on only nine occasions and have bred once.

A pair are stated by Whiteman (1936) to have bred by the waterfall at the head of the lower lake in Hexton Park just prior to the 1914–18 war. This record was satisfactorily supported and substantiated by subsequent communications with B. L. Sage but the race to which the birds belonged cannot be deduced or assumed.

Sage (1959) gave five other records. One was shot at West Mill (Hitchin) on 17 October 1848. Another 'apparently' but therefore not certainly of the British race *C. c. gularis* was seen in a flooded field near Hatfield on 5 April 1916. Other single birds were seen at Hitchin in mid-February 1936, found injured near Ware in October 1937, and seen by the River Chess on the county boundary near Chenies on 4 and 11 May 1941. The race of these birds was not determined (Hayward 1947, Brown 1949).

The other three and most recent records are all of birds of the Northern race *C. c. cinclus* known as the Black-bellied Dipper. One present on the River Rib near Bengeo from 29 December 1962, to 17 February 1963, was trapped and ringed. It was said by the river keeper to have been present for a few weeks previously. At Lemsford Springs NR one was present from 20 November 1974, to 21 February 1975, and another, present from 25 January to 28 March 1981, was accompanied by a second bird from 8 to 27 March. Song and courtship display were noted from the last two birds which roosted behind the waterfall at the outlet of Brocket Hall Lake.

No Dipper of the British race has yet been conclusively identified in Hertfordshire. This revises the statement made by Sage (1959) who thought there were two instances of birds of this race having been identified.

Figure 6.15 *Black-bellied Dipper at Lemsford Springs NR in March 1981.*
Photo: © Barry Trevis

Wren

Troglodytes troglodytes

MAP 60 An abundant resident.

Wrens breed in all parts of Hertfordshire and are not known to have been anything but common in the county. As stated by Mead and Smith (1982) the densest populations are found in woodlands, deciduous or coniferous, with a thick ground or shrub layer. They also found that sites, such as those on the Ashridge Estate, dominated by planted conifers or natural birch may often have a breeding pair every hectare. Gladwin (1983) estimated that there has been no significant change in the breeding population in central Hertfordshire between 1956 and 1980. In the fieldwork upon which this statement was based Gladwin found a breeding density of one pair per 1.14 hectares in woodland in the Bramfield area in 1977 and 1978.

Wrens are particularly vulnerable to cold winter weather and populations are subject to large variations. In the winter of 1962/63 the population was reduced by as much as three–quarters and in 1981/82 by about a half. Recovery from such losses may normally take three or four years.

Communal roosting in nestboxes, under eaves, and in holes in trees has often been observed in the county.

Figure 6.16 shows the number of Wrens ringed at Rye Meads in each calendar month from 1963–82. The peak in July and August reflects the

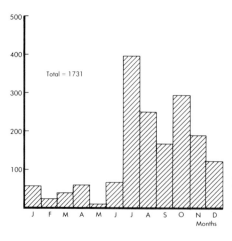

Figure 6.16 *Number of Wrens ringed at Rye Meads, in each calendar month in the period 1963–82*

appearance of newly fledged young and post–juvenile dispersal. The peaks in October and November, and March and April, appear to be due to local seasonal migrations of mostly juvenile and first year birds as well as to changes in netting areas on the site. Holdsworth (1974a) found similar increases in Wrens at Maple Cross in autumn and also postulated that these were local birds which found the site more attractive at that season. His data also shows an increase in visiting birds in March and April as they presumably pass through returning to local breeding sites.

Dunnock

Prunella modularis

An abundant resident.   **MAP 61**

The Dunnock breeds commonly in all parts of the county, nesting in a wide range of low vegetation from hedgerows and shrubs to medium and tall herbage. Mead and Smith (1982) found the population to have remained very steady in the 15 years to 1980 although the population graph from the *Common Bird Census* plots shows a small decrease in the later years. Gladwin (1983) found that numbers had decreased in central Hertfordshire between 1956 and 1980 and were slowly continuing to do so.

The Dunnock is probably the Cuckoo's most important host species in Hertfordshire. Mead and Smith (1982) state that 'up to 3 per cent of Dunnocks that rear young rear a Cuckoo and not a brood of Dunnocks'.

Local concentrations of Dunnocks occur in autumn, and many of the birds involved display the restless, noisy behaviour typically associated with migratory activity. The post breeding population peak in July followed by the arrival of new birds in October at Rye Meads is clearly illustrated by Figure 6.17. Rye Meads is only one of many sites where such concentrations have been noted. Analysis of ringing recoveries, however, shows that the birds are of very local origin and movements of more than 5km are rare. Nau (1965) found there is no significant difference between the wing formula of Dunnocks occurring at Rye Meads in autumn and data for British breeding

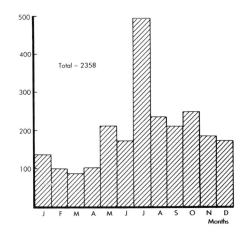

Figure 6.17   *Number of Dunnocks ringed at Rye Meads, in each calendar month in the period 1963–82*

birds *P. m. occidentalis*. There is therefore no reason to suppose that autumn Dunnocks at Rye Meads, and by extension in the county generally, are of other than British origin. There is however one exception. On 6 January 1963, during a particularly severe winter a Dunnock with the second primary 4mm longer than the seventh primary was trapped at Rye Meads (Nau 1965). This measurement is significantly outside the range for British Dunnocks and well within that for birds of the continental race *P. m. modularis*.

Robin

Erithacus rubecula

MAP 62 An abundant resident and partial migrant.

Sage (1959) described the Robin as a common and largely sedentary resident. Mead and Smith (1982) found the species to be abundant in the years 1967 to 1973 and distributed throughout the county. Particularly in the early 1960s and subsequently, there has been a large increase in central Hertfordshire (Gladwin 1983) as the species found new opportunities in newly developed low-density residential areas.

Analysis of ringing data from Bramfield Forest, Digswell Lake and Tewinbury suggests that many Hertfordshire Robins may establish and breed in territories less than 0.40 km from the nest from which they fledged.

Figure 6.18 shows the number of Robins ringed at Rye Meads in each calendar month from 1963–82. The peak from July onwards reflects the appearance of each year's young and also the very local autumn movements

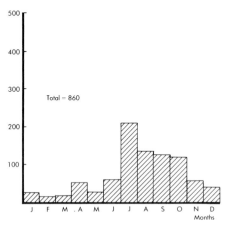

Figure 6.18 *Number of Robins ringed at Rye Meads, in each calendar month in the period 1963–82*

made by birds seeking to establish individual winter territories. A small proportion of British Robins, mostly females, migrate SSW. into France and Spain for the winter. The April peak in Figure 6.12 could reflect the return of some of these birds as well as the local movements of birds leaving the territories, most of which have normally relocated and paired by early March.

Large 'falls' of Robins of the greyer backed, orange rather than red-breasted continental forms *E. r. rubecula* regularly occur on the east coast of Britain in the autumn, usually in October. There is no evidence that significant numbers of these birds penetrate inland as far as Hertfordshire. A bird ringed at Low Hauxley, Northumberland, on 20 October 1976 and trapped and released at Rye Meads only ten days later on 30 October, was not noticeably greyer or more orange than local birds.

Nightingale

Luscinia megarhynchos

Rare annual summer visitor and passage migrant.　　　　　　**MAP 63**

In 1957 the Nightingale was a fairly common summer visitor to most areas where there was suitable cover (Sage 1959). At that time it was still found in all of the more wooded areas of the county being particularly numerous in places like Berkhamsted Common, Bramfield Park Wood, Broxbourne Woods (including Wormley Wood), Northaw Great Wood, Hatfield Park, Hertford Heath, Newton Wood and Watery Grove, Sherrardspark Wood, and Symondshyde Great Wood. Otherwise it was most frequently to be found in woodlands around Ashridge, Bayford, Braughing, Chipperfield, Chorleywood, Essendon, Hertford and The Pelhams.

By 1957, when Sage (1959) found the species had decreased in many localities, numbers had been declining in the county for at least 40 years. None the less it was still quite common. In 1961, for example, T. W. Gladwin and B. S. Nau found between 97 and 108 singing males between mid-May and mid-June in the woodlands between Brickendon, Broxbourne, Hoddesdon and Hertford Heath. Their census area included Goldings Wood, Hertford Heath, Balls Wood, Box Wood, all the woods in the Broxbourne complex including Thunderfield Grove, Wormley Wood and Derry's Wood, and Blackfan Wood, Light's Wood and several smaller woodlands around Brickendon. Since then numbers have continued to decrease to the level where the species is now a regular but rare breeding bird in Hertfordshire. Mead and Smith (1982) found that data from the fieldwork for the *Hertfordshire Breeding Bird Atlas,* carried out between 1967 and 1973, revealed 'a marked decline since the 1950s.' In 1980, when the British Trust for Ornithology organised a national breeding season survey of the species, only 23 singing males were found in the county despite 'a fairly comprehensive and accurate cover of the county being achieved' (Sawford 1981). The number of singing males counted in any year probably exceeds the number of breeding pairs as the failure to relocate some birds a few days later suggests counts include some passing migrants.

The cause of the decline appears to be the cessation of the harvesting and management of broad-leafed woodland by rotational coppicing and the loss of native deciduous woodland in general. Dense thickets of young coppice with relatively low density Oak standards and rich ground vegetation are now scarce in Hertfordshire, and many thick hedgerows and small areas of scrub, particularly Blackthorn thicket, have been removed.

There is no firm evidence of any significant passage of Nightingales through the county in autumn.

Bluethroat

Luscinia svecica

A very rare vagrant.

There are five recorded occurrences of Bluethroats in Hertfordshire.

A male of the nominate red-spotted form *L. s. svecica* was seen at Aldenham Reservoir on 4 March 1942 (Ridpath 1942). Another male was present at Marsworth Reservoir, Tring, on 23 September 1969. A first-year female was caught and ringed at Tewinbury on 12 September 1970, and another seen at Tring Reservoirs on 1 September 1976. The race or form of the last three could not be determined. On 29 April 1978, a Bluethroat of the white-spotted form *L. s. cyanecula* was found dead in a garden at Spellbrook, near Bishops Stortford. The skin of this bird is now in the Norwich Castle Museum.

Black Redstart

Phoenicurus ochruros

MAP 64 Occasional spring and rare autumn migrant, and rare summer visitor which breeds occasionally.

Sage (1959) described the species as an irregular winter visitor and passage migrant and listed the 22 county records up to 1957 inclusive. The 20 records prior to 1958 for which dates are available are summarised with subsequent records in Table 6.33.

In the 25-year period 1958–82 Black Redstarts were observed in the county in every year except 1962. As can be seen by comparing the figures in Table 6.33, which excludes birds seen at known or possible breeding sites, there appears to have been an increase in the numbers occurring on spring

TABLE 6.33 *Number of Black Redstarts observed in Hertfordshire in each calendar month up to 1982, excluding birds seen at known breeding sites*

Period	Jan.	Feb.	Mar.	Apr.	May	June	Jul.	Aug.	Sep.	Oct.	Nov.	Dec.	Total
Up to 1957	—	1	5	5	—	—	1	—	1	2	4	1	20
1958–82	1	2	10	38	13	—	1	5	6	7	2	1	86

passage. This might be expected as one or two pairs bred in at least 12, and possibly 14, of the 25 years from 1958–82, evidencing new colonisation.

Winter records include single birds at Ickleford through January to 15 February 1981, at Abbots Langley on 26 February 1981, and at Hatfield airfield on 2 December 1982.

Black Redstarts apparently bred in Hertfordshire for the first time in 1958 and have been proven to, or have probably done so as follows:

1958	Meadows (1970) refers to a nest from which four or five young fledged on 21 June 1958 at Wrotham Park, Bentley Heath. This site formerly in Middlesex, became part of Hertfordshire as a result of boundary changes made in 1965. There seems to have been no earlier published reference to this record which is also mentioned by Fitter (1971). Unusually in Britain the nest was 3–4 feet from the ground in an ivy covered old estate wall, in a quiet rural area.
1963	A pair with three fledged young and a second brood in a nest was discovered in one of the changing rooms of the Merchant Taylors School, near Rickmansworth, on 18 June (*British Birds* 58:490).
1968–9	A pair reared two broods in each year from a nest accessed through the same hole in the upper brickwork of the former downside goods shed at Welwyn North Station
1970–2	Pairs bred in a malting, near Ware, in St. Albans and in Welwyn Garden City (Mead and Smith 1982).
1973–5	A pair bred successfully at Rye House power station.
1978–81	Although present in the intervening years, except 1977, breeding was only suspected in 1979 and 1982, not proven in 1976, and known not to have taken place in 1980. In 1974 the adult female remained on the site until at least 23 December.
1974	A pair possibly bred at Codicote where a second male was also present.
1975	A pair nested in farm buildings near Tring (*British Birds* 71:31).
1975–6	A pair bred successfully at Warren Springs Laboratory, Stevenage.
1976	Two pairs nested in old maltings at Ware.
1978	A pair bred at Welwyn Garden City.
1980	A pair bred successfully at Royston.

In 1979 a pair were seen at the former breeding site at Tring on 16 September. The breeding record for TL/41K in Mead and Smith (1982) was outside the county boundary.

Redstart

Phoenicurus phoenicurus

Occasional spring and autumn migrant and rare summer visitor.　　　**MAP 65**

Sage (1959) described the Redstart as a local summer visitor which was then fairly numerous in a few favoured localities. Numbers have since declined so that by 1982 the species had become scarce in the county.

Redstarts were already declining in some parts of Hertfordshire in the early part of the twentieth century. For example it had become extinct as a breeding species in the Hitchin area by 1920. Only a few years earlier Foster (1917) had described it as breeding in all parts of the district but evidently decreasing.

From 1958 to 1968 breeding Redstarts were still relatively numerous in many of their traditional sites in mature deciduous woodland. Fortunately, accurate counts of the breeding populations were obtained at most sites in one or more years of that period, and included the following:

    1959   7 pairs at Berkhamsted Common
    1961   24 pairs in Broxbourne Woods
           5 pairs in Hatfield Park
    1962   6 pairs in Northaw Great Wood
    1963   4 pairs in Mimms Woods
           15 pairs in Northaw Great Wood
    1964   5 pairs in Ashridge Park
           7 pairs in Hitch Wood
           19 pairs in Northaw Great Wood
    1965   9 pairs at Frithsden Beeches
           2 pairs in Knebworth Park
           13 pairs in Northaw Great Wood
    1966   15-20 pairs in Northaw Great Wood

Also during this period several pairs nested annually in old mature hedgerows on the area of gault clay around Puttenham.

In 1965 and 1966 all the sites listed above, except Mimms Woods, were known to be occupied by Redstarts. Allowing for the fact that reafforestation had reduced the Broxbourne Woods population to two pairs by 1966 it would seem that between 40 and 50 pairs of Redstarts bred in the county in each of those years.

The effect of the Sahel drought on the species wintering area took a heavy toll during the winter of 1968/69 and the summer of 1969 revealed a dramatic decline in numbers to no more than three pairs. In that year a pair bred at Mardley Heath, near Welwyn, and there were no more than two pairs present in Northaw Great Wood. Elsewhere the species was absent from the usual breeding places on Berkhamsted Common and Frithsden Beeches and could not be found in Ashridge Park.

Since 1968/69 the species has shown no signs of recovery in Hertfordshire although British populations have in general made a significant but not complete recovery. Between 1971 and 1978 no more than seven pairs nested in any one year. The sites at which breeding was observed in this period included Ashridge Park, Broxbourne Woods, Frithsden Beeches, Hitch Wood, Knebworth Park, North Mymms Park and Northaw Great Wood.

In 1979 four pairs were present in Ashridge Park, and in 1980 a pair bred in Well Wood, Northaw. Otherwise the breeding season records for the four years 1979 to 1982 refer to singing and evidently unmated males. Ten singing males in 1981 and 12 in 1982 were located in Ashridge (seven, nine), Broxbourne Woods (one in 1982), and Northaw Great Wood (three, two). No females were seen anywhere in the county in either of these years.

It would seem that Redstarts have always been rare or occasional passage migrants in the county. Exceptionally over 30, together with Pied and Spotted Flycatchers, were present in Bramfield Forest on 4 September 1965.

Tables 6.34 and 6.35 show the total numbers of Redstarts observed in Hertfordshire during the passage periods in the 14-year period 1969–82

TABLE 6.34 *The total number of Redstarts observed in Hertfordshire during the spring passage periods, 1969–82, excluding birds observed at traditional breeding sites*

European standard five day period							
21 11–15 April	22 16–20 April	23 21–25 April	24 26–30 April	25 1–5 May	26 6–10 May	27 11–15 May	28 16–20 May
2	8	7	5	7	6	3	1

NOTES: Maximum in any one year — six in 1969
Total of 39 in 14 years

inclusive, following the population collapse during the 1968/69 winter. Birds observed at traditional breeding sites are excluded from Table 6.34.

The earliest dates for the county seems to be those of single birds at Hitchin (found dead) on 5 April 1901 (Foster 1914), and at Rye Meads on 12

TABLE 6.35 *The total number of Redstarts observed in Hertfordshire during the autumn passage periods, 1969–82*

European standard five day period						
48 24–28 Aug.	49 29 Aug.– 2 Sept.	50 3–7 Sept.	51 8–12 Sept.	52 13–17 Sept.	53 18–22 Sept.	54 23–28 Sept.
1	2	4	5	4	11	10

NOTE: Maximum in any one year — seven in 1981.
Total of 37 in 14 years

April 1970. There are seven October records of single birds, all between 1976 and 1981. These were at Tring Reservoirs on 3 October 1976, and 26 October 1979; Bramfield Forest on 11 October 1977; in Tring on 28 October 1978; at Wheathampstead on 12 October 1980; at Potters Bar on 4 October 1981; and at Stevenage on 21 October 1981.

Whinchat

Saxicola rubetra

MAP 66 Scarce spring and common autumn migrant. Formerly bred.

Sage (1959) described this species as a fairly common summer visitor with a habit of appearing and nesting for a year or two at sites where it had not previously been seen. In the 1930s it was widely distributed as a breeding bird but was nowhere particularly numerous except perhaps in the Colne and Lea valleys and along the Chiltern scarp

Between 1958 and 1972 an already declining breeding population rapidly disappeared altogether. In 1958 four pairs nested at Rye Meads, and seven pairs in the Lea valley between St. Margarets and Hertford. The population in this area then declined rapidly. Further south in the Lea valley occasional breeding took place at Broxbourne (1959, 1960), Turnford (two pairs in 1964) and Wormley (1965). Elsewhere the species was still to be found along the Chiltern scarp and a few pairs in and around the Colne valley. A single pair bred at Old Parkbury GP until 1962, and one or two pairs variously at Bushey Heath, Chorleywood, Croxley Moor, Elstree and Moor Park up to 1965.

The fieldwork for the national atlas carried out between 1967 and 1972 (Mead and Smith 1982) found the species breeding in 10 tetrads in the present county area. These birds were located along the Chiltern scarp and along the water meadows and gravel pits in the valley of the Lea and its tributaries. It is possible that breeding pairs at Standon Lordship and Thundridge had been previously overlooked. Whinchats have not bred in Hertfordshire since 1972 when two pairs nested on Hertford Meads and one pair at Pirton. The decline may well be due to climatic changes involving colder and wet spring weather increasingly extending into May and even early June.

A male held territory at Batlers Green throughout the summer of 1977.

Each year small numbers, usually less than 10 and mostly males, are observed passing through the county in the last few days of April and early May. Odd birds are also occasionally seen in mid-summer. The earliest records, all of single males, were at Broxbourne GP on 29 March 1968, Old

TABLE 6.36 *Total number of Whinchats observed in Hertfordshire in autumn, 1958–82*

European standard five day period						
45	*46*	*47*	*48*	*49*	*50*	*51*
9–13	*14–18*	*19–23*	*24–28*	*29 Aug.–*	*3–7*	*8–12*
Aug.	*Aug.*	*Aug.*	*Aug.*	*2 Sept.*	*Sept.*	*Sept.*
16	27	38	70	62	95	69
52	*53*	*54*	*55*	*56*	*57*	*58*
13–17	*18–22*	*23–27*	*28 Sept.–*	*3–7*	*8–12*	*13–17*
Sept.	*Sept.*	*Sept.*	*2 Oct.*	*Oct.*	*Oct.*	*Oct.*
40	44	25	13	20	3	2

Parkbury GP on 13 April 1969, and at Marsworth Reservoir, Tring, on 17 April 1964.

The autumn passage through the county lasts from the end of July to early October. Birds may occur in most parts of the county. Table 6.36 shows the number of Whinchats observed in the county in each five-day period from 9 August to 17 October for the years 1958–82. Birds which stayed and were thus observed at a site in more than one of the five-day periods are included in the totals for each period in which they were seen. Statistical tests show that there has been no significant change in the numbers occurring on autumn passage in the 25 years 1958–82. The peak passage period from late August to mid–September is evident from the Table.

The latest records are of single birds at Woodhall Park, Watton-at-Stone, on 16 October 1966, and at Cheshunt GP on 17 October 1981.

Stonechat

Saxicola torquata

Regular winter visitor and very rare breeding species. **MAP 67**

At the beginning of the 20th century the Stonechat was a common breeding species on Hertfordshire's heaths and commons. Sage (1959) states that 'it used to breed quite numerously on the commons of West Hertfordshire, such as at Chorleywood, Chipperfield, Kings Langley, Berkhamsted and Northchurch'. Other sites where it was known to breed regularly included Harpenden Common, Hertford Heath, Nomansland Common and Gustardwood Common. Stonechats are particularly vulnerable to cold weather and these last four sites were all deserted during the 1916/17 winter which caused a major decline in numbers generally. Breeding continued at Watford until 1932, Croxley Moor and Hertford Heath until the mid-1930s, West Mill, Hitchin, in 1934, in the Hitchin district until 1936–8, and on Berkhamsted Common in 1939. Then followed more cold winters and the species has been proved to breed on only four occasions since. Single pairs bred at Moor Mill, Radlett, and on Hertford Meads in 1953. In 1968 a pair summered at Broxbourne GP and an unaccompanied juvenile was seen there on 23 June. However, the observers concerned stated that there was no proof of breeding at that site. Single pairs bred in Highfield Wood, Hoddesdon, in 1970, a juvenile being seen with the adult pair on 23 June and at Broxbourne GP in 1973. Males at Rickmansworth on 10 June 1975 and at Garston on 8 May 1979 and a female at Northchurch, near Berkhamsted, on 11 June 1981, are the only other recent breeding season observations.

Sage (1980) inadvertently refers to four pairs having bred in 1958 and to a pair at Kings Langley in 1968. This error appears to have been caused by certain records of the Whinchat being wrongly attributed to this species.

Stonechats in small numbers are regular winter visitors having been

TABLE 6.37 *The number of Stonechats observed in Hertfordshire in each month from September to March 1958–82*

Area	Sept.	Oct.	Nov.	Dec.	Jan.	Feb.	March	April
Lea valley south of Stanstead Abbots	9	64	50	42	30	32	17	3
Rest of Herts.	4	20	24	25	30	27	15	2
Total:	13	84	74	67	60	59	32	5

recorded in every winter except 1963/64 between 1957/58 and 1982/83. Numbers fluctuate considerably and are severly reduced by cold winters. Table 6.37 is an attempt to illustrate the winter status of the species in the county. The figures have been obtained by simple addition of the maximum number observed at each site in each calendar month from September to April for the years 1958–82.

As can be seen in Table 6.37 most of the observations are from the southern part of the Lea valley. Just under three quarters of the other observations are from the Colne valley and from Tring Reservoirs and immediate environs. English Stonechats are known to be partial migrants and wintering birds are almost certainly of British origin. The relative peak in the Lea valley in October to December may reflect such movements, the birds later dispersing.

Wheatear

Oenanthe oenanthe

MAP 68 A common annual spring and autumn migrant usually involving less than 60 observed birds in any one passage period.

There can be little doubt that Wheatears have never bred commonly in the county. Sage (1959) described it as a scarce summer visitor breeding locally and very common as a passage migrant. In the 19th century it was known to 'breed freely' on Therfield Heath and other sheep-walks most of which had been enclosed by 1860. Elsewhere along the Chilterns however, it appears to have bred infrequently and in very small numbers. The last certain breeding in Hertfordshire occurred in 1954 when two pairs successfully reared broods in rabbit burrows on Hertford Meads. This is known to be an isolated occurrence as the site had been regularly and intensively watched since 1947. In 1961 a pair may have bred at Nuthampstead. Despite the

214

suggestion of probable breeding (*Trans. Herts. Nat. Hist. Soc.* 30:246) the original record gives no evidence of breeding by a pair present during the summer of 1967 at Upwick, near Little Hadham. On 16 August 1980, an adult was observed feeding a juvenile at Croxley Moor, but there was no reason to suspect that breeding had occurred in Hertfordshire.

The only certain breeding record included in Mead and Smith (1982) refers, as stated by the authors, to a site just outside the county boundary in Bedfordshire. The only probable breeding record quoted by them refers to a pair present for a week in May 1970, near Albury. This observation was not followed-up and the most likely possibility is that the birds were passing migrants.

Spring passage through the county is widespread and continuous from mid-March to mid-May. The earliest dates are of single birds in North Hertfordshire on 6 March 1920 and 8 March 1913 (Foster 1914) and at Haultwick on 10 March 1968. As shown in Figure 6.19 the spring passage has two distinct phases. The first phase which continues into the second half of

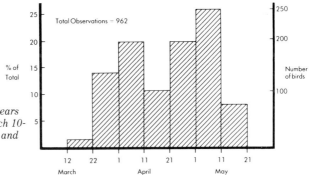

Figure 6.19 *Number of Wheatears observed in Hertfordshire in each 10-day interval between 11 March and 20 May, in the period 1958–82*

April involves only 'smaller' birds of the nominate form *O. o. oenanthe* which breeds in Britain. The second phase includes a significant proportion of larger brighter birds with characteristics of the Greenland race *O. o. leucorrhoa*. Detailed field observations made by T. W. Gladwin suggest that in some years more than half of the birds passing in May are typical of, or closer to, the Greenland form.

Few Wheatears have been ringed in Hertfordshire. At Rye Meads, for example, only 26 have been ringed in the five-year period 1958–82. None the less eight Wheatears ringed in the county between 28 April and 11 May had measurements exclusively associated with the Greenland race. A male found dead at Welwyn on 15 May 1980 was also of this form.

Single birds may continue to pass through on migration into early June; the latest being a female at Abbotts Langley on 13 June 1971.

In some years small numbers of returning birds appear in early July. The main autumn passage, however, is continuous from early August to early October. As shown in Figure 6.20 the return passage has a single peak. Over a third of the birds observed in autumn are seen during the last 10 days of August when many observers are out of the county, and about three quarters pass in the thirty-day period up to 10 September. Although, as a result of breeding, populations are at their maximum, fewer Wheatears pass through the county in autumn than in spring. Further, Wheatears of the Greenland form are rare if not absent. This suggests that most birds follow a different

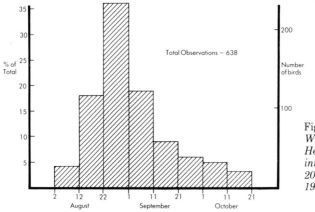

Figure 6.20 *Number of Wheatears observed in Hertfordshire in each 10-day interval between 2 August and 20 October, in the period 1958–82*

route in autumn than in spring. There are three November records of single birds; at Tring Reservoirs from 11 to 19 November 1976, at Pirton on 3 November 1979, and at London Colney from 18 to 25 November 1982.

An earlier analysis of the numbers of Wheatears observed in Hertfordshire between 1970 and 1979 (*Trans. Herts. Nat. Hist. Soc.* 28 Part 5:17, 1981) suggested that numbers had increased in both spring and autumn during that period. Analysis of observations from all sources for the period 1958–82 shows that numbers are subject to wide year-to-year variations but there has been no detectable change during that time. The range of variation is shown in Table 6.38.

TABLE 6.38 *Maximum, minimum and average number of Wheatears observed in Hertfordshire, 1958–82*

Passage period	Maximum	Minimum	Average
Spring (> 80: < 10)	90 (1968) 89 (1979)	7 (1974)	39
Autumn (> 40: < 10)	45 (1959) 41 (1960 and 1969)	— (1961) 7 (1970)	26

On occasions small numbers may accumulate at specific sites. Examples include 22, mostly males, at Hilfield Park Reservoir on 23 August 1959, and 14 near Bramfield on 8 September 1969.

Rock Thrush

Monticola saxatilis

A very rare vagrant.

The only Hertfordshire record is described by Sage (1959) as follows;

The first British example of this species was a male shot by Joseph Trigg at Therfield, near Royston, on 19 May 1843. It was skinned by John

216

Norman, of Royston, and was figured by William Yarrell in his *History of British Birds*. Later it passed into the collection of Mr F. D'Arcy Newcome, of Feltwell Hall, Norfolk. Subsequently it was procured by Lieutenant-Colonel T.S.N. Hardinge, who presented it to the Letchworth Museum, in which institution it still remains.

In 1976 the North Hertfordshire District Council re-organised and in 1980 relocated its museum services. As a result the skin is now in the care of the Natural History Department, North Hertfordshire Museums, at Baldock.

Ring Ouzel

Turdus torquatus

Irregular and scarce spring and autumn migrant.

Prior to 1958 the Ring Ouzel was a rare visitor; there being less than 25 published records of which some, probably referring to partially albino Blackbirds, are doubtful (Sage 1959).

The only authenticated breeding occurred at Offley in 1864 (Davis 1874) when a nest, eggs and adult bird were collected.

In the twenty-five year period 1958 to 1982 there were 24 occurrences in spring in 11 different years, and 10 occurrences in autumn in seven different years. All 24 spring observations were of males. However, the possibility that females may have been overlooked needs to be considered when making any judgements about the apparent predominance of males passing through the county in spring. Analysis of the spring records by date, set out in Table 6.39, reveals that the majority of the birds passed through Herfordshire in mid-April.

TABLE 6.39   *Number of Ring Ouzels observed in Hertfordshire in spring, 1958–82*

Period	Number of birds
24 March to 10 April	6
11 April to 25 April	15
26 April to 21 May	3
Total:	24

The only two May records were of single males at Stockers Lake on 8 May 1980, and a very late bird at Watery Grove on 15 May 1979.

Eight of the eleven autumn records, four of which were in 1981, cover the period 12 September to 17 October. The other three records were of single males at Stanstead Abbotts on 29 October 1977, Apsley on 30 October and 6 November 1971, and Cheshunt on 17 November 1968. The limited autumn records are mostly of males.

Blackbird

Turdus merula

MAP 69 Abundant resident, passage migrant and winter visitor.

One of the most abundant of Hertfordshire's birds, the Blackbird breeds in all parts of the county nesting in a wide variety of situations from window ledges in urban areas to small remnant hedgerows in the large, relatively featureless, arable areas south of Royston. Mead and Smith (1982) found that following recovery from the effects of the 1962/63 winter which reduced numbers by about 50 per cent, the farmland population has been subject to relatively minor fluctuations. Gladwin (1983) found evidence of an increase in suburban areas between 1956 and 1980. This was attributed to the establishment of lawns and mature shrubs in the relatively low-density residential developments of the early 1960s and an increase in tree-lined grass verges and open spaces in and around towns.

Each autumn large influxes occur at a number of sites such as Rye Meads and Maple Cross which are subject to regular and systematic observation. The autumn influxes at Rye Meads are well illustrated by Figure 6.21. The interpretation of these influxes is by no means straightforward. Prater (1970) found a lack of long-winged birds in the winter population at Rye Meads and as a result suggested that few continental migrants are caught there. This is also evident from analysis of retrap data at Maple Cross. Analysis of the foreign recoveries of Blackbirds ringed at Rye Meads supports this view. The number of foreign recoveries as evident from Table 6.41, is only 38 per cent of that which would be expected if Rye Meads populations reflected the average national experience. C. J. Mead has

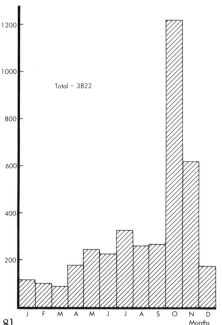

Figure 6.21 *Number of Blackbirds ringed at Rye Meads, in each calendar month in the period 1963–82*

x

x

x

TABLE 6.40   *Number of foreign recoveries of Blackbirds and Song Thrushes ringed in Hertfordshire 1909–83*

Country	Blackbird	Song Thrush
Finland	3	—
Norway	3	—
Sweden	6	—
U.S.S.R.	1	—
Denmark	4	—
Germany	5	—
Holland	1	1
Belgium	2	2
Channel Islands	—	1
Ireland	2	—
France	3	10
Spain	—	1
Italy	—	1

independently propounded the view that less than a third of Blackbirds in Hertfordshire in autumn are of continental origin. It therefore seems probable that a large component of the autumn influxes at sites like Rye Meads and Maple Cross is due to local migrations as birds leave woodlands and other habitats that are less suitable in winter. The return, mostly local movement in April is evident from the increase in birds ringed in that month, although increased ringing effort is also a factor.

Crudass and Nau (1965) also investigated the occurrence of immigrant Blackbirds at Rye Meads in autumn and winter and concluded that these probably come from a wide area extending from Scandinavia through Germany and the Low Countries to France. The accuracy of this conclusion is evident from Table 6.40 which shows the numbers of Hertfordshire ringed Blackbirds recovered abroad.

There is strong evidence of sexual biases in autumn and winter concentrations of Blackbirds in the county. Over 250 at Rye Meads on 23 October 1960, were mostly males yet 70 at the same site twenty days later, on 12 November, were nearly all females. On 10 October 1970, a flock of 50 females arrived with Redwings and Fieldfares at Stockers Lake, Rickmansworth. In contrast most of a flock of between 110 and 120 observed near St. Albans on 3 November 1968, were males. T. W. Gladwin has found that males predominate in the garden feeding winter populations in Digswell and Welwyn Garden City.

Fieldfare

Turdus pilaris

An abundant spring and autumn migrant and winter visitor.

Analysis of past records, particularly those quoting flock sizes, reveals that, at least since 1890, the status of this species has remained largely unchanged. It is an abundant spring and autumn migrant and winter visitor. There is strong evidence that the numbers occurring in Hertfordshire have increased, possibly by as much at 60 per cent, in the fifteen-year period 1968 to 1982.

The main arrival of Fieldfares usually starts in the last ten days of October reaching a very distinct peak in the first half of November. It is a diurnal migrant and large numbers are often to be seen passing west at this time. As indicated in Table 6.41 most, if not all, of the birds reaching the county originate from Scandinavia.

TABLE 6.41 *Number of foreign recoveries of thrushes ringed at Rye Meads, 1959–83*

Country	Blackbird	Fieldfare	Song Thrush	Redwing	When recovered
Finland	—	2	—	1	
Norway	2	2	—	—	Spring
Germany	1	—	—	—	and
Holland	—	—	1	—	Summer
Belgium	1	—	1	1	
Channel Islands	—	—	1	—	
France	1	2	5	1	Autumn
Spain	—	—	1	1	and
Italy	—	1	1	1	Winter
Turkey	—	—	—	1	
Total:	5	7	10	6	
Expected recoveries (based on national averages)	13	6	4	4	

NOTE: All the recoveries of Blackbirds, Fieldfares and Redwings are of birds ringed in autumn and winter

Sage (1959) gives no early autumn records. In recent years, however, the species has been observed once in July, four times in August, and on 10 occasions in September in eight of the years between 1964 and 1979. There was one at Frogmore Hall from 20 July to 3 August 1974; 12 at Abbots Langley on 1 August 1964; one at Waterend, Wheathampstead, on 27 August 1977; and an adult female in an unmoulted condition was caught and ringed at Box Wood, Stevenage, on 28 August 1978. The latter was suspected of having recently been breeding. Eight of the September records refer to between one and four birds. Exceptionally there were flocks of 200 at Tring Reservoirs on 9 September 1969, and 50 at Tewinbury on 24 September 1970.

On arrival in autumn Fieldfares feed almost exclusively on berries, particularly Hawthorn. As the berry crop becomes exhausted numbers decrease significantly and the birds that remain resort to feeding on the invertebrate populations of short grasslands, e.g. meadows, playing fields, grass airfields. Further decreases in numbers also occur at the onset of particularly cold weather causing prolonged glazing.

Flocks of up to 300 birds are common and larger flocks of up to 500 frequently observed; even larger numbers are not unusual. Sage (1959) quotes three records of flocks of a 1000 or more. Up to 1000 were present at Borehamwood in the early part of 1945; between 500 and 2000 at Wilstone

Reservoir, Tring, in December 1945; and over 1000 at Watford SF on 9 February 1947. Subsequent records include 1000s on hawthorn bushes on Berkhamsted Common at the beginning of 1963; 2500 feeding on Panshanger airfield from 18 December 1966, into January 1967; 1000 near Hitchin on 22 April 1973; 1000 at Abbots Langley on 1 February 1974; 1500+ at Pirton on 21 April 1974; 1000 at Tring Reservoirs on 3 January 1979; and 1000 near Lilley on 2 February 1982.

Large numbers also occur at roosts. Favoured sites appear to be willow and hawthorn scrub and coniferous woodland. Over 4000 entered a roost, used for several years, in half-grown larch at Bramfield Forest on 29 February 1964. Maximum numbers held in a scrub roost at Cheshunt GP, used annually since 1976, were 5400 on 25 December 1978, rising to 9000 on the 30th and falling to 8000 by mid-January; 1000 from 25 to 31 December 1979; 1250 on 2 December 1980; 500 on 3 April 1981; 620 on 14 December 1981; and 1000 on 18 December 1982.

In autumn there are a greater number of flocks than in spring. However, flock sizes are on average much larger in spring than at any other time. As a result of the accumulation of birds returning from the west and preparing to migrate back to Scandinavia, Fieldfares are usually at their most numerous in the county in the second half of March.

The main departure occurs in late March and early April but recent years have seen a significant increase in the records of birds seen in late April and May. Sage (1959) gives only three records of late flocks. There were 150 near Hexton on 23 April 1955; 12 at Wilstone Reservoir, Tring, on 25 April 1953; and 40 at Widford on 9 May 1957. Since then there have been many observations of flocks in late April, and 23 May records for the years 1958, 1960, and from 1973 to 1982 except 1975. Twelve records are of up to five, three of between 6 and 15, and six of between 25 and 100+ birds, all between 1 and 9 May. The two latest records are of single birds at North Mymms on 15 May 1960, and Graveley on 21 May 1982. It is interesting to speculate as to whether or not the increase in May records is a prelude to future breeding in the county.

There are at least eleven instances of Fieldfares being retrapped in subsequent years at the site where they were originally ringed in Hertfordshire. One ringed at Rye Meads on 14 December 1968 was retrapped there on 28 November 1970 and 6 December 1975.

Song Thrush

Turdus philomelos

A very common resident and passage migrant.   **MAP 70**

Sage (1959) described this as a very common and generally distributed resident and winter visitor. Line transects carried out by Gladwin and Nau around Bramfield, Broxbourne and Hertford in 1956 and 1957 suggested that it was then about as numerous as the Blackbird. Between 1967 and

1973 Mead and Smith (1982) also found it to be an extremely common resident but numbers have since declined significantly. Gladwin (1983) found that the population in central Hertfordshire had declined by as much as a half between 1956 and 1980 and was still decreasing. This finding is supported by one other source. The *Common Bird Index for Hertfordshire*, graphically presented in Mead and Smith (1982) shows a continuous and rapid decline since 1969. In comparison, at Rye Meads, where numbers have remained fairly stable, (as shown in Table 6.42) the number of Song Thrushes compared with Blackbirds ringed is indicative of a relative

TABLE 6.42   *Number and relative percentages of Song Thrushes and Blackbirds ringed at Rye Meads, 1963–82*

Period	Number ringed			Percentage of total	
	Song Thrush	Blackbird	Total	Song Thrush	Blackbird
1963–72	1370	1616	2986	46	54
1973–82	1439	2206	3645	39	61

increase in the latter species. None the less Song Thrushes are still very common in all parts of the county, rural as well as urban.

The Rye Meads figures almost certainly understate the decline. Whilst most Blackbirds occurring at Rye Meads and presumably therefore elsewhere in Hertfordshire are of local origin, the same is not true of Song Thrush. This is evident from Table 6.41 which shows that the proportion of Song Thrushes ringed at Rye Meads and recovered abroad is two and a half times the national average whilst the equivalent figure for Blackbird is less than a half. Many British Song Thrushes winter in France and Iberia (*see* Table 6.40) and the high foreign recovery rate at Rye Meads reflects the movements of these birds through the county. These movements are also apparent in Figure 6.22. The relative increase in March and high number in April reflect the return spring movement.

Song Thrushes are vulnerable to hot summers, e.g. 1976, and cold winters and the decline may be partly due to the recent incidents of such weather. Other possible causes, e.g. habitat loss and poor food availability on farm land and the recent trend towards longer colder springs, have not been

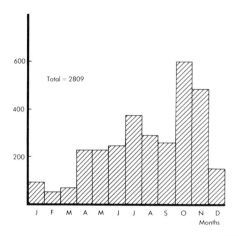

Figure 6.22   *Number of Song Thrushes ringed at Rye Meads, in each calendar month in the period 1963–82*

222

eliminated as contributory factors. At the onset of cold weather many birds which would otherwise have remained throughout the winter also move to France and Iberia. These cold weather movements are evident from the increases in long distance recoveries, both abroad and towards the SW. in Britain, that occur during particularly cold winters.

Despite the large numbers of Song Thrushes ringed in the county only two birds of the continental race *T. p. philomelos* have been found. Both were caught and ringed at Waterend, Wheahampstead, on 19 October and 20 November 1980. Thus, although large arrivals of continental birds are seen on the east coast in autumn, it seems that few penetrate inland as far as Hertfordshire. The vast majority of birds seen are therefore of the British race *T. p. clarkei.*

Redwing

Turdus iliacus

A common and often abundant spring and autumn migrant and winter visitor.

Records show that Redwings have been a common and often abundant winter visitor since at least the middle of the 19th century and no doubt long before that. An analysis of flock sizes suggests that there has been no significant change in the numbers occurring in Hertfordshire in the period 1968 to 1982. Analysis for longer periods lacks sufficient data. Some observers have commented that Redwings are usually more numerous than Fieldfares in, for example, East Hertfordshire and Northaw Parish. Ringing recoveries show that birds visiting the county have their origins in Scandinavia and Northern Russia and, as shown in Table 6.41, may occur over a wide area of Europe in winter. The species suffers from high mortality in cold winters. With two exceptions, described below, the large number of corpses inspected and birds trapped for ringing have all been of the continental or nominate race *T. i. iliacus.*

The first Redwings are usually seen in the first few days of October although small numbers are infrequently seen in late September. The earliest arrival date appears to be on 15 September 1973, when a flock was heard passing over Radlett. The main arrival commences in the second half of October and continues through November. Large numbers are often to be heard passing at night both in spring and autumn.

On arrival the birds feed almost entirely on berries and most leave when these are exhausted or at the onset of particularly cold weather. The remaining population feeds largely on soil invertebrates found in short grasslands.

Huge variations in numbers occur from year to year. Flock sizes tend to be about half of those of Fieldfares. Numbers up to 150–200 are frequently seen. However, larger flocks are unusual and there are only nine records of flocks or concentrations exceeding 500 birds. The largest were of 1000 roosting near Home Wood, Cuffley, in October and November 1962, 1000s on hawthorn bushes on Berkhamsted Common in early January 1963, and 2000 on Norton Common, Letchworth, on 15 November 1978.

Although more Redwings than Fieldfares have been ringed in the county, unlike the latter species there are only five instances of birds being retrapped in subsequent years at the site where they were ringed. Two were at Maple Cross and three at Rye Meads. It therefore seems probable that Redwings are less loyal to any particular wintering area. Indeed, winter recoveries from countries such as Italy, Greece and Turkey indicate the species to be much wider ranging and a much greater wanderer than the Fieldfare.

Most birds depart in March and records after the middle of April are exceptional. There are two May records of single birds at Hoo Wood on 4th, and Bushey Heath, Watford, on 26 May 1973.

In summer one was present near Hemel Hempstead from 27 June to 12 July 1972, and one was found freshly dead at Goffs Oak on 12 July 1978.

Birds of the Icelandic race *T. i. coburni* are evidently very rare having been recorded twice. One was found dead at Rye Meads on 31 March 1963, and another was caught and ringed at Mill Green, Hatfield, on 13 January 1979.

Mistle Thrush

Turdus viscivorus

MAP 71 A common resident.

Although less numerous than the Blackird and Song Thrush, Mistle Thrushes are resident in all parts of the county. Mead and Smith (1982) found the species to be commonest in the southern, central and western areas of Hertfordshire and least numerous in the prairie-like arable areas of the north-east.

For most of the year Mistle Thrushes search for food on cut or grazed, i.e. short, established grassland. Gladwin (1983) pointed out that particularly between 1956 and 1965 the greater part of urban and suburban developments made provision for wide, cut, grass verges, open areas, playing fields and trees. Further, much residential development during that period included modest sized gardens. The lawns, verges, open areas and playing fields planted at that time have become established and rich in invertebrate foods. Similarly, shrubs and trees have matured providing berries in autumn and winter with nest sites in spring. From a study of the species carried out in and around the towns of Hertford and Welwyn Garden City, Gladwin (1983) was able to conclude that the development of these alternative 'parkland-like' habitats had resulted in a large increase in the species in and around the county's towns. None the less the species is particularly vulnerable to cold weather and large short-term decreases do occur as happened in 1962/63.

From late June to early October, and sometimes later, small flocks are frequently observed. The majority of these flocks number between 10 and 20 birds. Sage (1959) considered these to be migratory flocks but subsequent evidence indicates these late summer flocks to be loose formations of local birds and family parties. Between 1958 and 1982 late summer and autumn flocks of more than 40 birds have been observed on only three occasions. There were 40–50 at Broxbournebury on 6 July 1960; 74 at Stockers Lake on 11 October 1979; and 70 at Waterend, Wheathampstead, on 9 August 1981.

Gladwin's continuing study has found that the berries of Rowan, Yew, Holly and Ivy are among important preferred foods in autumn and winter. A valuable Yew woodland, in county terms, included in the study area is that which has formed in All Saints' churchyard, Hertford. Here, as elsewhere, as many as six pairs of these birds may be seen in late autumn, each defending a food store by driving off all other birds that attempt to feed on the berries.

Spring flocks have been observed on three occasions. There were 14 at Newgate Street, Cuffley, on 14 February 1965; 40 at Hatfield on 20 April 1967; and 50+ at Hilfield Park Reservoir on 28 April 1973. One possible explanation of these flocks is that they were returning birds from less sedentary northern populations. Otherwise there is no evidence of any significant migration of Mistle Thrushes into or through Hertfordshire. However, a recovery for which there is no obvious explanation concerns one ringed at Maple Cross on 27 June 1971, and controlled at Gibraltar Point (Lincs) on 22 August 1972.

Cetti's Warbler

Cettia cetti

Scarce resident and rare breeding species since 1975.

The first significant influx of Cetti's Warblers into Britain from the continent was probably that which occurred in the autumn of 1971. Four years later, on 14 December 1975, the first Cetti's Warbler to be found in Hertfordshire, a female, was caught and ringed near Rickmansworth where the bird remained until 9 January 1976 (*British Birds* 69:347).

On 1 May 1976 a singing bird, presumed to be a male, was located at Stanborough Reedmarsh, Welwyn Garden City. This bird, which was accompanied by a second bird from 8 to 27 May, remained until at least 10

August. There was no evidence of any attempt to breed (*British Birds* 70:432, and 71:26).

In 1977 a pair, of which the female had been ringed in Jersey, was at Tring Reservoirs from 22 June to 1 July. The female had a pronounced brood patch but there was no evidence that the birds had attempted to breed in the county.

At least two different birds were present at Rye Meads during the autumn and winter of 1977/78. In the summer of 1978 a nest was found at Rye Meads. This was the first attempted breeding by the species in the county. Unfortunately the eggs were infertile. Another two birds, possibly a pair, were observed at Cheshunt on 28 June 1978 and another was present at Wilstone Reservoir, Tring, during October. Between October 1978 and March 1979 single birds were regularly recorded at Rye Meads and Cheshunt and it seems reasonable to conclude that they over-wintered at these sites. By 29 April 1979 three birds were singing in the Rye Meads–Stanstead Abbotts area. Five first year males present at Rye Meads in August were considered to be locally bred (Rye Meads Ringing Group). Single birds were again present throughout the autumn and winter at Rye Meads and Cheshunt, and two — one of which was seen mobbing a Tawny Owl — were present at Stanstead Abbotts on 24 December.

At least two males were present at Rye Meads in May and June 1980, in which summer a pair reared two broods at Stanstead Abbots GP. This was the first successful breeding by Cetti's Warblers to be recorded in Hertfordshire. Breeding was not proven at Rye Meads which is adjacent to Stanstead Abbots GP. It seems probable that two broods present at Rye Meads in August 1980 (*British Birds* 75:173) were those that had fledged at the Stanstead Abbots GP site. According to *British Birds* 75:172-3, two were singing at another site in the county in 1980 where one pair nested.

A single bird remained at Rye Meads throughout the 1980/81 winter.

In 1981 pairs bred successfully at Rye Meads and Croxley Hall GP and are presumed to have done so at Rye House power station where one and, possibly, two birds were observed carrying food on 12 June having been present since 16 April. A male was also present at Panshanger from 13 to 21 April: not August as stated in *British Birds* 76:19. Three males were singing at Cheshunt GP in June.

At the end of 1981 at least one bird appeared to be attempting to over-winter at Rye Meads. That winter, particularly in January 1982 contained

TABLE 6.43   *Number of Cetti's Warblers in Hertfordshire, 1975–82*

Year	Minimum number of full-grown birds observed	Number of pairs which bred or evidently attempted to	Number ringed at Rye Meads
1975	1	–	–
1976	3	–	–
1977	4	–	1
1978	5	1	2
1979	10	–	5
1980	8	2	5
1981	14	3	3
1982	3	–	–

some intensely cold periods and only three individuals were observed in the county in 1982. One was present at Amwell Quarry on 27 March; a male was singing at Cheshunt GP from 9 May to 7 July; and there was a male at Batchworth Lake on 31 May.

The decline in numbers associated with the cold 1981/82 winter is evident from Table 6.43 which summarises the occurrence of the species in the county.

There are two ringing recoveries involving Hertfordshire birds. The female of the pair at Tring Reservoirs from 22 June to 1 July 1977 had been ringed in Jersey on 25 July 1976, and a male ringed at Rye Meads on 12 August 1979 was trapped and released at Wicken Fen, Cambridgeshire, on 23 May 1980.

Grasshopper Warbler

Locustella naevia

A regular but locally scarce summer visitor.   **MAP 72**

In Hertfordshire the Grasshopper Warbler breeds mostly in scrub in young conifer plantations. Such sites rapidly become unsuitable as the conifers start to dominate the habitat, and the birds may occupy them for as little as four or five years. Smaller numbers occasionally breed in damp habitats dominated by tall herbs such as sedges, reeds and reed sweet grass which includes some bramble, hawthorn or other low scrub. The species is rare on dry commons and downlands dominated by bracken and deciduous scrub, as at Berkhamsted Common and on some of the chalk slopes in the north of the county, although it regularly breeds in similar habitats in counties like Kent and Sussex. The preference for intermediate habitats that are rapidly modified by vegetative succession and quickly become unsuitable, tend to obscure underlying population trends. Assessment is made even more difficult by the species secretive behaviour, making proof of breeding hard to obtain.

Sage (1959) described it as a local summer visitor whilst Mead and Smith (1982) found that between 1967 and 1973 it was present in most parts of the county and bred or probably bred in 125 of the 504 tetrads covered by the *Breeding Bird Atlas*. As many as 60 singing males were located in some years of the atlas fieldwork, a figure that has not been equalled since. Interpretation of the atlas has to take account of the difficulty of establishing which singing males, if not on passage, are paired. However, the fieldwork for the Atlas was carried out immediately after the peak period of coniferous reafforestation by the Forestry Commission in the early 1960s. Thus, in Hertfordshire, preferred habitats were more widely available than at any other time. Further, 'national' population indices, based on occurrences at British coastal bird observatories, were at outstandingly high levels between 1968 and 1970 (Riddiford 1983). Riddiford found some evidence of a general decline and proposed four possible causes including the effects of the

227

Sahelian drought in Africa and changes in Britain's spring and summer climate. The other two possible causes considered are the loss of scrub habitat and the effects of coniferous reafforestation. These last two have certainly been the most significant in determining population levels in the county between 1958 and 1982. Significantly in 1982, when 31 males were located at 15 sites, there were 11 singing males on 21 June in a recently felled area of Wormley Wood. It would seem therefore that current population levels are capable of almost immediate colonisation of new suitable habitats when these become available.

Between 1958 and 1982 Grasshopper Warblers have bred at some time or other in most parts of the county. As indicated above, the largest numbers have been in scrub among newly planted conifers and specifically in the woodland complexes around Bramfield, between Brickendon and Broxbourne, and at Northaw where the species was absent until the mid-1960s. The woodlands which include Bramfield Forest, Bramfield Park Wood, Harmergreen Wood and Puttockhill Wood contained 22 pairs in 1965, 30 pairs in 1967, 31 pairs in 1968, 32 pairs in 1969, but only 7 pairs in 1971. At Northaw there were between 20 and 30 singing males in newly planted parkland in 1978. The reafforestation of Broxbourne Woods was over a longer period than at most other sites and numbers have rarely exceeded 10 pairs in any one year. This may reflect the relative ecological poverty of the habitat on these acid soils.

The first birds are occasionally heard in mid-April but the main arrival usually takes place in late April and early May. Earliest records are of one at Oughtonhead on 6 April 1981, and four at Symondshyde Great Wood on 7 April 1973. Ringing studies in Bramfield Forest in the 1960s revealed that birds leave the breeding sites in early to mid-August. There are a few September observations the latest being of one at Stockers Lake on 30 September 1971.

Savi's Warbler

Locustella luscinioides

A very rare vagrant.

There have been two recorded occurrences of the species in the county. The first record was of a bird seen and frequently heard singing at Stanstead Abbots GP from 22 to 27 April 1979 (*British Birds* 74:484). On 20 and 21 May 1981 a male was reeling from a small island in the Seventy Acre Pit at Cheshunt (*British Birds* 75:518).

In view of the recent expansion of this species on the continent, particularly in France and Germany, and the fact of small numbers breeding in East Anglia and south–east England, the occasional appearance of Savi's Warbler in Hertfordshire is not surprising.

Aquatic Warbler

Acrocephalus paludicola

A very rare vagrant.

The first Hertfordshire record was of a single bird at Hilfield Park Reservoir on 14 and 15 August 1960 (*British Birds* 54:191). Another was seen at Wilstone Reservoir, Tring, on 18 September 1976 (*British Birds* 70:433).

Sedge Warbler

Acrocephalus schoenobaenus

Common spring and autumn migrant and locally common summer visitor.

MAP 73

If anything the numbers of Sedge Warblers occurring in the county have increased since Sage (1959) described it as a common summer visitor. The species nests in rank aquatic habitats and in dry scrub bordering a wide variety of wetlands. Increases in numbers are largely due to the greater number of suitable habitats resulting from the expansion of wet gravel pits. However, the population at many individual sites, as indicated by the *Common Birds Census* indices (Mead and Smith 1982) has declined due, it is suggested, to the effects of the drought in the African Sahel. Mead and Smith (1982) found it to be widely distributed throughout the county, being present along most valleys and waterways and in the low dense rank habitats bordering lakes, reservoirs, flooded gravel pits and ponds. Gladwin (1983) found that it had increased in central Hertfordshire between 1956 and 1980 due to an increase in suitable habitats but also noted that there were fewer at individual sites. Recent estimates of population include 205 pairs between Cheshunt and Amwell in 1980, of which 82 pairs were at Rye Meads and Stanstead Abbots GP and 86 pairs at Cheshunt GP, 71 pairs between Amwell and Welwyn Garden City along the Lea valley in 1982, and 73 pairs in the Colne valley (including 16 pairs at Troy Mill and 12 pairs at Stockers Lake) also in 1982. In 1981 there were 39 singing males at Tring SF, *c.* 20 males at Tring Reservoirs and 10 pairs at Oughtonhead. In 1980 the numbers of spring males counted were 45+ in the Hitchin area, 30+ at Tring

Reservoirs and SF, and 15+ at Northchurch. Calculations applying these figures on a *pro rata* area basis to all suitable habitats in the county indicate that the breeding population in 1982 was not less than 700 pairs, and was probably between 775 and 850 pairs (mean estimate = 809 pairs). In parts of North Hertfordshire small numbers regularly breed in dry scrub. In some years nests containing young are found up to the second week of August.

The first Sedge Warblers usually appear in the first ten days of April with the bulk of the spring passage and arrival occurring in the second half of that month and early May. Early birds have been seen in the last few days of March in at least seven years. The earliest appears to be one seen at Rye House Marsh on 27 March 1977. A record of one at Rye Meads on 9 March 1978 (*Trans. Herts. Nat. Hist. Soc.* 28 Pt3:60, *Birds in the Lea Valley* 1978:21, *London Bird Report* 43:57) is the subject of a transcription error. The earliest bird at Rye Meads that year was on 9 April (*Ninth Report of the Rye Meads Ringing Group* 1983:16).

The autumn passage is extensive. Some local birds leave in July and thereafter there seems to be a continuous passage throughout August to mid-September. Small numbers continue to be seen in most years up to the first decade of October and sometimes a little later. The latest records are of singles seen at Old Parkbury on 15 November 1964, and caught at Tring Reservoirs on 12 November 1905 (*Bull. Brit. Orn. Club* 31:47).

Sedge Warblers are long distance migrants which deposit proportionally larger fat reserves than any other warbler. At Rye Meads birds have been found to double their body weight prior to autumn migration (Gladwin 1963a.) The foreign recoveries of Sedge Warblers ringed in Hertfordshire are set out in Table 6.44.

TABLE 6.44   *Number of foreign recoveries of Sedge Warblers and Reed Warblers ringed in Hertfordshire, 1959–82*

Country	Sedge Warbler	Reed Warbler
Holland	1	–
Channel Islands	2	1
France	5	1
Switzerland	1	–
Spain	–	3
Portugal	1	4
Morocco	1	3
Mauritania	–	1
Mali	1	1

Paddyfield Warbler

Acrocephalus agricola

A very rare vagrant.

One was seen and photographed outside the Drayton Bank hide at Wilstone Reservoir, Tring, on 9 November 1981 (*British Birds* 75:519). The species main breeding area is in South Russia just north of the Black Sea, Turkistan and adjacent areas of Asia. This is the only record of this species in Hertfordshire and was only the seventh to be recorded in Britain.

Marsh Warbler

Acrocephalus palustris

A very rare vagrant.

Sage (1959) accepted two records of single birds seen and heard at Wilstone Reservoir, Tring, on 24 June and 4 July 1941, and on 17 and 18 July 1942. Since then there have been four published records as follows:

One ringed at Rye Meads on 16 July 1960 (*see below*).
Four pairs bred at Rye Meads in 1961 (*see below*).
One singing at Stockers Lake from 25 May to 4 June 1978 (*British Birds* 73:23).
One trapped at Waterend, Wheathampstead, on 8 June 1980.

In 1961 four pairs of supposed Marsh Warblers nested at Rye Meads in a habitat comprising medium tall herbage, including nettles, willow herb, and low dense willow and hawthorn scrub. These birds built relatively shallow nests with 'basket-handles' — one being found attached to the branches of a willow — and demonstrated great variation in song and powers of mimicry. The difference in the behaviour and songs of these birds from that of reed-bed nesting Reed Warblers on the same site was a primary factor in the conclusion, reached by many, that these birds were Marsh Warblers. Variations in both populations caused uncertainty about separation in the field using plumage characteristics alone. The problem was meticulously studied and reported upon by Crudass and Devlin (1965). Essentially they found that many of the accepted criteria for separating Reed and Marsh Warblers were unreliable. They found a wider variation in colouration and measurements of Reed Warblers than had hitherto been reported and that the variability of the song of the Reed Warbler had been 'seriously under-rated by field observers'. The present writer (Gladwin) was one of the original observers of the 1961 supposed Marsh Warblers and on the basis of Crudass and Devlin's findings and subsequent field experience of both species, particularly variation in Reed Warbler behaviour, believes these birds were Reed Warblers behaving in a way at that time unfamiliar to field observers.

The explanation for the behaviour may be that as a result of fierce competition for too few traditional reed-bed nest sites, 'surplus' birds colonised adjacent less-preferred habitats. The high level and variation of song could then be a response to intense competition within these alternative habitats.

The bird ringed at Rye Meads on 16 July 1960 was identified by Dr B. S.

Nau and the present writer using criteria, primarily based on wing formula, which are now known to be unsatisfactory. Re-examination of the data and of a photograph of this bird's wing formula are also inconclusive and this record can therefore no longer be satisfactorily referred to the Marsh Warbler.

In view of the above, descriptions of all the records of this species in the county need to be re-assessed.*

Reed Warbler

Acrocephalus scirpaceus

MAP 74 Common spring and autumn migrant and local summer visitor.

Sage (1959) described this species as a local summer visitor with a patchy breeding distribution. Apart from those at Marsworth and Wilstone Reservoirs, Tring, there were apparently no large reed-beds in the county until recent times. Most of the breeding records quoted by Sage refer to small colonies of up to six pairs in small riverside and lakeside reed fringes.

As a result of their specialised requirements, the distribution of the Reed Warbler in the county is also that of reed (*Phragmites*) dominated habitats. The increase in flooded gravel workings, particularly in the Colne and Lea valleys, in the last 25 years has resulted in an increase in such habitats and therefore in the Reed Warbler population. Large reed-beds are, however, still too few in Hertfordshire and this type of habitat needs to be conserved and expanded wherever possible. Important sites are Rye Meads where 68 nests were found in 1980, Stanborough Reedmarsh, Stockers Lake, Tewinbury and Tring Reservoirs. Recent estimates of population include 160 pairs in the Lea valley south from Hertford (includes 60 pairs at Rye Meads in 1982, *Ninth Report of Rye Meads Ringing Group*), 42 pairs in the Lower Colne valley (including 19 pairs at Stockers Lake), 44 pairs at 12 small sites around Redbourn and St. Albans, 24 pairs at Stanborough Reedmarsh and Mill Green (per T. W. Gladwin), and 22 pairs at Tring Reservoirs (per B.T.O.). In the north of the county up to 14 pairs may breed in the Hitchin area. Using these figures as a basis, the breeding population of the county can be accurately estimated to be between 300 and 350 pairs.

There have been instances of Reed Warblers breeding in relatively dry, mixed habitats of tall herbs, e.g. on the edge of a barley field and in nettles and willowherb with scrub. This, together with the species talent as a mimic,

---

* A typed manuscript entitled *Notes on Bird Observations* sent to Lord Lytton in September 1943 by The Revd. E. P. Whalley is deposited in the library of the Natural History Department, North Hertfordshire Museums, at Baldock. The document refers to the identification of both Reed and Marsh Warblers at Stanborough Reedmarsh, Welwyn Garden City, in June and July 1943. It also describes the author's basis for the identification, largely upon song, and similar earlier experiences in Suffolk and Sussex. There can be little doubt that the birds were incorrectly identified because the variability of Reed Warbler song was not recognised at that time.

can cause observer confusion leading to misidentification. Such a situation occurred at Rye Meads in 1962 and is described under Marsh Warbler.

The main spring passage and arrival usually occurs in the last few days of April and the first half of May although the first birds are occasionally seen as early as mid-April. Apart from unsubstantiated and therefore unacceptable reports published in the *Hertfordshire Bird Reports* of single birds at Oughtonhead on 6 April 1981, and 8 April 1982, the earliest is of one seen at Rye Meads on 12 April 1982.

A large passage, initially comprising mainly dispersing juveniles, occurs from July into September. The main autumn departure and migration is generally a little later than that of the Sedge Warbler. In most years a few are still to be seen in early October the latest being singles at Rye Meads on 17 October 1982, and Turnford Marsh, Cheshunt, on 25 October 1977.

As evidenced by recoveries of birds ringed in Hertfordshire, set out in Table 6.44, migration routes to wintering areas in West Africa lie along the western side of Iberia and through NW. Africa.

Great Reed Warbler

Acrocephalus arundinaceus

A very rare vagrant.

More (1865) states that Frederick Bond had seen three eggs of this species that had been taken in Hertfordshire on a date and at a location which were unknown. The species cannot be considered to have occurred or even bred in the county on the basis of this unsubstantiated third-hand reference.

The only record of this species in Hertfordshire remains that of a bird seen and heard at Marsworth Reservoir, Tring, on 27 April 1946 (Sage 1959).

Melodious Warbler

Hippolais polyglotta

A very rare vagrant.

The only two Hertfordshire records are of single birds observed at Rye Meads on 12 and 13 August 1961 (*British Birds* 55:578), and at Marsworth Reservoir, Tring, on 12 September 1971.

Dartford Warbler

Sylvia undata

A very rare vagrant.

Dartford Warblers have been observed on seven and possibly eight occasions as listed by Sage (1959):

A pair were present on Common Wood Common, near Chipperfield, on 1 May 1897, but breeding was not proved. Otherwise single birds have been seen on Berkhamsted Common as follows. A male on 27 May and 11 July 1922; one on 21 March 1927; a male on 24 March 1938, and 7 May 1939; and one on 10 November 1946. A bird seen in silhouette at a distance of 10 yards on 9 November 1947, was probably of this species.

Barred Warbler

Sylvia nisoria

A very rare vagrant.

The only two records are of single juveniles caught and ringed at Rye Meads on 19 August 1972, and 16 August 1975.

Lesser Whitethroat

Sylvia curruca

MAP 75   A common summer visitor and autumn migrant.

Sage (1959) also described this skulking and relatively inconspicuous species as a common summer visitor noting that it was 'reasonably numerous' around Bishops Stortford, Hertford, Hitchin and Tring. At that time it was scarce if not rare in most of south-west, south and central Hertfordshire. Although everywhere far less numerous than the Whitethroat, it was mostly and commonly to be found in relatively tall hawthorn hedges and blackthorn scrub on the boulder clay in the east and north-east of the county, and on the chalk of the Chiltern scarp.

Since 1959, populations in the cereal dominated arable farmlands on the boulder clay have declined substantially, mainly due to the removal and

234

machine cutting of hedgerows. At the same time the species has spread into most parts of Hertfordshire and in particular has colonised dense woodland edges and scrub along railway and motorway cuttings and embankments. It is now particularly common in the central areas around Hertford, Stevenage and Welwyn Garden City; in the south around Cuffley, Broxbourne and Wormley; and in the south-west around Chorleywood, Chipperfield and Bovingdon. It is still as common as ever in the hedgerows and scrubland on the chalk and at sites such as Berkhamsted Common. In most if not all areas it is now more numerous than the Whitethroat. This is evident at Rye Meads where, as illustrated in Figure 6.23, it now outnumbers the latter species by about 4:1; a complete reversal of the relative situation that existed in the early 1960s.

Figure 6.23 *Percentage of Whitethroats in the total number of Lesser Whitethroats and Whitethroats ringed at Rye Meads, 1963–83*

Lesser Whitethroat populations are subject to large annual variations which tend to obscure any overall changes that may have occurred. Gladwin (1983) found that the population in central Hertfordshire had increased between 1956 and 1980, but was aware of the great variability in year to year numbers. However, the spread into central and other parts of the county, described above, is all or partly offset by losses in the arable farming areas. The *Common Bird Census* index for Hertfordshire (Mead and Smith 1982) shows an overall decline since 1966. At Rye Meads, however, the numbers of Lesser Whitethroats ringed has increased from 22 in 1962 to reach a peak of 150 in 1980 and 123 in 1983 (*see* Table 6.45). This increase coincides with the emergence of extensive hawthorn and bramble scrub which this species favours as evidenced by the fact that many birds stay on the site for two to four weeks after ringing.

The first spring birds usually appear in the last ten days of April but as found at Rye Meads (Melling 1974) and Maple Cross the Lesser Whitethroat appears to be a rare spring migrant in the county. Spring observations are largely due to the arrival of the local breeding population. However, in late summer and autumn, large movements occur from mid-July to mid-September with a significant peak being reached in mid-August (Melling 1974). Ringing studies in Bramfield Forest and at Maple Cross have found a similar pattern.

The autumn passage of the Lesser Whitethroat is the latest of all the common *Sylvia* warblers and records of single birds in early October are not unusual. The latest were two at Tring Reservoirs on 31 October 1979.

Ringing recoveries of Hertfordshire birds in Italy are consistent with this species NW.–SE. movements across Europe, to and from Egypt and beyond, and the Middle East.

Whitethroat

Sylvia communis

MAP 76 A common and widely distributed summer visitor and spring and autumn migrant.

This species was at one time so common that Sage (1959) devoted only eight words to it, describing it as 'a very common and generally distributed summer visitor'.

In the winter of 1968/69 a huge decline in numbers occurred which appears to be directly due to severe drought in its wintering area in the Sahel.

TABLE 6.45 *Number and relative percentages of Lesser Whitethroats and Whitethroats ringed at Rye Meads, 1961–83*

Year	Number ringed			Percentage of total	
	Lesser Whitethroat	Whitethroat	Total	Lesser Whitethroat	Whitethroat
1961	–	16	16	–	100
1962	22	65	87	25	75
1963	26	66	92	28	72
1964	19	67	86	22	78
1965	32	13	45	71	29
1966	80	51	131	61	39
1967	7	71	78	9	91
1968	22	62	84	26	74
1969	18	10	28	64	36
1970	22	11	33	67	33
1971	16	14	30	53	47
1972	17	8	25	68	32
1973	26	10	36	72	28
1974	53	36	89	60	40
1975	55	23	78	71	29
1976	22	18	40	55	45
1977	37	42	79	47	53
1978	41	28	69	59	41
1979	61	20	81	75	25
1980	150	39	189	79	21
1981	115	48	163	71	29
1982	71	25	96	74	26
1983	123	31	154	80	20
Total:	1035	774	1809		
Average:	45	34	79	57	43

As shown by *Common Birds Census* indices (Mead and Smith 1982) and by Gladwin (1983) numbers have continued to decrease ever since. Signs of recovery in some years, e.g. in 1976 and 1977 when 'normal' numbers were reported from some sites, have not been sustained. By 1982 populations were probably less than 20 per cent of pre-1968/69 levels. Prior to this the species was far more numerous than the Lesser Whitethroat. Evidence of this is provided by examination of the relative numbers ringed at Rye Meads and set out in Table 6.45 and Figure 6.23. Expressing the totals ringed in terms of relative percentages tends to smooth out year by year differences in ringing effort and provides a useful relative index. In general the increased Lesser Whitethroat population is now some four times more numerous than that of the Whitethroat. This represents a complete reversal of fortunes for these species.

Large numbers of Whitethroat are no longer seen, or trapped and ringed, whilst passing through the county in spring. Passage extends from mid-April to early June with the peak movement occurring in the first half of May (Melling 1974). The earliest record is of one at Turnford Marsh, Cheshunt, on 5 April 1974.

Autumn passage starts with a huge dispersal of juveniles in early July and continues until early to mid-September. Thereafter observations are rare. The latest records are of single birds at Holyfield Marsh GP on 20 October 1980, and near Royston and at Rye Meads on 4 October 1970.

Garden Warbler

Sylvia borin

Rare spring and common summer visitor and autumn migrant.   **MAP 77**

Sage (1959) described the Garden Warbler as 'a common and well-distributed summer visitor' and noted that in some areas it was then a little less numerous than the Blackcap.

Although it is found in most woodlands and in all parts of the county, being most numerous in dense mature scrubland and young plantations, it is now much less numerous overall and found in far fewer locations than the Blackcap. This is partly, and probably mainly, due to the general loss of thickets and scrub habitats in the farmland areas although the effects of the Sahel drought in its wintering area must also be considered to a possible major contributory factor. Further evidence is provided by a study of *Common Bird Census* indices (Mead and Smith 1982). In contrast, the populations in some woodland complexes, although subject to considerable year to year variations, may not have changed significantly in the last 25 to 30 years. This may be because the available population always tends to fill preferred habitats in woodlands before colonising 'smaller' habitat units.

As found at Rye Meads (Melling 1974) and Maple Cross there is no significant passage of Garden Warblers through the county in spring other than that due to the arrival of breeding birds into the Home Counties

237

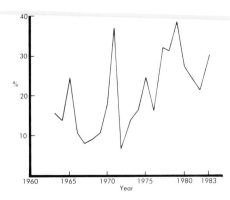

Figure 6.24 *Percentage of Garden Warblers in the total number of Garden Warblers and Blackcaps ringed at Rye Meads, 1963–83*

generally. The first birds are usually seen in the last days of April with the main arrival following in the first half of May. Apart from an unsupported published report of one at Oughtonhead on 8 April 1982, the earliest bird was one seen at Letchworth on 15 April 1972.

Garden Warblers are common autumn migrants in the county. The main passage occurs in the second half of July and August (Melling 1974) and involves many juveniles. The numbers ringed at Rye Meads (*see* Table 6.46) are to some extent a measure of breeding success. Expressing the numbers of Garden Warblers as a percentage of the total number of Garden Warblers and Blackcaps ringed smooths out year by year differences in ringing effort and produces an index of relative population levels. As can be

TABLE 6.46 *Number and relative percentages of Garden Warblers and Blackcaps ringed at Rye Meads, 1963–83*

Year	Number ringed			Percentage of total	
	Garden Warbler	Blackcap	Total	Garden Warbler	Blackcap
1963	4	23	27	15	85
1964	9	63	72	13	87
1965	11	35	46	24	76
1966	8	66	74	11	89
1967	4	45	49	8	92
1968	6	63	69	9	91
1969	6	48	54	11	89
1970	15	72	87	17	83
1971	17	29	46	37	63
1972	8	100	108	7	93
1973	9	58	67	13	87
1974	25	133	158	16	84
1975	20	65	85	24	76
1976	4	21	25	16	84
1977	24	52	76	32	68
1978	29	66	95	31	69
1979	30	48	78	38	62
1980	65	178	243	27	73
1981	46	147	193	24	76
1982	40	151	191	21	79
1983	101	234	335	30	70
Total:	481	1697	2178		
Average:	23	81	104	22	78

seen from Table 6.46 and Figure 6.24 far fewer Garden Warblers than Blackcaps occur at Rye Meads but some relative recovery does appear to be taking place.

Numbers decline rapidly in early September and the only October record is that of one at Rye Meads on 12 October 1981.

The sole winter record is of one seen in a garden at Stevenage on 27 February 1974.

Blackcap

Sylvia atricapilla

An abundant spring and autumn migrant and summer visitor. **MAP 78**

The status of the Blackcap remains as described by Sage (1959), a common summer visitor breeding in most woods and copses in the county. As shown by Mead and Smith (1982) it is distributed widely throughout the county. The *Common Birds Census* indices (Mead and Smith 1982) show a slight increase in population since 1963 whilst Gladwin (1983) found it to have increased significantly in central Hertfordshire between 1956 and 1980. Breeding in a wide range of scrub, hedgerow, gardens and woodland habitats it can be almost abundant in some woodlands. In Northaw Great Wood, for example, there were 47 singing males in 1964 and 31 in 1978. The Blackcap is second only to the Willow Warbler in the order of abundance of the *Sylviidae* in Hertfordshire.

In spring the first migrants are usually seen in March. However, it is difficult to determine whether early records refer to wintering birds bound for central and northern Europe, or birds returning northwards from Spain and North Africa. Large numbers of Blackcaps pass through the county in spring. As demonstrated at Rye Meads (Melling 1974) the bulk of this passage takes place between mid-April and early May.

From late June breeding birds and juveniles start dispersing from their nesting territories and large numbers appear at sites such as Rye Meads where there is an abundance of insects and berries. Like other *sylvia* warblers Blackcaps prepare for migration by feeding on Blackberries and Elderberries. The main departure and autumn passage occurs in August with small numbers continuing to pass during September. Melling (1974) demonstrated that Blackcaps at Rye Meads are nine times more numerous in autumn than in spring.

Table 6.46 shows the numbers of Blackcaps and Garden Warblers ringed at Rye Meads between 1963 and 1983. The general increase in numbers is undoubtedly due to the development of suitable habitats during that period.

Sage (1959) found no winter records of Blackcaps in the county. The first birds to be reported in the months December to February were single males present at a bird table in Watford on 16 and 17 January 1965, and at Croxley Green from 7 to 26 February 1968. Since then the numbers observed in the winter months have steadily increased. Between 1965 and 1982 at least 72 different Blackcaps were reported in the months from December to February. Of these, 55 were males and 13 females. There are few records of single birds in which the sex is unstated.

The number of Blackcaps observed in each month from December to February are set out in Table 6.47. Birds observed at a site in more than one

TABLE 6.47 *Number of Blackcaps observed in Hertfordshire in each month from December to February, 1965–82*

	Dec.	Jan.	Feb.
Males	20	33	27
Females	7	6	8
Unsexed	3	1	–
Total:	30	40	35

month are included in the totals for each month in which they were seen. Records for November and March are excluded from the analyses as many of these may be late and early migrants respectively.

Most wintering birds are seen in gardens where they mostly appear from late December onwards. It is probable that such appearances are due to local birds moving in from the nearby countryside in search of alternative and more appropriate foods at the onset of cold weather. Many of the birds are noted at bird tables and have been seen to eat bread, biscuit crumbs, ivy and other berries, apples and fat. Observation of ringed birds has shown that they are able to survive mild and average winters in the county.

Wood Warbler

Phylloscopus sibilatrix

MAP 79 A local summer visitor.

Sage (1959) also found this species to be a local summer visitor but additionally considered it to be quite numerous on migration.

Although the population is subject to large year to year variations, there appears to have been no significant overall change in the distribution and numbers breeding in Hertfordshire between 1958 and 1982. As pointed out by James (1981) in a detailed study of the distribution and ecology of this species, Hertfordshire, at the edge of its range has the highest population in the East Anglian region. Both Mead and Smith (1982) and James (1981) found its distribution in the county to correspond with the semi-natural or more specifically ancient woodland described by Hinton (1980).

Ashridge Forest, where up to 20 singing males have been found in most years since 1958, continues to be the stronghold of the species. Small numbers, i.e. less than four pairs at any one site, probably nest annually in

Broxbourne Woods, Northaw Great Wood, and various woodlands around Knebworth and Stevenage. Elsewhere Wood Warblers have bred or been suspected of breeding in at least 38 different woodlands between 1958 and 1982. The erratic pattern of infrequent breeding and desertion of these latter sites has been a recognised feature since at least the beginning of the twentieth century (James 1981). These fluctuations are normally to be expected at the edge of such a species range. Overall, in an average year, about 35 pairs of Wood Warblers probably nest in the county.

James (1981) also examined the habitat preferences of Wood Warblers in the county. He found that the majority preferred close canopy woodland with some shrub cover being essential. Although birds present in beech stands are usually breeding, birch is the dominant species in the large majority of territories, and the distribution of Wood Warblers in Hertfordshire best fits that of oak–birch (acid) woodlands. In contrast, James (1981) found the species to be 'almost totally absent from either oak–ash or oak–hornbeam woodland unless it is alleviated by a few birches'.

In general Wood Warblers arrive from late April through May and depart in late July and August. The earliest and latest records are of single birds at Oughton Head on 8 April 1982 and at Wormlet Wood on 11 September 1959. Apart from movements due to the local breeding population there is no evidence of any significant migration of Wood Warblers through Hertfordshire.

Chiffchaff

Phylloscopus collybita

A common spring and autumn migrant and summer visitor.   **MAP 80**

Sage (1959) described the Chiffchaff as a fairly numerous summer visitor but noted it to be more thinly distributed than the Willow Warbler and in some years to be almost scarce. Mostly found in deciduous woodlands with good herb and low shrub layers, populations remained high until the early 1970s. Thus Mead and Smith (1982) found that between 1967 and 1973 it was common and widely distributed throughout the county. Thereafter numbers declined rapidly. Gladwin (1983) found it had decreased in central Hertfordshire between 1956 and 1980 whilst the *Common Birds Census* index suggests a decrease of up to 50 per cent since 1966. This is further evidenced by ringing studies. As can be seen in Table 6.48 and Figure 6.25, the proportion of Chiffchaffs in the total number of Chiffchaffs and Willow Warblers ringed at Rye Meads has also approximately halved since the early 1970s. Expressing the totals ringed in terms of relative percentage tends to smooth out differences in ringing effort. Further, Willow Warbler populations have been fairly stable, having at most increased by 15 per cent but probably less. Thus the estimate that the population of breeding Chiffchaffs halved between 1970 and 1982 is probably realistic. None the

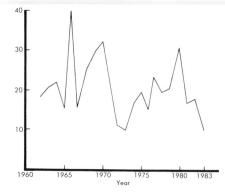

Figure 6.25 *Percentage of Chiffchaffs in the total number of Willow Warblers and Chiffchaffs ringed at Rye Meads, 1962–83*

less this common species remains widely distributed in woodlands throughout the county.

Large numbers of Chiffchaffs pass through the county during both passage periods. The pattern of migration in Hertfordshire is well described from studies made at Rye Meads (Melling 1974). In spring the first birds usually arrive at the start of the last decade in March. A heavy passage and arrival then continues into the first ten days of April, sharply declining thereafter such that most breeding birds have arrived by the middle of the month. Movements resume with the onset of juvenile dispersal at the end of June. The main autumn passage and departure, however, occurs

TABLE 6.48 *Number and relative percentages of Chiffchaffs and Willow Warblers ringed at Rye Meads, 1962–83*

Year	Number ringed			Percentage of Total	
	Chiffchaff	Willow Warbler	Total	Chiffchaff	Willow Warbler
1962	16	73	89	18	82
1963	23	88	111	21	79
1964	33	114	147	22	78
1965	10	53	63	16	84
1966	88	131	219	40	60
1967	17	87	104	16	84
1968	41	129	170	24	76
1969	46	109	155	30	70
1970	63	133	196	32	68
1971	22	78	100	22	78
1972	11	90	101	11	89
1973	24	225	249	10	90
1974	45	239	284	16	84
1975	71	296	367	19	81
1976	27	157	184	15	85
1977	44	151	195	23	77
1978	38	166	204	19	81
1979	46	180	226	20	80
1980	107	259	366	29	71
1981	44	235	279	16	84
1982	82	402	484	17	83
1983	43	387	430	10	90
Total:	941	3782	4723		
Average:	43	172	215	20	80

242

throughout September finishing as suddenly at the end of that month as the spring passage does in April.

A small number, never to date exceeding eight, have been seen in the county between December and February in most winters since 1958. Sage (1959) gives only one winter record, of a bird at Wilstone Reservoir, Tring, from 10 to 18 February 1913. Thus it would appear that regular over-wintering in Hertfordshire is a recent development. Most birds are seen in willow and similar scrub habitats bordering watercourses, gravel pits and reservoirs in the Colne and Lea valleys. The fact that some Chiffchaffs remain through and survive average winters has been proven by birds ringed and retrapped at Maple Cross and Rye Meads. One, for example, ringed at Rye Meads — a regular wintering site on 29 December 1968 was retrapped on January 25 and March 16 1969.

Willow Warbler

Phylloscopus trochilus

An abundant spring and autumn migrant and summer visitor.

MAP 81

At least since historical records have been kept, and as indicated by Sage (1959), the Willow Warbler has never been other than abundant and well distributed throughout the county. It is the most numerous of the *Sylviidae*, which includes genus *Regulus*, that occur in Hertfordshire. Willow Warblers of the nominate race *P. t. trochilus* are found breeding in most forms of open woodland and copses, large and small, along some well established hedgerows, and in habitats of medium to long herb with some scrub. Mead and Smith (1982) found it to be abundant and widely distributed between 1967 and 1973. The *Common Birds Census* indices evidence a small increase in population between 1966 and 1982. Similarly Gladwin (1983) found it had increased in central Hertfordshire, perhaps by as much as 20 per cent, between 1956 and 1980. In contrast Chiffchaffs, as partly evident from Table 6.48, have declined.

In spring the first birds arrive in early April and sometimes in the last few days of March. Earliest records are of single birds at Bedmond and St. Albans on 17 and 20 March 1973 respectively, and at Tring Reservoirs on 20 March 1977. The main arrival, however, takes place in a period of less than ten days, usually in mid-April. This feature of the spring arrival and passage through the county is well illustrated by Melling (1974). Very occasionally it has been delayed. In 1975, for example, most of the breeding population did not appear until mid-May.

Autumn passage begins in early July with the dispersal of huge numbers of juveniles and, as evident from ringing studies at Rye Meads, continues at a high level throughout August. Thereafter numbers decline rapidly in the first half of September (Melling 1974). Studies in Bramfield Forest found that most breeding adults had departed by early August. As in spring large 'falls' of Willow Warblers are regularly observed in autumn. Over 1000 which arrived in 63 ha of Bramfield Forest on the night of 31 August 1969 had gone by 2 September. Sudden peaks of 'falls' in August involving similar or greater densities at smaller sites are frequently reported. Thus the Bramfield observation may be typical of this species autumn movement through the county. Willow Warblers are rarely seen after mid-September and records for October and November are few.

There are three winter records of single birds at Mardley Heath (in song) on 7 December 1979, at Wilstone Reservoir, Tring, on 28 December 1982, and at Rye Meads on 14 and 15 January 1978.

One found dead at Aldenham on 25 April 1949 was examined at the British Museum (Natural History) and referred to the northern race *P. t. acredula* (*London Bird Report* 1949:17). This is the sole recorded occurrence of this sub-species in the county.

Goldcrest

Regulus regulus

MAP 82 A locally abundant resident.

Sage (1959) described the Goldcrest as a fairly common resident and winter visitor. Prior to 1917 it was said to be fairly common around Tring (Hartert and Jourdain 1920) and fairly common as a nesting species in North Hertfordshire (Foster 1914). Otherwise the limited information available suggests it was to be found in most other parts of the county. Numbers were severely reduced by the great frost of 1916/17. Hartert and Jourdain (1920) referring to that winter and the Tring area stated that it had been 'exterminated in that neighbourhood'. As records show that it almost 'entirely disappeared' from Berkshire and Buckinghamshire in that year it seems unlikely that it faired any better in Hertfordshire. Recovery clearly took several years. Records show that the species was again common around Hexton in 1936 and presumably elsewhere where coniferous woodland existed.

In the 1950s and early 1960s large areas of deciduous woodland were replanted with coniferous, mostly exotic, species. Most such reafforestation occurred in the large woodland blocks in the south, centre and west of the county. As shown by Mead and Smith (1980) most coniferous woodland contains large breeding populations.

The species is particularly vulnerable in cold winters and populations may vary considerably. In the mid-1970s (Mead and Smith 1980), following a sequence of mild winters, populations were at a very high level and for a few years birds were even found breeding in single conifers in gardens.

In autumn small flocks regularly appear in October and November away from the coniferous woodlands, in hedgerows, scrub, and almost any shrub or semi-woodland habitat. Indications are that these observations are mainly due to movements of relatively local, mainly juvenile, birds out of the breeding sites, rather than long distance migrants.

Firecrest

Regulus ignicapillus

Scarce visitor and resident not proved to have bred.

Sage (1959) listed five records of which three were subject to various degrees of uncertainty. The two records he accepted were of a pair on 21 January 1951, at Startops End Reservoir, Tring, where one remained until 23 March, and one near Aldbury, Tring, on 15th October 1957.

One present at Rye Meads on 8 October 1961, and a male seen at Northaw on 15 April 1967, were only the third and fourth accepted occurrences in the county.

In May 1961, four were found in the New Forest, Hampshire. Numbers slowly increased and in 1971 a small breeding population was discovered in Norway Spruce in Wendover Woods, Buckinghamshire (Batten 1973) only 3.2 km from Tring. Since then the Buckinghamshire population has flourished and small numbers have been seen in Hertfordshire in most years, mainly and not surprisingly around Ashridge and Tring. The species has not yet been proved to have bred in the county.

The records from 1968 onwards divide into the following three categories and are described accordingly in the paragraphs that follow.

(a) Breeding season (June) records of singing birds; all with one exception from the west of the county.
(b) Other records from the western area.
(c) Records from the rest of Hertfordshire.

Breeding season records are as follows:

1968   A singing male was seen and heard twice near Heronsgate and at Chipperfield (Mead and Smith 1980).

1974–5 At Ashridge one was seen on 28 April 1974, and a male seen and heard singing on 13 June 1975.

1979   A male seen and heard singing on 13 June, was probably the same bird heard singing on several other occasions in the same month at Aldbury Common.

1980   There were four singing males at Ashridge in June, and a pair held territory by the Grand Union Canal, Tring, from 8 May until at least 14 June.

1981   The only record from Ashridge was of a male seen on 12 May but not thereafter. A male was seen and heard singing in Brocket Park from 10 May to 11 July. This is the only breeding season record away from the west of the county.

(1982) Two singing males near Pitstone Common, Ashridge, were just outside the county boundary.

Nine birds, seven at the reservoirs, have been seen in and around Tring on 27 April and 29 September 1971, 11 November 1972 (ringed at Pendley), 28 March 1973 (two), 8 April 1975, 15 April 1979, 6 April 1981 (at Wigginton), and 18 October 1981.

Other records of 28 birds are as follows:

1968   Singles at Potters Bar on 15 April and at Croxley Common Moor on 13 November.

1972   Singles at Coleman Green on 27 February, Nyn Park on 29 December, and ringed at Oaklands (Welwyn) on 31 December, and two on Hertford Heath from 1 to 10 December.

1973   Singles at Hilfield Park Reservoir on 3 March, and Chestnut GP on 27 April. At Lemsford Springs there was one on 24 February, two on 13 October and one from 20 October (to 17 March 1974) which roosted with Goldcrests in a dense growth of ivy on a crack willow.

1974   One at Lemsford Springs to 17 March, and from 20 November (to 1st March 1975), again roosting in ivy with Goldcrests.

1975   Singles at Lemsford Springs to 1 March, Watery Grove on 8 April, Turnford Marsh, Cheshunt, on 22 April, and in Whippendell Woods on 9 May.

1976   One at Hoddesdon on 28 January.

1979   Singles at Purwell Ninesprings, Hitchin on 9 April and Hilfield Park Reservoir on 2 May.

1980   Singles at Lemsford Springs on 22 and 30 March, Graveley on 2 April, and Hilfield Park Reservoir on 4 April, and two at the latter site on 28 October.

1981   Singles at Lemsford Springs on 23 March and Watery Grove, Stevenage, on 5 April.

1982   Singles at Bennington on 27 March, Amwell on 10 April, and at Rickmansworth at the end of September and on 28 December.

The breeding season birds at Ashridge and other records from the Tring area are probably a consequence of the breeding population in Wendover Woods (Bucks.). Similarly it is interesting to note that Brocket Park, where a single male sang in the summer of 1981, is adjacent to Lemsford Springs where the species has been seen in spring on three occasions and has overwintered twice.

The majority of records refer to males and only four, including that at Tring in 1951, to females.

Of the thirty-seven birds observed away from possible breeding sites since 1968, 20 were seen in late March and April and six between late September and November. In addition the birds that overwintered at Lemsford Springs in 1973/74 and 1974/75, a well-watched site, arrived in October and November and left in March. This would suggest October–November, and March–April movements from and to woodland breeding sites.

Spotted Flycatcher

Muscicapa striata

Occasional autumn migrant and common summer visitor.

MAP 83

This species was described by Sage (1959) as a common and generally distributed summer visitor. Prior to the preliminary fieldwork for the national atlas carried out in 1967 the species was accepted as being so common and widespread that observers took little more than a passing interest in it. The record cards for the county prior to 1967 contain only two single entries. Mead and Smith (1980) found it to be breeding commonly in all parts of the county between 1967 and 1972. Since then numbers have decreased considerably, possibly by as much as two thirds. None the less it is still common in most parts of the county although rather local in some areas of NE. Hertfordshire, only being numerous in some villages and more wooded areas.

The bulk of the breeding population usually arrives from mid-May into early June. The earliest records appear to be of single birds near Little Chishill on 18 April 1971, at Pirton on 28 April 1969, and at Tring Reservoirs on 29 April 1977.

It is a hole nesting species found mainly in larger gardens, orchards, churchyards, parklands and woodlands. Large family parties are frequently seen, remaining close to the nest site through July and into August, and occasionally into early September. Examples include 40+ at Ickleford Common on 25 August 1979, and 25 at Oughton Head on 3 September 1977.

Most breeding birds leave in August although a small number usually remain into early September.

There is no evidence of any significant spring passage in the county. If any birds do pass through bound for other breeding areas they presumably do so without stopping. In autumn small numbers occur that cannot be attributed to local birds. The largest numbers recorded were 15+ in Bramfield Forest on 20 September 1969, and 41 on tennis-court fencing at County Hall, Hertford, following a storm on 21 September 1982. Including these records the total numbers of Spotted Flycatchers seen in Hertfordshire in September from 1969 to 1982 in European Standard Five-Day Periods 51 to 54 were as follows:

Period 51	(8th–12th)	39	Period 53	(18th–22nd)	84
Period 52	(13th–17th)	24	Period 54	(23rd–27th)	5

The only October records are of single birds at Priory Park, Hitchin, on 2 October 1977, Ickleford Common on 6 October 1979, Theobalds Park on 12 October 1978, and Rye Meads on 14 October 1974.

Pied Flycatcher

Ficedula hypoleuca

Scarce spring and occasional autumn migrant that may have bred once.

Sage (1959) hesitantly accepted a record of a pair said to have bred prior to 1917 in a hole in an apple tree at Oughton Head Farm, near Hitchin (Foster 1917). Curiously Foster makes no further reference to this record in Hine (1934) nor is it referred to by Hayward (1947). This record has therefore been reviewed and the available evidence is considered insufficient to confirm the species as ever having bred in Hertfordshire.

Prior to 1958 there were 27 records of single birds in spring (16 in April, 10 in May and one in June) and eight records involving at least 10 birds in autumn (Sage 1959). As shown in Table 6.49, 35 birds have been seen in spring and 89 in autumn in the 25-year period 1958-82. It is evident from this

TABLE 6.49   *Total number of Pied Flycatchers observed in Hertfordshire before and since 1958*

Period	Spring	Autumn
Prior to 1958	27	c.10
1958 to 1982	35	89

Table that the species has occurred much more frequently in autumn in the latter period than hitherto. Tables 6.50 and 6.51 show the total numbers observed in each five-day period during the spring and autumn passage from 1958 to 1982. The long autumn passage period may reflect the August

TABLE 6.50   *Total number of Pied Flycatchers observed in Hertfordshire in spring, 1958–82*

				European standard five day period				
20	*21*	*22*	*23*	*24*	*25*	*26*	*27*	*28*
6–10 April	*11–15 April*	*16–20 April*	*21–25 April*	*26–30 April*	*1–5 May*	*6–10 May*	*11–15 May*	*16–20 May*
4	1	6	4	4	5	2	6	1

NOTES: Maximum in any one year – six in 1979
Total of 33 birds seen in 17 of 25 springs

TABLE 6.51   *Total number of Pied Flycatchers observed in Hertfordshire in autumn, 1958–82*

				European standard five day period					
45	46	47	48	49	50	51	52	53	54
9–13 Aug.	14–18 Aug.	19–23 Aug.	24–28 Aug.	29 Aug.- 2 Sept.	3–7 Sept.	8–12 Sept.	13–17 Sept.	18–22 Sept.	23–27 Sept.
9	3	4	10	3	13	13	20	6	4

NOTES: Maximum in any one year – 12 in 1968
Total of 85 birds seen in 19 of 25 autumns

departure of British populations followed by the passage of Scandinavian origin.

The earliest and latest spring records are of a male at Chorleywood on 4 and 11 April 1960; one at Ashridge on 7 June 1970; and one at Moor Mill on 9 June 1954. The earliest autumn record is of one at Gilston Park on 25 July 1982.

There are no October records although, strangely, later birds were seen at Ashridge on 14 November 1965; Broxbournebury on 25 November 1966; and Hertford Heath on 1 December 1972.

The largest numbers recorded on any one occasion are five at Letchworth from 4 to 7 September 1958; five at Old Parkbury on 12 August 1959; 10 in the Tewin–Welwyn area on 15 September 1968; and five in Bramfield Forest from 12 to 14 September 1971.

Bearded Tit

Panurus biarmicus

An occasional winter visitor that has bred.

Prior to 1959 the Bearded Tit had not been seen in the county since 1905. Sage (1959) lists four records of which one may refer to an imported bird, as follows:

1848　A pair at Oughtonhead in November.
　　　A pair was shot near Tring Reservoirs on 21 December (*Trans. Herts. Nat. Hist. Soc.* 5:77).

1888　A male at Bishops Stortford on 12 July (*Trans. Herts. Nat. Hist. Soc.* 10:35)

[1905　One seen in the west of the county in late January may have been one of the birds imported from Holland and released at Wilstone Reservoir, Tring (*Trans. Herts. Nat. Hist. Soc.* 13:52; Hartert and Jourdain 1920).]

Since 1959 varying numbers have occurred in 22 of the 24 winters from 1959/60 to 1982/83, the exceptions being 1962/63 and 1969/70; and have bred or attempted to breed on at least five occasions. As evident from the list of ringing recoveries (*see* Table 6.53) most occurrences are the result of eruptions from the traditional reed-bed breeding sites in Norfolk and Suffolk. The eruption in the autumn of 1965 included birds from the

TABLE 6.52　*Hertfordshire recoveries of ringed Bearded Tits*

(a) *Ringed elsewhere and recovered in Hertfordshire*　　Recovered

9	9	1965	Walberswick, Suffolk	23	10	1965	Rye Meads, Hoddesdon
17	9	1965	Walberswick	23	10	1965	Rye Meads
21	9	1965	Knardijk, Ijsselmeer, Netherlands	9	10	1965	Rye Meads *
10	9	1970	Stodmarsh, Kent	21	3	1971	Maple Lodge, Rickmansworth
3	7	1971	Minsmere, Suffolk	30	11	1971	Maple Lodge
11	9	1972	Minsmere	19	11	1972	
				and 3	11	1973	Rye Meads
13	9	1972	Minsmere	19	11	1972	Rye Meads
19	9	1977	Walberswick	26	11	1977	Rye Meads
9	7	1978	Titchwell, Norfolk	26	11	1978	Rye Meads
8	9	1978	Walberswick	5	11	1978	Rye Meads
20	9	1978	Fordwich, Canterbury, Kent	22	10	1978	Rye Meads
20	9	1978	Fordwich	22	10	1978	Rye Meads
4	8	1979	High Halstow, Rochester, Kent	20	12	1980	Rye Meads
2	10	1979	Stodmarsh	17	2	1980	Rye Meads
6	7	1980	Walberswick	6	12	1981	Rye Meads
23	7	1980	Walberswick	31	10	1981	Rye Meads
27	9	1980	Walberswick	6	12	1981	Rye Meads

(b) *Ringed in Herfordshire and recovered elsewhere*

28	10	1971	Maple Lodge	18	9	1973	Minsmere
25	11	1972	Rye Meads	18	9	1973	Minsmere
10	12	1977	Rye Meads	23	5	1980	Isle of Grain, Kent

* The first recovery of a foreign ringed Bearded Tit in the British Isles

Netherlands. The recovery of a Dutch ringed Bearded Tit at Rye Meads on 9 October, only 18 days after ringing, was the first recovery of a foreign ringed Bearded Tit in the British Isles. The list of recoveries also includes a bird trapped at Rye Meads in successive winters. It is interesting to note that most recoveries are within a short period. Simple aggregation of the numbers present at each site on a month by month basis provides a good estimate of the minimum numbers present in the county. These are set out in Table 6.52.

TABLE 6.53 *Minimum number of Bearded Tits present in Hertfordshire in each of the months September to April, 1959–82*

Sept.	Oct.	Nov.	Dec.	Jan.	Feb.	Mar.	Apr.
6	225	265	225	166	145	127	41

Analysis of the numbers in Table 6.52 shows that the birds occurred as follows:

Colne valley	6%
Rye Meads and Stanstead Abbots GP	51%
Stanborough Reedmarsh	21%
Tring Reservoirs	18%
Other sites	4%

The Colne valley includes Maple Lodge, Old Parkbury GP, Rickmansworth GP, and Stockers Lake. Other sites for which all observations are included are Broxbourne GP, Cheshunt GP, Harpenden, Hilfield Park Reservoir, Purwell near Hitchin, Sawbridgeworth Marsh, Tewinbury and Kings Weir GP at Wormley.

The largest numbers observed together were 30 at Rye Meads on 11 November 1972 (*Seventh Report of the Rye Meads Ringing Group*), 28 at Rye Meads and Stanstead Abbots GP on 30 October 1977, and 40 at the same site on 28 October 1978, of which 20 to 30 were still present in January 1979. Numbers trapped for ringing include 165 at Rye Meads (1964-82) and 13 at Maple Lodge (1971-82).

Ringing studies at Rye Meads show that many birds overwinter usually departing in February and March. Observations suggest that Bearded Tits are diurnal migrants which follow flyways associated with natural features such as the Chiltern Hills and Colne and Lea valleys (Gladwin 1976). Apart from breeding birds, discussed below, the latest observations are of single birds at Rye Meads on 14 May 1980, and from April to 1 June 1975.

Between 1966 and 1973 Bearded Tits bred or attempted to breed at Stanborough Reedmarsh, Welwyn Garden City, on five different occasions. Gladwin (1976) provided a detailed account of these events which are summarised as follows:

1966 Two pairs nested. One nest was found from which at least three young fledged and a second pair were seen to be accompanied by four recently fledged young. At least thirteen birds were present in July and it is probable that at least one pair had a second brood.

1968 Two pairs nested; at least five young fledged.

1971 Two pairs nested but no young fledged.

1972 Two pairs started nest building in March, which would appear to be early, but fire destroyed the reed-bed probably before any eggs were laid.

1973 One pair were seen carrying nesting material but the reed-bed was again destroyed by fire.

Long-tailed Tit

Aegithalos caudatus

MAP 84 A fairly common resident.

Both Sage (1959) and Mead and Smith (1982) found this species to be moderately common but missing from certain areas. Although widely distributed numbers are lowest in the chalk zone along the north of the county and in areas with little or no significant deciduous woodland or suitable cover.

Long-tailed Tit populations may be severely reduced by particularly cold winter weather and numbers therefore vary considerably from year to year. None the less Gladwin (1983) found no evidence of any overall change in numbers in central Hertfordshire during the 25-year period 1956–80. *Common Bird Census* indices also indicate that there has been little or no change between 1966 and 1982.

Outside the breeding season Long-tailed Tits are usually seen in flocks, sometimes mixed with other tit species. Recoveries and retraps of ringed birds are mostly close to the ringing site and rarely more than 10 km from it. Flock sizes vary considerably. Analysis shows that 89 per cent of all flocks seen in the county in autumn, when populations are at their maximum, contain no more than 20 birds. Flocks of more than 30 birds are infrequent. The only flocks of more than 50 birds reported were 71 at Rye Meads on 5 November 1960 and 75 in Hockeridge Woods, Berkhamsted, on 17 January 1951. The record of 304 at Cheshunt GP on 15 October 1972 (*Trans. Herts. Nat. Hist. Soc.* 27:222) is a misprint for 30 to 40.

Some flocks are simply formed of one or more family parties but others are more complex. At Maple Cross, for example, 15 Long-tailed Tits caught on 31 December 1983 included one ringed as a juvenile on 24 July 1983, and five of a flock of 11 full-grown birds ringed on 12 September 1982. This regrouping is particularly interesting regardless of whether or not the original flock of 11 was a single family party. Holdsworth (1974b) also found that there is some interchange of membership between flocks occurring at Maple Cross.

Marsh Tit

Parus palustris

A scarce to fairly common resident. **MAP 85**

Sage (1959) described the Marsh Tit as a common but somewhat local resident that was probably more numerous than the Coal Tit. By the period 1967 to 1973, when the fieldwork for the *Herfordshire Breeding Bird Atlas* (Mead and Smith 1982) was carried out, it had become the scarcest and least widely distributed of all the six resident tit species (five *Parus* spp and *Aegithalos caudatus*). Since then the decline has continued. Gladwin (1983) reported a continuing decrease of at least 75 per cent in central Hertfordshire between 1956 and 1980. The local *Common Bird Census* index shows identical losses. In Hertfordshire the decrease has been double that of the national average; the reason for it is not clear. The decline cannot be explained by habitat losses or changes alone. Found mainly in parkland and ancient woodland with large trees Marsh Tits have disappeared from some sites which appear to have changed little. It is still, however, far commoner than the Willow Tit in North Hertfordshire (T. J. James).

Willow Tit

Parus montanus

A common resident. **MAP 86**

By the mid-1950s there was still some uncertainty about the population and distribution of this species in Hertfordshire (Sage 1959). Most records for that period are from the west and south west of the county and it was said to be more numerous than the Marsh Tit around Harpenden. Overall however, the Marsh Tit was by far the more numerous and more widely distributed of the two species. The Willow Tit was known to be scarce in the northern chalk belt and in the boulder clay zone in the east and north-east. It was known to be absent from the valley of the River Beane between Hertford and Watton at Stone, and rare in the woodlands around Bramfield and Tewin.

By 1967 to 1973, as shown by Mead and Smith (1982), the Willow Tit had become a relatively common breeding bird in most woodlands with suitable scrub habitats, being scarce only on the chalk in the north, on the boulder clay, and in the southern area from Borehamwood to Bushey and Watford. Whilst the increase was largely due to the colonisation of new areas, numbers had also increased in the few areas where the species was already well established. T. J. James (pers. com.) states that the Willow Tit first bred in Northaw Parish in 1964 and has since become common there.

Since 1973 the increase has continued. Mead and Smith (1982) found that the population on some sites had clearly increased two- or three-fold over the last 15 years. Gladwin (1983) calculated an increase in central Hertfordshire of some 300–400 per cent between 1956 and 1980. None the less the species is still scarce in North Hertfordshire where it remains outnumbered by the Marsh Tit.

Outside the breeding season the Willow Tit has become a regular visitor to gardens in rural and some semi-urban areas and as many as 10 to 15 are not infrequently seen in mixed flocks of tits.

Coal Tit

Parus ater

MAP 87   A very common resident.

Sage (1959) described the Coal Tit as a common resident with a distinct preference for conifers. Likewise, the *Breeding Bird Atlas,* (Mead and Smith 1982) found it to be fairly common in all areas with conifers.

As a result of reafforestation with coniferous species, mostly in the early 1960s, the Coal Tit population has increased greatly (Gladwin 1983). It is abundant in plantations of climax or nearly mature European Larch or Larch hybrids and may be found in relatively small coniferous units in rural or semi-urban areas. It is a rare breeding bird in woodlands dominated by broad-leaved species.

Outside the breeding season Coal Tits roam more widely, small numbers being seen in deciduous woodlands and gardens. Mixed flocks of tits seen in the county in autumn and winter often contain small minority numbers of Coal Tits. The largest number recorded appears to be 15 to 20 in a flock seen at Bramfield on 28 September 1969, which otherwise comprised 200 Blue Tits, 40 Great Tits, 50 Long-tailed Tits and 12 Willow Tits.

Blue Tit

Parus caeruleus

MAP 88   An abundant resident.

As found by Sage (1959) and Mead and Smith (1982) this species is abundant in all parts of the county. It is most numerous in beech, oak, and oak–hornbeam woods where, in some cases, it is at least three times more numerous than the Great Tit. In 1962, prior to reafforestation, there were an average of one pair in every 1.1ha of broad-leaved woodland in Bramfield Park Wood.

In coniferous plantations it is less common than the Great Tit. Further, average fledging rates from nestboxes in coniferous plantations in Bramfield Forest of 2.1 per brood are less than half of those from boxes in linear deciduous woodland at Lemsford Springs and Digswell Lake, and in gardens in the low density residential areas at the north end of Welwyn Garden City.

Gladwin (1983) considered the population in central Hertfordshire to have increased between 1956 and 1980. This was attributed to the increase in nestboxes and feeding stations, particularly in older gardens containing mature shrubs and trees where caterpillar and other insect foods are readily available when eggs hatch.

In winter many Blue Tits form flocks sometimes containing smaller numbers of other tit species. Unfortunately too little data is available to define typical flock sizes. However, it does seem that flocks containing more than 200 Blue Tits are probably unusual.

Great Tit

Parus major

A very common resident.   **MAP 89**

As described by Sage (1959) the Great Tit is still a very common resident. It is a common bird of gardens, urban as well as rural, mature hedgerows and woodlands, being most abundant in deciduous woods. In some oak–hornbeam woodlands in the centre of the county there are as many as one pair in every 1.7 ha. Mead and Smith (1982) found it to be common in every part of the county. The population has probably remained significantly unchanged for many years. Gladwin (1983) found that in central Hertfordshire an increase in urban populations, encouraged by garden feeding and the provision of nestboxes, no more than made up for pairs lost as a result of hedgerow removal in the rural farming areas.

In autumn and winter relatively large concentrations, rarely exceeding 100 birds, are frequently seen feeding on beech mast and yew berries. Large mixed flocks of tits containing small numbers of Great Tits are a common feature in autumn and winter.

Ringing recoveries show that most Hertfordshire birds remain within a few kilometres of the site where they were bred for the whole of their lives. There is no evidence of migrant birds from the continent reaching the county.

Nuthatch

Sitta europaea

MAP 90 A fairly common resident.

Sage (1959) described the Nuthatch as being fairly common throughout the county with the exception of the Bishops Stortford area. Since then numbers have increased although its distribution remains much the same. Mead and Smith (1982) found it to be well distributed in most areas but virtually absent from woodlands on the northern chalk zone and the boulder clay in the east and north-east. However T. J. James (pers. com.) has found Nuthatches in most moderate-sized ancient woodland coppices around Nuthampstead, Clothall, Wallington, and Sandon, but scarce around Hitchin and Ashwell where there is no real ancient woodland. It is a common bird in parklands and woodlands containing mature deciduous trees. In the last 20 years it has appeared increasingly at garden feeding stations and now breeds in nestboxes and natural sites in many gardens containing suitable trees. Gladwin (1983) estimated that Nuthatches had increased in central Hertfordshire by 100 to 200 per cent between 1956 and 1980, and attributed much of this to the successful colonisation of gardens. The *Common Birds Census* indices for the county indicate an increase of just over 100 per cent.

Treecreeper

Certhia familiaris

MAP 91 A common resident.

Treecreepers are found in all types of woodland habitats, large and small, rural and semi-urban, and even in many mature hedgerows. As found by

256

Mead and Smith (1982), the species is resident in all parts of the county. Sage (1959) considered Treecreepers to be much more numerous than Nuthatches. Despite the recent success of the latter species this is still the case. Gladwin (1983) could detect no significant change in the population in central Hertfordshire between 1956 and 1980, a finding supported by *Common Birds Census* indices for the county. The species has temporarily benefited from the additional nest sites provided by diseased elms.

Golden Oriole

Oriolus oriolus

A very rare vagrant that has bred twice.

Sage (1959) lists 17 occurrences of Golden Orioles in the county up to 1957. Since then there have been a further 11 records.

Breeding has only been satisfactorily proven on two occasions. In June 1881 a nest with three eggs was found near Ware (*Trans. Herts. Nat. Hist. Soc.* 2:83). In the early 1970s a pair nested at a closely guarded site in the west of the county and possibly subsequently. Adults and newly fledged young were seen by the finder and a member of the British Trust for Ornithology's staff (per C. J. Mead).

The sixteen non-breeding records quoted by Sage (1959) include two for which the precise dates of observation are not known. Twelve of the remaining records are from the months of May (four), June (six) and July (two). In autumn the only record is of one in Kings Walden Park in September 1952. The most remarkable record, however, is of one stated to have been seen in a garden in Bishops Stortford in February 1936 (Linsell 1953). James and Sawford (1979) describe a specimen, now in the North Hertfordshire Museum at Baldock, recorded from Hitchin, 1878, but not mentioned by Sage (1959). One of the Bayfordbury specimens from that museum is missing.

The ten recent non-breeding records, all between mid-April and early July, are as follows:

1962   A male seen and heard in Broxbourne Woods on 7 June.
1967   A male seen and heard in Bramfield Forest on 22, 23 and 29 April.
1969   A male singing at Bricketwood Common on 31 May.
1977   A male singing in Ashridge on 12 May.
1979   A male singing at Rabley Heath on 30 May.
1980   A male in song in Northaw Great Wood on 26 May.
1981   A male in Northaw Great Wood from 11 to 19 April.
      A male at Cheshunt GP on 30 and 31 May.
      One singing at Ashridge on 28 June.
      A female at Little Gaddesden on 5 and a pair on 8 July.
(*British Birds* 76:23)

Two unconfirmed second-hand reports of birds at Northaw Great Wood from 1 to 5 May and in Knebworth on 11 May 1982 (*Trans. Herts. Nat. Hist. Soc.* 29 Pt2:27) are not included as no details were submitted to the County Records Committee.

Red-backed Shrike

Lanius collurio

A very rare summer visitor that has bred.

Once described as fairly common (Sage 1959) the Red-backed Shrike is now a very rare visitor to the county. The decline of the species was described by Gladwin (*Trans. Herts. Nat. Hist. Soc.* 27:65-66) as follows:

> A decline in its numbers was first noted about 1916. The stronghold of the species was in the chalk areas in the north of the county, although it was to be found in most parts. Foster, in Hine (1934), considered the species to be 'quite well-known as a summer visitor' and, 'a common object on the telegraph wires bordering the Great North Road between Stevenage and Biggleswade'. In 1947 Hayward, *Trans. Herts. Nat. Hist. Soc.* 22:184, stated that 'one or two pairs still nest on most commons in the west of the county and odd pairs in other districts, while it appears to be more plentiful in the north, which was always its stronghold'. We now know that the species was still common at that time (1947-8) around Hertford (c. 15-20 pairs), Hertford Heath (5-10 pairs), Hoddesdon (20 pairs) and Welwyn Garden City (8 pairs).

The decline continued and since 1958 breeding has occurred or pairs seen as follows:

1958   A pair bred at Berkhamsted.
          A pair at Therfield Heath, Royston, on 19 July.
          An adult and a juvenile at Broxbourne on 19 August.
1960   Two pairs bred at Hoddesdon.
          Three pairs bred at Dawley Warren, Tewin, a site considered to have been previously overlooked.
          One pair probably bred on The Roundings, Hertford Heath.
1961   A pair were present and probably bred on Therfield Heath.
          A nest with four young was found on Chorleywood Common on 22 June.
1962   A pair seen on Oughtonhead Common on 16 May.
          Two males and a female at a known breeding site at Great Amwell on 17 May.
1964   One pair bred at Hexton.
          One pair bred at West Herts. Golf Course, Watford.
          Two pairs present at Great Amwell.
1965   One pair bred at Oughtonhead Common.
          One pair bred at Hexton.
          A pair returned to Great Amwell but did not stay to breed.
1966   Two pairs present and probably bred on Therfield Heath.

1967   One pair attempted to breed on Therfield Heath but the nest was destroyed.

1968   Single pairs nested at Hexton and on Telegraph Hill.

1972   A pair present at Moor Park golf course on 1 May were not seen again.

1974   A pair present at Oughtonhead Common during June were said to have bred (*Trans. Herts. Nat. Hist. Soc.* 28:22) but the record shows uncertainty about any evidence of breeding.

During the period 1958 to 1974 there were also 24 records of single birds seen at various sites throughout the county.

Since 1974 there have been only five reported observations as follows:

1977   An immature at Tring Reservoirs on 23 and 30 August.

1979   A male at Oughtonhead Common on 8 July.

1980   A male at Oughtonhead Common on 9 June.

1981   A female at Stanstead Abbotts on 9 May.

       A male at Flamstead on 14 and 15 August.

Red-backed Shrikes usually depart during late July and August and the latest record, and the only one in September between 1958 and 1982, is of an immature at Therfield Heath from 26 to 28 September 1969.

Great Grey Shrike

Lanius excubitor

A scarce but regular winter visitor.

The status of this species has probably not changed significantly during the present century at least. As described by Sage (1959) it continues to occur regularly having been seen in every year from 1958 to 1982. During this period there were some 113 records involving at least 92 different birds. The number of different birds has been calculated on the assumption that a chronological sequence of records, albeit from different sites, may refer to one individual. Some birds may be loyal to a particular site for several years. In Bramfield Forest, for example, one was present from 13 November 1963 to 30 March 1964, from 11 November 1964 to 26 February 1965, on 1 November 1965, from 1 November 1966 to 22 April 1967, from 6 January to 25 April 1968, and again in November 1968 and November 1970. The number of birds seen in each calendar month from 1958 to 1982 was as follows:

October	10	January	29
November	28	February	26
December	25	March	31
		April	18
		May	1

Individuals which were observed in more than one month are included in the totals for each month in which they were seen. The records cover the period 12 October to 9 May. In addition, one was present at Thundridge from 9 to 17 July 1968. Details of this bird established it as being of the northern race *L. e. excubitor.*

An unusual sight was of one chasing a Scarlet-headed Blackbird *Amblyramphus holosericeus* at Broxbourne SF on 20 November 1960.

Woodchat Shrike

Lanius senator

A very rare vagrant.

There are two records, both listed by Sage (1959), as follows:

c. 1847–56 A bird preserved by W. Norman at Royston was shot either near Baldock in the spring of 1856 or was possibly that shot at Sandon about 1845.

1873 One near Hertford in May is considered to be the bird referred to in *The Fauna and Flora of Haileybury* (1926).

Jay

Garrulus glandarius

MAP 92 A common resident.

As described by Sage (1959) the Jay is a common resident which breeds in woodlands, parklands and low-density residential areas where the gardens and environs contain mature trees. It is found in such habitats throughout the county being less numerous in the east and north-east where suitable areas are fewer. In the late 1950s and early 1960s the population suddenly increased significantly; Gladwin (1983) found that in central Hertfordshire where there had been much reafforestation, it had doubled between 1956 and 1980. Since 1966 the population has been relatively stable as shown by the *Common Birds Census* indices (Mead and Smith 1982). The resident population belongs to the British race *G. g. rufitergum.*

Outside the breeding season flocks of between 10 and 15 birds are commonly observed. Larger numbers together are, however, rare.

Exceptional records are of 57 which flew SSE. over Broxbourne in two parties on 16 November 1962, and over 29 at Frithsden Beeches on 25 January 1964.

Irruptions of birds from the continent have been observed along the east coast of Britain in at least five of the twenty-five years from 1958 to 1982. However, there are no records of birds showing the characteristics of the continental sub-species *G. g. glandarius* in the county.

Magpie

Pica pica

A very common resident.   **MAP 93**

At one time a very rare bird, numbers started to increase sometime about 1920 (Sage 1959). By 1957 the species had become common in the western, southern, central and some northern districts. It was still scarce on the chalk east from Baldock, in the area north-east and east from Buntingford and Stevenage to the county boundary, along the Stort Valley, and in the Lea valley below Hertford. Since then numbers have continued to increase. By the period 1967 to 1973, when the fieldwork for the *Breeding Bird Atlas* (Mead and Smith 1982) was carried out, it had become common in all parts, except on the chalk between Baldock and Royston, and along the eastern parts of the county around Albury, Brent Pelham, Anstey and Nuthampstead. Numbers had increased everywhere, particularly in the urban fringes. Gladwin (1983) found that numbers in central Hertfordshire had increased by 400 to 500 per cent between 1956 and 1980 in which year the Ashwell area in the north was colonised. Central Hertfordshire was defined as Ordnance Survey 10km squares TL21 and TL31 which include a large area around Hertford and the Lea valley where the species was still very scarce in 1957. At Rye Meads, for example, where single birds were seen on only seven occasions in 1961, there were six breeding pairs in 1982. *Local Common Birds Census* indices (Mead and Smith 1982) suggest the population has probably doubled since 1973.

Flocks of up to 20 are now commonly seen in the county and since 1975 there have been 17 reports of large flocks of between 20 and 50 birds. The largest single flock reported was of 60 at Hilfield Park Reservoir on 11 March 1982 where a communal roost has existed for several years.

261

Nutcracker

*Nucifraga
caryocatactes*

A very rare vagrant.

There was an unprecedented irruption of this species into East Anglia and SE. England in the autumn of 1968 (*British Birds* 63:353–73). All of the birds observed in Hertfordshire were of the slender-billed race *N. c. macrorhynchus*. The 10 Hertfordshire records, listed below, all in the autumn of 1968, are the only recorded occurrences of the species in the county.

> Two at Hitchin on 29 and 30 August.
> One at Letty Green from 9 September to 13 October.
> One at Bramfield Forest on 11 September.
> One at Berkhamsted from September to 6 October.
> One at Rothamsted Park, Harpenden, on 3 October.
> One near Pirton on 5 October.
> One near Hexton from early October to 3 November.
> One at Watford during November.
> One near Brookmans Park on 10 November.
> One at Digswell on 19 and 20 December.

Jackdaw

Corvus monedula

MAP 94 A common resident.

As described by Sage (1959) and Mead and Smith (1982) the Jackdaw is a common resident breeding throughout the county in church towers, other old buildings and hollow trees. Gladwin (1983) found that numbers in central Hertfordshire had increased steadily between 1956 and 1980 and were probably continuing to do so. The *Common Birds Census* index for the county also shows an increasing trend up to 1980 (Mead and Smith 1982).

From autumn through to spring many Jackdaws roost communally, often with Rooks. Symondshyde Great Wood, Titnol's Wood and the woodlands within the western perimeter of Hatfield Airfield have been major roost sites for large numbers of *corvidae* since at least 1945. Of up to 11 000 *corvidae* present between 1964/65 and 1972/73, it was variously estimated that 75–80 per cent were Rooks, and 15 per cent (1650) Jackdaws. Numbers of Rooks have since declined and the maximum number of *corvidae* recorded in the 1981/82 winter was 3200, of which 60 per cent (1920) were Jackdaws, on 31 December 1981. Other communal roosts involving 1000 or more Jackdaws have been regularly noted at Birchall Wood, Cole Green, and in woodlands at Woolmer Park, Woodhall Park and Weston where there were 1500 on 15 February 1981. A crow roost has long existed beside Tringford Reservoir. This roost, used throughout the year, usually contains up to between 200 and 400 Jackdaws in winter and between 20 and 60 in summer. The maximum counted there was 580 on 6 March 1978.

A bird ringed as a juvenile at Älvsborg, Sweden, on 5 June 1939, and recovered at Radlett on 10 March 1940 remains the sole certain occurrence of the Scandinavian race *C. m. monedula in* Hertfordshire (*British Birds* 41:174). British Jackdaws belong to the race *C. m. spermologus* which breeds throughout Western Europe except Scandinavia.

Rook

Corvus frugilegus

A common resident breeding species, and probably a winter visitor from **MAP 95** outside the county. This is the same status given by Sage (1959).

A great deal of attention has been given to the breeding status of this species within the county over a long period of time, as a result of which it is known that, although still widespread, it has decreased significantly since the early 1960s. Details of surveys of rookeries in the county are given by Sage and Nau (1963), Sage (1972), and Sage (1977), and the results are shown in Table 6.54.

The steady decline in both the total number of nests and the number of individual rookeries over a period of 15 years is clearly shown in the Table. Overall, the rate of change from 1960/61 to 1975 was 7054 (44.82 per cent) in

TABLE 6.54   *Hertfordshire rookery statistics, 1960/61–75*

	Year	Total	Decrease	Percentage Decrease
(a) Nests	1960/61	15739	–	–
	1971	10708	5031	31.96
	1975	8685	2023	18.89
(b) Rookeries	1960/61	521	–	–
	1971	402	119	22.84
	1975	375	27	6.72

the number of nests, and 146 (28.02 per cent) in the number of actual rookeries.

Another aspect which is of considerable interest concerns changes in size of individual rookeries, and this is shown in Table 6.55.

It can be seen that a feature of the changes that occurred over this period was the fragmentation of the larger rookeries into smaller units. As the Table shows, the percentage of rookeries in the two lower size groupings (1–25 and 26 — 50 nests) increased from 84.26 per cent in 1960/61, to 85.82 per cent in 1971, and 90.40 per cent in 1975.

The two rookeries with more than 200 nests in 1961/61 were Frogmore Hall (Watton-at-Stone) with 203 nests, and the agglomeration centred on Ashwell village with 526 nests. By 1971 the Frogmore Hall rookery was down to 185 nests, and the large Ashwell agglomeration was reduced to two rookeries of 20 and 28 nests respectively; the only rookery with more than 200 nests in that year was the one by the B.158 at Bayford with 235 nests. In 1975 the Bayford rookery had 242 nests, and one at Peg's Lane, Widford (with 125 nests in 1971) had 213 nests.

Unfortunately the same degree of effort has not been devoted to the study of the location and size of communal roosts, and the pattern of flight lines to and from these roosts. Indeed, the only area that has received anything more than passing attention in that lying just to the NW. of Hatfield. In January 1967 there was a communal corvid roost (about 80 per cent Rooks) of about 10 000 birds in Symondshyde Great Wood, at which flocks arrived from both north and south. In 1968 a pre-roosting gathering area was located at nearby Coopers Green, and in January and December 5000+ birds habitually collected there. The same gathering site was in use again in January and December 1969 when it was estimated that about 11 000 birds (75 per cent Rooks) were involved. Later, in November 1977, a roost of 5000–6000 (80

TABLE 6.55   *Size composition of Hertfordshire rookeries, 1960/61–75*

Number of nests	1960/61			1971			1975		
	Number of rookeries	Percentage of total		Number of rookeries	Percentage of total		Number of rookeries	Percentage of total	
1–25	309	59.31		266	66.17		268	71.47	
26–50	130	24.95		79	19.65		71	18.93	
51–100	58	11.13		44	10.95		24	6.40	
101–200	22	4.23		12	2.98		10	2.67	
200+	2	0.38		1	0.25		2	0.53	
Totals:	521			402			375		

Figure 6.26   *Rook, declining as a result of the reduction in grasslands.*

Photo: © Tom Gladwin

per cent Rooks) was located at Ball's Covert just NW. of the main runway at Hatfield aerodrome. By December 1981 this roost had moved a short distance to Home Covert and had declined to about 3200 birds (40 per cent Rooks, 60 per cent Jackdaws). This decline in the numbers of Rooks roosting in the area is obviously related to the decrease in the breeding population in surrounding areas.

Another roost was sited to the SE. of Welwyn Garden City at Cole Green, and on 22 July 1967 (the winter roosts begin to form in July) contained about 2500 birds. In January and December 1969 this roost held some 8000 birds (90 per cent Rooks). In 1978 a roost was found in Lannock Wood, Weston, and held about 3000 birds on 30 September. It was still in use in 1981 when it had some 2000 birds in January, 5000 in October, and 3000 in December. Three small roosts were found in 1979 — one of about 800 at Letchworth in January, one of about the same number at Rabley Heath in February, and another of 750+ at Langleybury in late September. In 1980 some 700 were noted roosting in the Panshanger, near Hertingfordbury, in January, and 400 at Tring Reservoirs in late February. The Panshanger roost contained about 2000 birds on 1 March 1981.

Carrion Crow

Corvus corone

The two distinct forms of the Carrion Crow are dealt with separately in the following sub-sections. The two forms are:

(a)   Carrion Crow *Corvus corone corone*
(b)   Hooded Crow *Corvus corone cornix*

(a) Carrion Crow

Corvus corone corone

MAP 96 A very common resident.

By the end of the 19th century and possibly earlier, the Carrion Crow *C. c. corone* had become a rare bird in the county. Sage (1959) describing it as a common resident traced the start of the increase to the period of the First World War from 1914 to 1918. The increase has continued and by the years 1967 to 1973, when the field work for the *Breeding Bird Atlas* (Mead and Smith 1982) was carried out, it was breeding commonly in all parts of the county including gardens and town centres with isolated tall trees or large bushes. By 1980 Gladwin (1983) calculated that numbers in central Hertfordshire had trebled since 1956. This is not inconsistent with the 200 per cent increase indicated by the *Common Birds Census* indices for the period 1967 to 1979 (Mead and Smith 1982). Like the Magpie, the Carrion Crow is a great beneficiary of animal carcases resulting from traffic deaths. As the population has increased so has the number of unconventional nest sites. In recent years nests have been discovered on cranes, electricity pylons, on the washing plant at two gravel pits, and in the upper lattice of an aerial mast.

Although a solitary breeding species many Carrion Crows do form communal roosts and feeding flocks. Analysis of the 128 records giving flock sizes since 1958 shows that 72 per cent of all autumn and winter flocks, including roosts, contain less than 100 birds and 19 per cent contain between 101 and 200 birds. These figures include 'loose' flocks or gatherings at feeding sites such as rubbish tips and sewage farms. The balance of 9 per cent, for flocks of over 200 birds, may be very high as some observers only report high or unusual observations. The largest flocks reported were 260 in a roost at Chorleywood in February 1971, maxima roosting at Tring of 325 on 20 September and 320 on 8 November 1978, and a flock of *c.* 500 at Weston on 15 February 1981. Consistent with recent population increases it is not surprising that these records refer to recent years and far exceed the previous largest numbers given by Sage (1959) who found only three records of between 100 and 180 birds.

Carrion Crows will also roost communally with Rooks and Jackdaws. The largest numbers yet recorded in such a roost were up to 500 with as many as 10 000 to 11 000 Rooks and Jackdaws in the Symondshyde and Coopers Green woodlands between 1967 and 1977.

(b) Hooded Crow

Corvus corone cornix

The Hooded Crow *C. c. cornix* is a rare winter visitor and autumn and spring passage migrant. It was once a common winter visitor when, being most numerous around Royston, it also became known as the Royston Crow (Sage 1959). From 1912, or thereabouts, to 1957 it was evidently no more than an occasional winter visitor. Since then there are some 15 recorded occurrences in 11 of the 25 years from 1957 to 1982 as follows:

1960   One at Hoddesdon on 24 December.

1961   One at Tring Reservoirs on 8 March.

1962   One at Rye Meads on 21 and 27 October.
At Cuffley there were two on 28 October and one on 29 and 30 October and 1 December.

1966   One at Wilstone Reservoir, Tring, on 6 November.

1966-7 One at Stanborough on 10 November 1966 and from 11 January to 17 April 1967.

1967   One at Tring Reservoirs on 19 March.

1969   One at High Leigh, Hoddesdon, on 23 January.

1971   Two at Hollingson Meads, Pye Corner, on 27 March.

1975   One at Tring SF on 22 November.

1976   Singles at Buckland on 14 January, and Tring Reservoirs from 21 to 30 March.

1977   One over Quickswood, Clothall, on 17 April, and one at Tring Reservoirs on 15 December.

1980   One at Hastoe, Tring, from 24 January to 21 February. One at Stockers Lake from 20 March to 6 April.

Raven

Corvus corax

A very rare vagrant that formerly bred.

The last recorded breeding of this apparently once common species occurred in Brocket Park in 1846. Thereafter Sage (1959) gives six records between 1880 and 1894, all in the months from October to February. Another (month not stated) was seen and heard near Haileybury College in 1888 (*Trans. Herts. Nat. Hist. Soc.* 25:191). Since then there have been a further seven records as follows:

1905   A pair at Aldenham Reservoir on 27 July.

c. 1905 One shot near Letchworth.

1914   One near Hitchin in January (Foster 1917).

1930   One flew N. over Harpenden Station on 10 September.

1950   One flew NE. over Radwell in early March.

1955   One circling and gliding NNW. over Great Barwick on 2 July.

1968   Two soaring over Bramfield Forest on 23 May.

The possibility that some or all of these birds had escaped from captivity cannot be excluded.

Starling

Sturnus vulgaris

MAP 97 An abundant resident, passage migrant and winter visitor.

Described by Sage (1959) as a very common resident, it was found by Mead and Smith (1982) to be abundant in every part of the county and so it remains. A hole nesting species it is abundant in urban as well as rural areas.

In October and November very large numbers arrive from continental Europe to winter in the county. These birds are diurnal migrants and the autumn movements are readily observed.

Starlings form huge communal roosts. A long established roost used by post breeding birds from late May or June to early November exists in reed-beds and adjacent scrub at Wilstone Reservoir, Tring. This roost contained some 20 000 birds on 25 October 1941 and 10 000 in June 1943. Numbers in recent years included 10 000 on 23 July 1981, 15 000 on 17 July 1979, 25 000 on 8 August 1978, reaching a peak of 36 000 on 25 September before falling to 2000 by 8 November. Thus numbers at this roost do not appear to have changed significantly for at least 40 years. Similar post breeding roosts reaching maxima of up to 30 000 in early autumn are to be found in small woodlands throughout the county. Not all birds join these large congregations. Small roosts containing only a few hundred birds are common-place throughout the year, and these may be due to local birds.

In winter several roosts of between 10 000 and 50 000 birds are reported annually and even larger woodland roosts of 100 000 or more birds are reported in some years. Roosts estimated to contain 500 000 birds were present at Great Gaddesden on 26 January 1957 and Abbots Langley from January to March 1973. The roost at Abbots Langley again contained 500 000 birds from October 1973, reaching an estimated 1 000 000 between January and March 1974. Analysis of the number and size of roosts reported shows no evident change in population levels. However the numbers roosting on buildings in towns like Hertford, St. Albans and Watford have declined in recent years, possibly due to the unsuitability of modern buildings.

Rose-coloured Starling

Sturnus roseus

A very rare vagrant.

There are five records, the first three listed in Sage (1959), all in late autumn or winter, as follows:

1855 A male was shot at Wallington, near Baldock, on 20 December having been seen a few days earlier.

1952   One at Much Hadham on 25 October.
1956   An immature female was seen in Weston Park on 21 December.
1967   One at Hemel Hempstead on 10 January (*British Birds* 61:355).
1978   An adult at Cheshunt on 4 December (*British Birds* 72:540).

House Sparrow

Passer domestius

An abundant resident.   **MAP 98**

The House Sparrow is, as described by Sage (1959), abundant throughout
the county, particularly around all forms of human settlements, although
numbers have declined significantly. Mead and Smith (1982) considered it
probable that numbers have been falling since 1910 or thereabouts. In
central Hertfordshire, Gladwin (1983) found that between 1956 and 1980
there had been a noticeable decrease in rural populations. The huge
reduction in traditional stackyards, farmyards in which horses, chickens
and other livestock are fed in the open, and fields with seed bearing 'weeds'
has certainly reduced food availability and this may account for the decline.
In contrast, urban populations may have increased. Not only has there been
an increase in urban area but also in the amounts of food provided at bird
tables and otherwise in gardens, parks and other public open spaces.

Flocks of up to 1000 birds are regularly seen, particularly in fields of
ripening cereals and on stubble following the harvest. House Sparrows also
form large communal roosts. There were, for example, over 5000 roosting at
Westmill, Hitchin, in February 1981.

There are several records of nests still containing young in early to mid-
October. House Sparrows nest in a wide variety of situations, some of the
more unusual observed in the county including the bases of nests still
occupied by Herons and Rooks, and in dense 'tangles' of barbed wire.

Unfortunately this is a much understudied and under recorded species.

Tree Sparrow

Passer montanus

A common resident.   **MAP 99**

Sage (1959) described the Tree Sparrow as a fairly common but local
resident. Numbers then increased and the *Hertfordshire Breeding Bird
Atlas* (Mead and Smith 1982) shows that by the period 1967 to 1973 it had

become widely distributed throughout the county during the breeding season. Between 1958 and 1965, despite losses in the 1962/63 winter, the increase had been rapid. New breeding areas, often involving quite large numbers of birds were reported annually. Thus in 1964, for example, 50 pairs bred at Frithsden Beeches, 73 pairs in the Parish of Northaw, and 15 pairs in Northaw Great Wood where nesting had not previously been observed. Tree Sparrows seem to suffer badly in cold winters and numbers fluctuate considerably. Gladwin (1983) found that although numbers had increased overall in central Hertfordshire between 1956 and 1978, by 1980 there had been a sudden sharp fall. This sudden decrease of about a half, is also evident from the *Common Birds Census* indices (Mead and Smith 1982) and observations at other well studied sites. At Rye Meads, for example, a colony in nestboxes reached a maximum of 32 pairs in 1977, declined to only 13 pairs in 1979, but had increased again to 29 pairs by 1982.

Most Tree Sparrows nest in holes in hedgerow and woodland trees and readily form colonies when available nest sites allow. Nestboxes have long been a popular option. In 1910, for example, 12 out of 50 nestboxes erected at Norton, near Hitchin, were occupied by this species. More recently, in 1975, 183 young fledged from 52 broods which hatched from 212 eggs in 22 nestboxes in Prae Wood, St. Albans. Tree Sparrows show a great deal of adaptability in their choice of nest sites. Within the county nests have been found in the bases of Rooks nests, in the cross-bars of power cable pylons, and are frequently observed in Sand Martin burrows.

Outside the breeding season Tree Sparrows feed in large flocks and also roost communally. Flocks of up to 200 have been regularly and frequently reported in recent years, and numbers up to 500 are not unusual. The largest single flocks reported were of 2000 at Chorleywood on 30 December 1970, 1000 at the same site on 2 January 1973, and 1500 at Lemsford on 2 February 1979.

Tree *x* House Sparrow
Passer montanus x *P. domesticus*

One at Hilfield Park Reservoir on 1 June 1982 was considered to be a male showing the characteristics of a hybrid Tree Sparrow with House Sparrow.

Chaffinch
Fringilla coelebs

MAP 100 A very common resident, spring and autumn migrant, and winter visitor.

Stated by Sage (1959) to be abundant throughout the county, the Chaffinch was then one of the most numerous of Hertfordshire's breeding birds. However, between 1956 and 1961 huge numbers died almost certainly as a result of the use of organo-chlorine insecticides and in some areas it became quite scarce. Numbers have since increased and as shown by Mead and Smith (1982) it is again a very common breeding species in all parts of the county being least numerous away from the wooded areas in North Hertfordshire. The British breeding population belongs to the sub-species *F. c. gengleri*.

The large diurnal arrivals of Chaffinches from the continent in October and November are a familiar sight. Huge numbers pass through the county but many stay for the winter, returning to the continent in late March and April. Thus Chaffinches ringed in Hertfordshire have been recovered in Norway, Sweden, Germany, Holland and Belgium. These belong to the continental sub-species *F. c. coelebs*.

Between October and early April flocks of up to 200 are common and larger flocks of up to 500 or 600 have been reported in some years. The largest flocks appear to have been in Bramfield Forest where there were 700 on 3 April 1969 and 1000 in February 1968.

Brambling

Fringilla montifringilla

A regular winter visitor.

The status of the Brambling is as described by Sage (1959), a regular winter visitor whose numbers are subject to considerable year to year variations. Scarce in some winters, e.g. 1963/64, Bramblings may be abundant in others, e.g. 1968/69.

The first birds are usually seen in late October with the main arrival taking place in November. The earliest autumn record appears to be of three seen at Pirton on 17 September 1978.

Analysis of the county records reveals that the great majority of winter flocks contain less than 50 birds whilst flocks of between 100 and 200 are unusual. Records of higher numbers are of 400 with Chaffinches and Yellowhammers in Bramfield Forest from January to mid-March 1968, up to 250 at the same site from December 1968 to 3 April 1969, and 400 near Tingley Wood on 24 January 1978. Over 500 were counted in 15 flocks at Ashridge on 22 November 1968. A high proportion of winter records are from beech woods, particularly those along the Chilterns.

Prior to departure in late March and early April, Bramblings often form large pre-migratory flocks of one or two hundred birds which are seen in most years. The largest such flocks reported, with one exception, were of 300 at Rye Meads on 23 March 1958. The exception was a flock estimated at some 10 000 birds present in the area around Berkhamsted, Potten End and Great Gaddesden during the first ten days of April 1971. The latest spring records appear to be of two at Ashridge on 2 May 1976 and one at Maple Cross on 4 May 1979.

There are two late summer records. A juvenile was caught and ringed near Ashridge on 4 August 1971, and another seen at Tring Park on 9 August 1976.

Bramblings ringed in Hertfordshire have been recovered in Norway, Sweden, Denmark and Yugoslavia.

Serin

Serinus serinus

A very rare vagrant.

There are three county records as follows:

1973 One between Aldenham and Hilfield Park Reservoirs on 21 March. (*British Birds* 67:337).

1976 A male at Ashwell on 19 December (*British Birds* 71:524).

1982 A male in song in the Stort valley, near Harlow, on 26 May was not found again on subsequent visits by the observers. (*British Birds* 76:521).

Greenfinch

Carduelis chloris

MAP 101 A very common resident.

The Greenfinch remains a very common resident (Sage 1959) which breeds in scrub, hedgerows, woodlands and mature gardens in all parts of the county (Mead and Smith 1982).

The *Common Birds Census* index for the county suggests that populations have been relatively stable since 1963. Consistently, Gladwin (1983) could find no evidence of any change in the numbers breeding in central Hertfordshire from 1956 to 1980 despite an increase in numbers feeding in gardens.

Outside the breeding season many Greenfinches form large flocks and numbers up to 500 are not unusual. Flocks of 1000 or more have been reported on five occasions, the largest being of 1500 in a mixed flock with Linnets between Weston and Baldock on 3 December 1966, 1500 feeding on grain at Tewinwater on 11 September 1968, and 1500-2000 at Chorleywood on 23 December 1970.

A large proportion of recoveries of Hertfordshire ringed birds are from distances of less than 20km. Analysis of recoveries over 50km suggests there is a small late autumn and winter movement to the south and south-west, with a return movement in late March and April.

Goldfinch

Carduelis carduelis

A common resident and spring and autumn migrant.   **MAP 102**

Although described as common, both Sage (1959) and Mead and Smith (1982) found the distribution of the Goldfinch to be 'patchy'. Further, as shown by the *Common Birds Census* indices (Mead and Smith 1982) populations are subject to considerable variation. A particulary large fall, described by Mead and Smith (1982) as serious, occurred in 1969 and it was hypothesised that this may be due to the wet summers, increased use of weedkillers and other agricultural practises such as the use of hedge flails. Gladwin (1983) found that in central Hertfordshire numbers decreased in the rural zone between 1956 and 1980 but partially compensatory increases were occurring in new urban areas as gardens and trees matured. Overall the Goldfinch is possibly only a little less numerous in 1982 than it was 25 years ago, and is found breeding in good numbers in some parts of the county. None the less populations in most agricultural areas are thin.

Many British Goldfinches winter in France and Spain and large movements through the county occur in spring and autumn. Spring flocks are usually small, numbers only rarely reaching or exceeding 50. Large post breeding flocks form in July and persist through autumn and winter. Flocks of up to 100 are regularly reported, and larger flocks of up to between 200 and 300 seen in most years. The autumn passage has a distinct peak in early October.

A significant number of Goldfinches ringed in Hertfordshire in summer and autumn have been recovered in Belgium, France and Spain.

Siskin

Carduelis spinus

A regular but local winter visitor   **MAP 103**

There has been no evident change in the status of the Siskin since Sage (1959) described it as a regular winter visitor which is often quite numerous.

273

Numbers are subject to considerable year to year variations. Occasionally, however, it appears to be quite scarce. In 1958, for example, there were only five records of up to seven birds at three sites. In most winters small numbers are observed in most alder woodlands and occasionally in birch. Most flocks contain less than 25 birds whilst the largest seen usually contain from 50 to 60. Flocks of between 100 and 150 birds have been recorded on 19 occasions in 13 of the 25 years from 1958 to 1982. The four records of larger numbers are of 170 at Northaw Great Wood on 21 March 1976, 250 at Stockers Lake on 2 January 1982, and a flock of 555 with Redpolls at Cheshunt GP on 12 December, which had decreased to 200 on the following day, the 13 December 1981. In recent years small numbers have been increasingly appearing at bird tables, particularly in February and March, where they feed on fat and nuts.

Most Siskins arrive in late October and November and are rarely seen after mid-April. The earliest autumn record appears to be of three at West Hyde on 15 September.

In 1965, and each year from 1967 to 1972, two singing males were present in Bramfield Forest in May and June. The birds were always in the same small area of coniferous woodland at the western end of Basil's Park. Despite regular observation no females or other evidence of breeding were seen. Mead and Smith (1982) however, interpreted the territorial behaviour of these birds as evidence of attempted or intended breeding. Breeding in the county was eventually confirmed in 1982 when a pair reared four young near Hemel Hempstead.

Linnet

Carduelis cannabina

MAP 104 A common resident and spring and autumn migrant.

Both Sage (1959) and Mead and Smith (1982) described this resident species as breeding commonly in all parts of the county. Gladwin (1983) found some evidence of a small decrease in central Hertfordshire between 1956 and 1980, a finding supported by the *Common Birds Census* index (Mead and Smith 1982). None the less the Linnet remains a very common bird throughout the county, breeding in hedgerows and scrub in rural and outer urban areas.

Significant numbers of Linnets ringed in the county have been recovered in south-west France and Spain where many British birds winter. The large numbers which pass through the county between mid-March and the end of April, and in October and November are presumably migrating to and from this area. Linnets form large post breeding flocks in July and remain in flocks whilst on migration and throughout the winter. Many birds do not leave Britain for the winter, except when the weather is exceptionally cold.

Flocks of up to 300 to 400 are regularly seen in autumn and spring. However, whilst winter flocks are mostly of between 50 and 100 birds, larger numbers are not unusual. Exceptionally the largest flock was of 2500 to 3000 in a mixed flock with Greenfinches, Chaffinches and Tree Sparrows at Chorleywood on 23 December 1970 reducing to 1500 by 16 January 1971. Other large flocks were of over 1000 at Rye Meads on 18 November 1972, 2500 at Ashwell on 21 November 1976, and 1500 at Lemsford on 2 February 1979. Sage (1959) gave the previous largest flock as 300 seen at Chorleywood on 7 January 1954. Between 1958 and 1982, however, there were reports of at least 27 different flocks of 300 or more birds. Despite the occasional large flocks Linnets are now generally absent from much of N. and NE. Hertfordshire in winter.

Twite

Carduelis flavirostris

A scarce passage migrant and winter visitor.

Although Foster (in Hine 1934) stated that this species was found in winter on the Pegsdon, Barton, Warden and Hexton Hills, Sage (1959) described it as a scarce winter visitor, having found only the following five records for Hertfordshire:

1883	A pair caught near Aldbury in December.
1884	Two pairs caught near Ivinghoe in February.
1940	One on Bishops Stortford GC on 2 February.
1946	Twenty near Ware on 19 December.
1953	Two near Startops End Reservoir, Tring, on 15 November.

Since then Twite have been recorded in the county in a further 14 years as follows:

1960	At Rye Meads there were three on 28 and two on 29 October.
1961	Two at Rye Meads on 21 October.
	One at Tring Reservoirs on 29 October.
	Three at Old Parkbury on 6 December.
1962	One at Rye Meads on 25 November.
1964	Two roosting in low scrub, Bramfield Forest, on 12 January.
1965	One at St. Lawrence End on 13 November.
	One at Wilstone Reservoir on 27 December.
1965–6	At Tewinbury, eight on 26 December and 2 January and seven on 4 January roosting in reeds.
	One at Weston Park on 12 December.
1972	A male at Pirton on 3 December.
1974	A male at Lemsford Springs roosting in reeds with Corn Buntings from 17 November to the end of the year.
	Five at Nyn Park, Northaw on 7 April.
1977	Six at Royston SF on 12 December.
	Three or more at Ashwell on 27 December.
1978	Seven at Royston SF on 2 April.

1979   Two at Boxmoor Common on 11th January.
At Baldock, two on 1 and one on 4 January.
Two at Wallington on 23 March.

1981   Up to 10 at Baldock with 300 Linnets from at least 19 to 22 December.

1982   One at Amwell GP on 17 January.

A significant number of recent records are from the Chilterns.

Redpoll

Carduelis flammea

The following two sub-species which occur in Hertfordshire are separately described in the sub-sections that follow:

(*a*) Mealy Redpoll *C. f. flammea*
(*b*) Lesser Redpoll *C. f. disruptis*

(*a*) Mealy Redpoll

Carduelis flammea flammea

A regular winter visitor in small numbers.

Sage (1959) described the Mealy Redpoll as a rare winter visitor and from the available records this would appear to have been the case. Further, between 1958 and 1982 observers submitted few records which were confidently referred to this sub-species. However, as will be shown, it seems probable that the Mealy Redpoll is a regular winter visitor that is largely overlooked.

From 1967 to 1970 the Mimram Valley Ringing Group carried out ringing studies at Bramfield Forest and Tewinbury. In each autumn and winter small numbers of Mealy Redpolls and birds exhibiting characteristics between *C. f. flammea* and *C. f. disruptis* were trapped and ringed at both

276

sites. Such birds totalled less than 5 per cent of all Redpolls trapped, the majority being Lesser Redpolls.

Gladwin (*Trans. Herts. Nat. Hist. Soc.* 27:67) described the records for 1969 as follows:

Several Mealy Redpolls were trapped and ringed in Bramfield Wood on October 12th and 19th. Nine birds which were certainly of this form were significantly larger and heavier (about 2 grams) than birds of the form *disruptis* caught at the same time. Mealy Redpolls were also trapped and ringed in Ashridge Park during the autumn. Sage, in *A History of the Birds of Hertfordshire,* describes this form as a rare visitor. Recent experiences, however, suggest the form probably occurs regularly but is overlooked because of the difficulty of identifying it in the field. It should also be noted that the populations trapped at Ashridge Park and Bramfield Wood contained a number of 'intermediates' which exhibited plumage characteristics ranging between the two forms *flammea* and *disruptis.* These intermediates tend to have body sizes and weights typical of *disruptis.* Adults which had bred in Bramfield Wood, and their young, continued to be retrapped into November and none of these exhibited any plumage characteristics typical of the 'intermediates', suggesting that the latter were of a transient migrant population.

It would seem therefore that, although there are only two records since 1970, the last being of two at Baldock on 22 December 1981, small numbers of Mealy Redpolls are very probably of regular, even annual occurrence.

One ringed at Ashridge on 9 October 1962 was recovered at Eindhoven, Holland, on 28 November 1963 when it was identified as being a Mealy Redpoll.

(b)   Lesser Redpoll

Carduelis flammea disruptis

A common resident and winter visitor.   **MAP 105**

Describing it as a local but not uncommon resident, Sage (1959) also stated that 'there is little doubt that the Lesser Redpoll has increased considerably as a breeding species since the beginning of the century'. The trend continued and in the subsequent 25 years to 1982 the breeding population has increased by a further 500 or 600 per cent. Much of this growth is evident from the *Common Birds Census* indices (Mead and Smith 1982). Peak populations were probably reached in 1980 for by 1982 there was some evidence of a decline.

In the mid-1950s the distribution of the Lesser Redpoll was very patchy and there were few districts where it was known to breed regularly (Sage 1959). These included areas around Hitchin, Mardley Heath, along the Mimram valley from Digswell to Kimpton, and around Hertford, Broxbourne and St. Albans. By the period 1967 to 1973, as shown by Mead and Smith (1982), it was common in all the wooded areas of the county. Indeed in some, like the woodlands at Ashridge and Bramfield, it had become abundant. Since then numbers have increased further and it is probable that the *Hertfordshire Breeding Bird Atlas* now understates its distribution. The increase in population has been accompanied by a quite remarkable diversification of nest sites. Until about 1960 most nests found in the county were in birch woodland and coniferous plantations. Since 1970, however, it has also nested commonly in gardens and hedgerows. In summary it now seems to nest widely in medium-tall scrub or shrub habitats, as well as a wide variety of trees.

The largest flock referred to by Sage (1959), and described by him as 'exceptional', was found at Abbots Langley where there were 70-80 on 21 January and at least 100 on 10 February 1942. Since the early 1960s, however, flocks of several hundreds of Lesser Redpolls have been a common sight in the major woodlands between autumn and spring. There are records of four flocks of 1000 or more birds. In Bramfield Forest c. 1000 were present on 19 April 1964, from January to mid-April 1965, and on 5 October 1969. However, by far the biggest flocks seen to date were at Ashridge where there were 5000 to 10 000 birds between August and November 1969.

Two-barred Crossbill

Loxia leucoptera

A very rare vagrant.

There are three records, the first given by Sage (1959), as follows:

1890   One shot at Tharbies, near Sawbridgeworth, on 11 January.
1963   A male with five Crossbills *L. curvirostra* in Bramfield Forest on 22 December (*British Birds* 57:277).
1966   An immature male in Bramfield Forest on 18 September (*British Birds* 60:331).

It is now known that some Crossbills *L. curvirostra* exhibit double white wing-bars, albeit not as clearly defined as in *L. leucoptera*. Other characteristics are therefore also essential in the consideration of records some of which may need to be re-assessed.

Common Crossbill

Loxia curvirostra

MAP 106   An irregular visitor that has bred.

As described by Sage (1959) the majority of observations of this species are the result of irruptions or erruptions into Britain from the continent such as occurred in 1909, 1927, 1929, 1935, 1953, 1962 and 1966. After such irruptions some birds remain for up to two years and may breed.

Sage (1959) gives two breeding records of a nest found at an unnamed locality in 1907, and another taken at Letchworth in 1911. Foster in Hine

(1934) says that it has bred in the Hitchin area several times and that a nest had been recorded at Welwyn (Foster 1917). Whilst there is no evidence to support these statements the reference to Welwyn is particularly interesting. Following the extensive irruption in 1962 it became known that Crossbills were breeding in an area of relatively open old pine woodland at Oaklands, near Welwyn. On investigation it was discovered that small numbers had bred in the woodlands, probably annually, since at least 1944. Two households described the birds as having been regular, often daily, visitors to their bird baths and ponds since 'sometime towards the end of the Second World War'. Both families said how they had come to look for the appearance of young birds early in each spring and one produced diary records for the years 1948, 1951 and 1952 which supported this. Pine woodland of the type then found at Oaklands is rare in Hertfordshire and since one of Foster's correspondents lived nearby at Woolmer Green it is possible, although speculative, that his reference to a nest at Welwyn is from this site. Two pairs nested successfully at Oaklands in each year from 1962 to 1974, except 1969 when only one pair bred. In 1974 a 'golden' coloured male (singing) and at least two normal females were also present and a third pair may have attempted to breed. Several nests were located between 1962 and 1974, often 'lodged' in the fork of branches near the tops of the pines. Since 1974 the woodlands have been further infilled with more houses, and Crossbills have not nested there since.

Following irruptions birds have been seen in many parts of the county and sometimes remain for a year or two and occasionally breed. Such an irruption occurred in the summer and autumn of 1962. As a result Crossbills were present at various sites in southern, central and western Hertfordshire from late July 1962 to August 1964. The only record outside this general area was of four at Letchworth on 21 January 1963. Maximum numbers at the principal sites involved were:

Ashridge	c.40 from July to September 1962 at Ringshall where 29 were feeding on Whitebeam berries on 29 September.
Bramfield Forest	Less than 10 from September 1962 to August 1963, then maxima of 60 on 7 September 1963, 70 on 5 December 1963, and 40 on 12 January 1964. All had left by mid-February 1964. Most of the birds were in a small pine plantation and less frequently in two sections of European Larch planted in 1938.
Goldings Wood, Haileybury	Between 12 and 20 on many dates from 25 September 1962 to 6 March 1964.
Harmergreen	Present in pines around a low density residential area from 20 August 1962 to January 1964. Apart from 23 on 7 September 1963 numbers never exceeded eight.
Oaklands, Welwyn	Up to 30 in pines at the long established breeding site from July 1962 to at least September 1963.
Panshanger	Present, mainly in pines, from at least March 1963 to December 1963. Maxima reported were 32 on 28 April and 47 on 7 September.

Elsewhere numbers not exceeding 16 were reported from 15 other sites in the two years following the 1962 irruption.

The sites at Bramfield, Harmer Green and Oaklands are within two miles of each other, and Panshanger only two miles further. Thus it seems probable that there would have been some, if not considerable, movements between these areas.

Further influxes occurred in June and early July 1966. From then until March 1967 small numbers, never exceeding seven, were reported from much the same areas as those in which Crossbills were seen between 1962 and 1964. In 1967 a pair probably bred in Lamer Park, near Wheathampstead.

In the 15 years from 1968 to 1982 Crossbills have been reported on 17 occasions in 9 different years. Five records are for the autumn of 1972 when 17 were seen flying over Tring on 16 July and 77 on 10 August. All the remaining records refer to less than ten birds.

The site near Chorleywood for which Mead and Smith (1982) included a breeding record is outside the county boundary.

In 1980 two immatures were killed on a road at Kings Walden on 10 July and another immature seen at Moor Park, Rickmansworth, on 11 and 18 August but there is no suggestion these birds had fledged in Hertfordshire.

As the records show, Crossbills seen in the county exhibit a strong preference for pines.

Bullfinch

Pyrrhula pyrrhula

MAP 107 A very common resident.

Sage (1959) found the Bullfinch to be reasonably common in most parts of the county and described it as a common resident. In the 1950s and early 1960s the population in central Hertfordshire increased significantly. The increase, which presumably also occurred in other areas, appears to have been by a factor of between two and three times. As evident from the *Common Birds Census* indices numbers have since remained reasonably stable (Mead and Smith 1982). The species seems to be numerous wherever there are thick hedgerows, scrub or woodlands, and breeds in even small remnants of blackthorn and hawthorn thickets. Thus, as demonstrated by Mead and Smith (1982), it is widely distributed throughout the county. Mead and Smith (1982) did however find it absent from small parts of the agricultural zone in the north-east of the county. Recent observations have shown that it is now present throughout that area, although population densities are low as indeed they are in the urban areas.

Some Bullfinches remain in pairs throughout the winter but many roam the coutryside in small flocks. In spring they appear in orchards and gardens where their fondness for buds may result in considerable damage to fruit trees. Analysis of the county records shows that few flocks (4 per cent) contain more than 15 birds. Exceptionally the largest flocks recorded were of 70 with Greenfinches at Ridge on 13 February 1965, and 55 at Rye Meads on 14 January 1962. Much larger numbers pass through or use individual sites.

At Ashridge in 1969, for example, it was estimated that 100 different individuals were drinking at the same pool in one week.

Of 492 Bullfinches present in flocks of 10 or more birds reported from all parts of the county since 1958, 71 per cent were males.

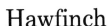

Hawfinch

Coccothraustes
  coccothraustes

A local, fairly common resident.   **MAP 108**

The Hawfinch remains as described by Sage (1959), a fairly common resident. It is a secretive bird, more often heard than seen, and very easily overlooked. Between 1967 and 1973 Mead and Smith (1982) found it bred or probably bred in 80 out of 504 tetrads and considered Hertfordshire to be one of its national strongholds. Found mostly in remnants of ancient woodland, particularly those containing wild cherry, hornbeam or beech, it is commonest in central and south-western areas and in the woodlands around Ashridge. Populations seem to be subject to wide year to year variations and it seems possible that they are particularly vulnerable during cold winters. None the less between 1965 and 1980 the population doubled in central Hertfordshire (Gladwin 1983) where nests have recently been found in gardens with mature trees at Bulls Green, Digswell and Tewin, and in the western part of Welwyn Garden City.

Small flocks of between 10 and 20 birds are reported between autumn and spring in most years. Exceptionally the largest flocks on record were of 65 in Woodhall Park on 24 February 1981, and 50 near Berkhamsted on 27 March 1895 (Sage 1959). Otherwise the highest numbers are the subject of eight records of between 20 and 26 birds. Five of these records being obtained since 1970.

Snow Bunting

Plectrophenax nivalis

A rare vagrant.

Sage (1959) lists 18 records of this species in Hertfordshire. However, the specimen from Offley is an albino Corn Bunting (James and Sawford 1979).

281

Of the ten records between 1881 and 1900 ony six include precise dates in September (1), December (1), January (3) and February (1). There is also a recently discovered record of a pair shot at Aldenham in January 1895. The other seven records given by Sage (1959) involving at last ten different birds are as follows:

1913 One at Letchworth in January (Foster 1914).
1926 One between Hatfield and Welwyn on 30 January.
1935 One at Wilstone Reservoir, Tring, on 13 and 20 October.
1944 One on 6 and two on 7 November at Wilstone Reservoir, Tring.
1945 Two at Wilstone Reservoir, on 10 November.
1952 One at Wilstone Reservoir, on 25 October.
1953 One at Wilstone Reservoir, on 9 October.
1957 A male at Hilfield Park Reservoir on 3 February.

Snow Buntings have subsequently been reported in a further eight years as follows:

1959 At least six at North Mimms on 13 December.
1960 A female at Rye Meads on 23 January and a male at Highley Hill, near Ashwell, on 1 October.
1961 Singles at Wilstone Reservoir, Tring, on 1 and 5 November (presumed to be the same bird), and at Rye Meads also on 5 November.
1972 Three flew south over Welwyn Garden City on 6 March. Four (two pairs) at Maple Cross on 26 November.
1974 A male at Tring Reservoirs on 28 October.
1978 One at Hilfield Park Reservoir from 15 to 18 November.
1979 A female with Corn Buntings and Yellowhammers NE. of Weston Hills, Baldock, on 1 January.
1981 One near Wilstone Reservoir, on 8 January.

Most records are for the months of October, November and January.

Yellowhammer

Emberiza citrinella

MAP 109 A very common resident.

Sage (1959) similarly described the Yellowhammer to be a very common resident. As demonstrated by Mead and Smith (1982) it is common in all parts of the county outside the urban areas. The *Common Birds Census* indices show that, apart from a short lived increase in the mid-1970s, the population has remained largely unchanged since at least 1964. Similarly, Gladwin (1983) could find no evidence of any significant change having occurred in central Hertfordshire between 1956 and 1980.

Yellowhammers are commonest in scrub, immature coniferous plantations, and particularly on the farmlands where they will even nest in small fragments of old hedgerows. From autumn through to spring many Yellowhammers form flocks. Most flocks contain less than 50 birds although numbers up to 200 are not uncommon. Exceptionally there was a flock of 500–1000 birds near Berkhamsted Common on 19 January 1941 (Sage 1941). Otherwise the largest flocks were of 300+ in Bramfield Forest from October to December 1967 and 300 in Comb's Wood, Benington, at the end of 1982.

Communal roosts also, it seems, rarely contain more than 200 birds. In Hertfordshire, Yellowhammers have been observed roosting in a wide variety of situations including long herbage, bracken, scrub, coniferous, plantations and even under snow (Gladwin 1985). There are long established reed-bed roosts containing up to 200 birds at Rye Meads and 100 at Tewinbury.

Sage (1959) considered the possibility that some winter flocks are composed of continental birds. Ringing studies have since confirmed that birds seen in Hertfordshire are of local origin. Indeed only four British ringed Yellowhammers have been recovered abroad, two in France and two in the Netherlands.

Cirl Bunting

Emberiza cirlus

A former very rare resident.

MAP 110

At best the Cirl Bunting has always been as described by Sage (1959), 'one of Hertfordshire's rarest breeding species'. From at least 1864, when a nest was found, a small breeding population existed on the chalk hills around Tring. In 1968, during fieldwork for the *Breeding Bird Atlas* (Mead and Smith 1982), the species was recorded in three tetrads on the Chiltern scarp near Tring and one pair were proved to have bred. However, *all* of these birds were outside Hertfordshire (C. J. Mead, pers. com.) and thus it is not known when breeding last occurred in the county. A male on 11 July 1964 was the last reported observation from the Hertfordshire part of this area. A flock of 10 at Wilstone Reservoir, Tring, on 4 February 1941 were also probably local birds.

It is probable that a remnant breeding population existed along the Mimram valley between Ayot St. Lawrence, Codicote and Kimpton up to at least 1967. Of possible significance are the known attempts to breed at Codicote in 1915 and 1918 (Sage 1959). Other records from this poorly studied area, all relatively recent, are as follows:

1956 A pair near Kimpton in June.
1961 A pair at Bower Heath, Harpenden, on 9 April.
1963 A pair and a singing male at Codicote Bottom throughout July but no evidence of breeding.
1964 A male at Kimpton on several dates in August.
1967 A male singing near Kimpton during the breeding season.

Breeding records away from these areas, all given by Sage (1959), are of a nest found at Croxley in 1935, attempted breeding at Bishops Stortford in 1938, and a pair suspected of breeding near Rickmansworth in 1948 and 1949. The few records from other parts of the county up to 1957 are mostly of single observations from widely scattered localities. In addition to the records listed above, Cirl Buntings have been observed since 1958 as follows:

1959   A male at Hilfield Park Reservoir on 20 July.
1962   A female at Old Parkbury, Radlett, on 30 June.
1964   A female at Kings Langley on 23 and 29 January. Six in the stackyard at Tewin Hill Farm on 15 February. One at Tring WaterWorks on 11 July.
1967   Two at Redbournbury on 2 September and 22 October.
1968   Twenty, declining to 16, in a mixed flock of finches and buntings at mixed seed and grain provided for Pheasants in Bramfield Forest from 5 February to 1 April; two remaining until last seen on 21 April.
        A female at Leatherfield Common, Benington, on 28 April.
1972   A male at Pirton on 17 September.
1977   One at Moor Park golf course on 15 June.
1981   An immature at Bricket Wood in September.

Ortolan Bunting

Emberiza hortulana

A very rare vagrant.

There is one record. An adult male at Chorleywood on 8 February 1953 (Sage 1959).

Rustic Bunting

Emberiza rustica

A very rare vagrant.

There is one record. A young male was caught in the nets of a bird-catcher near Aldenham on 19 or 20 November 1882 (Sage 1959).

Little Bunting

Emberiza pusilla

A very rare vagrant.

There is one record. A male at Hilfield Park Reservoir on 20 April 1960 (*British Birds* 54:197).

Reed Bunting

Emberiza schoeniclus

A local resident and spring and autumn passage migrant.   **MAP 111**

Since Sage (1959) described the Reed Bunting to be a common resident numbers declined dramatically in the early 1960s, largely recovered in the early to mid-1970s and then decreased again. The first decline is well illustrated by the situation at Berkhamsted and Northchurch Commons where 15 to 20 pairs bred between 1953 and 1962 but none in 1963 after a severe winter or 1964, following which 5 males were again holding territory in 1965. Habitat changes are one contributory factor. Reed Buntings often colonise newly planted conifer plantations. In 1963 11 pairs bred in Broxbourne Woods and 14 pairs in Bramfield Forest. The following year, 1964, 31 pairs bred in Bramfield Forest. Numbers declined thereafter as the habitat became less suitable. At Rye Meads where 100 pairs bred in 1973, numbers fell to about 80 pairs in 1974 and 30 pairs in 1982. This decrease is also attributed to a change in habitat (*Ninth Report of the Rye Meads Ringing Group*). Between 1967 and 1973, when populations were showing some recovery, Mead and Smith (1982) found it to be a 'fairly common nesting bird' patchily distributed throughout the county. As might be expected the distribution is largely that of wet habitats. Gladwin (1983) found it had increased in central Hertfordshire between 1956 and 1980, mainly due to an increase in suitable habitats. However, a series of cold winters appear to have resulted in further considerable losses such that by

1982 it is probable that the total breeding population of the county was at the lower end of the range 300 to 500 pairs. In 1981 64 pairs were located in 6 of 13 *Common Birds Census* plots, including 30 pairs in 23 ha at Tring SF. In 1982, when Tring SF was not censused, only 22 pairs were located in the five other plots holding Reed Buntings; a decrease of about a third in one year.

Small numbers of migrant Reed Buntings pass through Hertfordshire in both spring and autumn. These movements are still not sufficiently understood but are probably regional as few British ringed birds have been recovered abroad. In late March and the first half of April small migrant flocks are often to be seen on agricultural land and in wetland habitats almost anywhere in the county. These flocks usually contain a high. proportion of males. The largest such flock recorded in spring was of 80 (74 males) at Hertford Meads on 19 April 1969. Flocks of autumn migrants also tend to include a majority of males. Thirty-six Reed Buntings ringed at Bramfield in September 1969 comprised 27 males (15 adults) and 9 first-winter females.

Most Reed Buntings roost communally during the winter months. Reed-beds are preferred and between 100 and 200 have roosted for many years at Rye Meads, Tewinbury and Tring Reservoirs and irregularly at Oughtonhead. There are many records of smaller roosts in bracken and scrub as well as reeds. The largest woodland roost on record was in Box Wood, Stevenage, which held 150 birds in January 1979.

Reed Buntings are known to be particularly vulnerable during cold winters when their appearance at garden feeding stations has become a regular feature of their behaviour.

Corn Bunting

Miliaria calandra

MAP 112 A common resident.

When Sage (1959) described the Corn Bunting as 'a local but by no means uncommon resident', it bred commonly along the Chilterns. Otherwise, apart from a small breeding population in the London Colney, Radlett and Shenley area, it was very thinly distributed on the arable lands of central, east and north-east Hertfordshire. However, Sage (1959) also noted that many of the records away from the Chilterns were due to a southward expansion of range which started sometime about, or a little before 1950. As evidenced by the *Common Birds Census* index, populations continued to increase until the mid-1970s (Mead and Smith 1982). Similarly the species continued to expand its range and Mead and Smith demonstrated that between 1967 and 1973 it was to be found on arable farmlands throughout the county, except along the southern belt from Watford through Potters Bar to Cheshunt. Very scarce in central Hertfordshire prior to 1956 it had become common by 1980 (Gladwin 1983); the population having increased from less than 10 to more than 100 pairs. Since 1975, or thereabouts, the population has been reasonably static and its distribution is now probably little different from that described by Mead and Smith (1982) except that it is much more numerous in the areas around Rickmansworth, Chorleywood, Aldenham, London Colney and Radlett. None the less numbers on a *Common Birds Census* plot near Radlett declined from 11 pairs in 1980 to one pair. The reasons are as yet unclear.

In winter Corn Buntings form large communal roosts, usually in reed-beds or scrub habitats. The largest roosts reported in the ten-year period 1959 to 1968 were of 120 at Northaw on 6 October 1961, and of 100 at Standon Lordship on 28 November 1959, Marsworth Reservoir, Tring, on 29 February 1961, and at Wallington on 16 February 1964. The records for the next ten years, 1969 to 1978, show considerable increases in roost sizes. The maxima at Tring, for example, reached 300 in December 1969, and 450 in March 1978 although there were wide variations in the intervening years. At Rye Meads a reed-bed roost increased from 20 birds in March 1962 to 100 in December 1973 and March 1978. A month later, in April 1978, a roost at adjacent Stanstead Abbotts was found to contain 206 Corn Buntings. In December 1978 a roost holding 100 birds was discovered at Ashwell SF.

In 1979, 150 birds were counted roosting at Weston Hills on 1 January and 100 at Berkhamsted GP on the 7th. Exceptionally, 450 were present at Maple Cross on 27 January and the roost at Tring reached a new maximum of 500 in December.

In 1980 and 1981 the maxima counted at Tring fell to 300 and 320 respectively. New roosts included 250 at Springwell watercress beds on 16 November 1980, 120+ at Tolpits Lake on 7 February 1981, and 100 at Pirton in December 1981.

Elsewhere long established but smaller roosts exist in reed-beds at Tewinbury and Stanborough Reedmarsh, and in scrub and woodland at some 15 to 20 locations.

7

Hertfordshire Breeding
Bird Atlas Maps

7.1 Introduction and Background

Hertfordshire has been well served by Sage's *History of the Birds of Hertfordshire* which was published in 1959. However he was unable to provide detailed distribution maps for, even then, there were too few active bird-watchers in the county to do the necessary fieldwork. It was the botanists who showed the way. In 1962 the Botanical Society of the British Isles published their national *Atlas of the British Flora* using the 10km squares of the National Grid as the basic recording unit. This was followed, in 1967, by Dony's *Flora of Hertfordshire* based on the more precise two kilometre squares appropriate for a county survey. Botanists do have certain advantages when it comes to mapping schemes — plants do not fly. However, many ornithologists came to appreciate that this was the future method for gathering distributional data and were soon exploring ways of applying it to birds.

The B.T.O. proposed to survey the summer distribution of breeding birds at the only time of the year when the more mobile species have their interest centred on one place — the nest. A few active birders suggested that the number of birds within each unit should be assessed by the fieldworkers. This was attempted in various different ways during pilot surveys for the National Atlas but the idea was eventually rejected. It was decided, at an early stage, that breeding should be proved beyond doubt wherever possible for each species within each unit surveyed. This system has now been used for the National Atlas in Britain and several other European countries and for many local surveys in Britain. For the country-wide surveys the recording units have been based on whatever suitable maps or map-grids have been available. In Britain and Ireland 10km squares, in the Netherlands 5km squares and in France on rectangles 20km × 27km: a sensible choice since each unit was precisely covered by a single map. For local surveys the 2km × 2km unit is now generally used. Its boundaries are the even numbered kilometre lines of the National Grid: each is thus an area of four square kilometres and is called a *tetrad* from the Greek *tetra* meaning four.

Fieldwork for the Hertfordshire Atlas started in 1967 when, as part of the pilot survey for the National Atlas, the 125 tetrads in the five 10km squares from Aylesbury (SP81) in the west to Welwyn (TL21) in the east were surveyed by members of the British Trust for Ornithology's staff, Chris Cox, Jim Flegg and Tom Gladwin. The results were encouraging but the proposition that tetrads should be used for the National Atlas was rejected. However, it was thought that there were sufficient observers in Hertfordshire for the whole county to be covered at the tetrad level. Thus, from 1968, the criteria used nationally for recording on the 10km square unit were used in Hertfordshire at the tetrad level: the combined records from its constituent 25 tetrads forming a complete 10km square record for the National Atlas. Any species recorded in the breeding season in possible breeding habitat, that is, for example, ignoring loafing non-breeding gulls, could be entered into the Atlas records in one of three ways:

Possibly breeding   *Column 1 record*
Entry in first column on the recording card.
A species seen in possible breeding habitat during its breeding season.
No further indication that it might actually be breeding.

Probably breeding   *Column 2 record*
Entry in second column on card.
Species seen in likely breeding habitat and suspected to be breeding.
Criteria included birds holding territory, persistently singing etc.

Proved breeding   *Column 3 record*
Entry in third column on the card.
Species definitely breeding — nest and egg or young found, parents feeding newly fledged young etc.

Each entry had a code — column one a simple tick, column two a single letter indicating the sort of evidence found and column three a double letter code, again indicating the evidence found. Effectively, as soon as a species was proved to breed in a tetrad further records of it could be ignored.

The recording card used in the county was very similar to that used for the national survey but, of course, showed a more restricted species list. It also asked for rather more information on coverage and, for a minority of species, an estimate of the number of breeding pairs within the tetrad.

Although the National Atlas fieldwork was to run from 1968 to 1972 it was decided to include the 1967 tetrad survey data in the local Atlas. Each year assessments were made as to how well the local coverage was progressing. By 1971 it was clear that there were few, if any, areas where new records for 10km squares would be obtained but that there were quite a number of tetrads which were poorly covered. Some of these gaps were plugged in 1972 but it was decided to make a special effort during 1973, after the National Atlas had finished. By the end of summer 1973 only two tetrads with any part of Hertfordshire in them had not been surveyed. In both cases minute parts of the county were involved and both tetrads have been completely excluded from the survey, they were TQ09 A and TL30 Y. Otherwise all tetrads with any part of Hertfordshire in them have been included and, to allow for a reasonable comparison, the whole of every tetrad was surveyed rather than what may be only a small part within the county. Also to make the Atlas as complete as possible the definition of Hertfordshire includes any area which has been part of the administrative county since 1859, when the Watsonian vice-county system was devised (Hertfordshire is v.c. 20).

The fieldwork was great fun. It appealed to the more or less suppressed collecting instinct within every observer, for one only had to move to the next tetrad for even the humble House Sparrow to become a new record. It was a challenge to the skilled ornithologists who took part and considered it a matter of some pride to prove as many species as possible rather than to have them on the card as lowly ticks. Many felt that their fieldcraft had gained tremendously from taking part. Finally it appealed to everyone as an obviously objective means of recording the county's breeding bird distribution.

Observers were encouraged to visit the tetrads for which they were responsible several times from March through to July. Some species, such as Mistle Thrush, are much easier to record early in the season whilst others, like Corn Buntings, are easier later. Direct disturbance of breeding birds was discouraged for proving breeding through observations of parents feeding newly fledged young is much easier and safer for the birds than actual nest-finding. There were few tetrads for which several cards were not received. Sometimes these came from the same observer in different years but, in most cases, several observers were involved.

Many observers were, of course, submitting records for their home area where many of the birds they were recording could really be counted as old friends. However even they often discovered areas within a short walk of home that they never knew existed and certainly birds which they did not believe bred so close. The instructions to Atlas workers relied crucially on the incomparable maps of the Ordnance Survey. Not only did they show the grid lines and therefore the boundaries of the tetrads and the reference numbers of the 10km squares but also they showed the local area. The 1 : 25 000 series (2½" : 1 mile) are in sufficient detail to show every building, field boundary, wood, copse, path and pond. The Atlas worker confronted with a strange tetrad would ideally look at this map and decide to visit the main stretches of water, woods etc. In recent years many towns and villages have spread very quickly swallowing what was countryside. Their spread, in certain parts of the county has also caused extensive gravel diggings which, in their turn, provide particularly good habitats for birds. Coverage within the county was so good that all such areas were found and recorded.

The completed cards were destined for CJM's card index in Tring, however, for much of the county during the final stages of the survey, they were first sent to organisers covering particular 10km squares. These organisers, with an intimate knowledge of their own patch, were in a very good position to make immediate checks for mis-identifications and mis-readings of maps resulting in the incorrect use of tetrad letters. Final checks were made when the cards reached Tring and later when the maps were plotted. At this stage additional information from the County Recorder's files was incorporated. Hertfordshire workers were responsible for all the county's tetrads within the London Natural History Society area and information was freely exchanged with the Bedfordshire Natural History Society for their Atlas. The slight differences between their maps, those for Hertfordshire and the 10km maps of the National Atlas mostly relate to the slight differences in time-scale of fieldwork.

7.2 The Maps

On the maps every small square is a tetrad. Each is given a letter (A to Z omitting O) which, with the 10km square reference, uniquely determines which four km² area is being referred to. The map below shows how this works. The lettering system is that recommended by the Ray Society for work by naturalists, it is totally logical, for the successive letters refer to tetrads with increasing grid reference numbers (the south-western corner A is 00, B is 02 and Z is 88). On the outline map and throughout the atlas the current county boundary is shown by the thick solid line. Old boundaries are shown by dotted lines. The 504 tetrads surveyed are all enclosed on all four sides by continuous lines. All contain part of Hertfordshire and were surveyed in their entirety (not just 'our' part). Note that TQ09 D, TL01 D, TL11 E and TL12 A are outside the county and TQ09 A and TL30 Y were not surveyed.

All species maps have dots (or circles) in their tetrads according to the following codes:

- • Possibly breeding
- ○ Probably or possibly breeding (generally records from the initial survey in 1967 but sometimes late records from observers notebooks)
- • Probably breeding
- ● Proved breeding.

On all the published tetrad maps the records refer to the exact tetrad where the bird was recorded. None have been moved to protect sites but, in a few instances, no map has been published so as to protect a vulnerable species. In a few other cases the map has not been published since there are so few records that they may be easily described in the text.

Figure 7.1   *County of Hertford – Map nomenclature based on the Ordnance Survey. In the top left-hand corner of each 10km square is a two-letter, two-figure code being a standard feature of all modern Ordnance Survey maps. The lettering system for the 25 tetrads (2km squares) within each 10km square is shown in the top left corner, being lettered A to Z omitting O.*

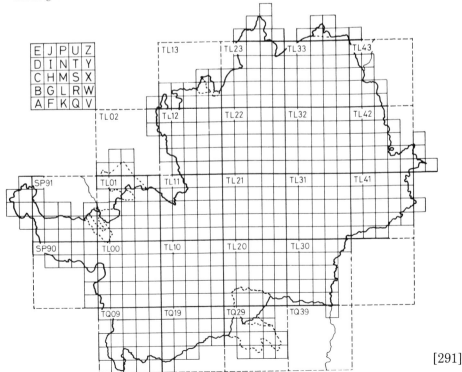

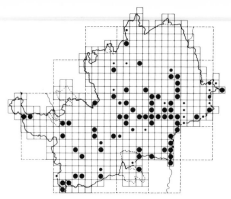

1 Little Grebe
Tachybaptus ruficollis

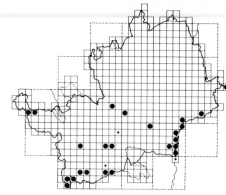

2 Great Crested Grebe
Podiceps cristatus

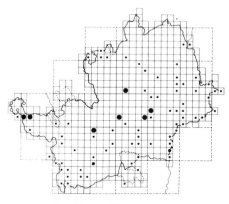

3 Grey Heron
Ardea cinerea

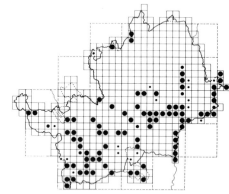

4 Mute Swan
Cygnus olor

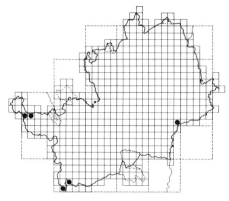

5 Greylag Goose
Anser anser

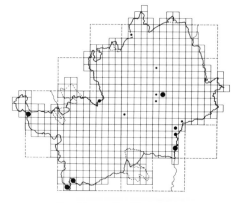

6 Canada Goose
Branta canadensis

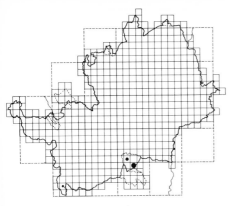

7　Mandarin
Aix galericulata

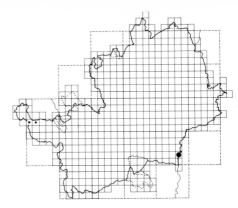

8　Gadwall
Anas strepera

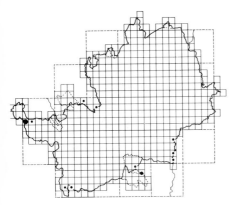

9　Teal
Anas crecca

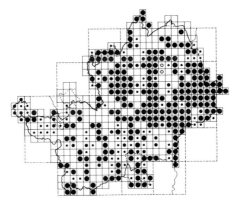

10　Mallard
Anas platyrhynchos

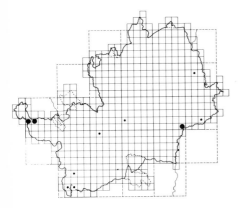

11　Shoveler
Anas clypeata

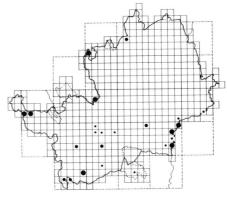

12　Pochard
Aythya ferina

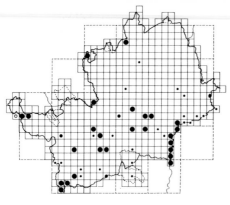

13 Tufted Duck
Aythya fuligula

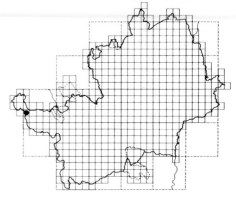

14 Ruddy Duck
Oxyura jamaicensis

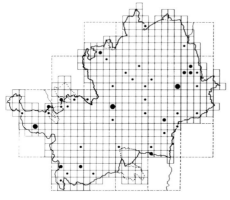

15 Sparrowhawk
Accipiter nisus

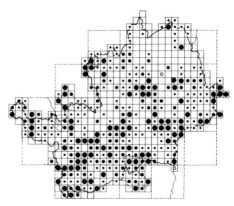

16 Kestrel
Falco tinnunculus

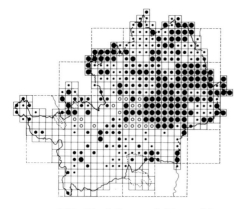

17 Red-legged Partridge
Alectoris rufa

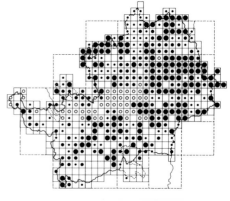

18 Grey Partridge
Perdix perdix

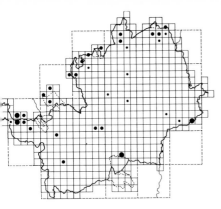

19 Quail
Coturnix coturnix

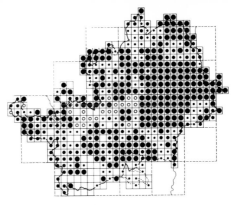

20 Pheasant
Phasianus colchicus

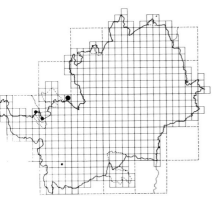

21 Lady Amherst's Pheasant
Chrysolophus amherstiae

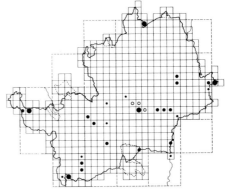

22 Water Rail
Rallus aquaticus

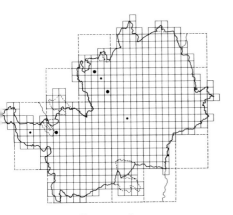

23 Corncrake
Crex crex

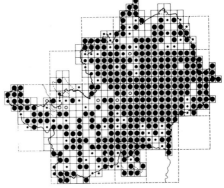

24 Moorhen
Gallinula chloropus

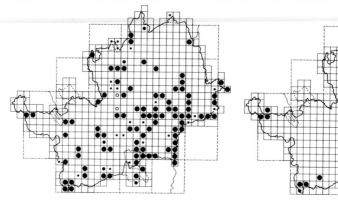

25 Coot
Fulica atra

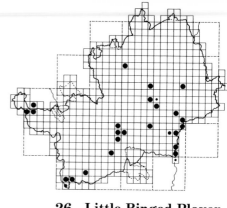

26 Little Ringed Plover
Charadrius dubius

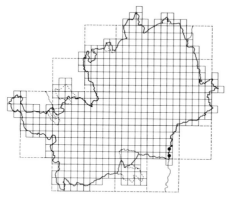

27 Ringed Plover
Charadrius hiaticula

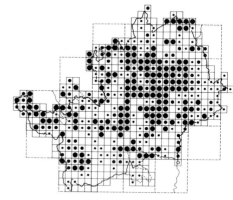

28 Lapwing
Vanellus vanellus

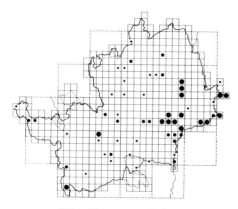

29 Common Snipe
Gallinago gallinago

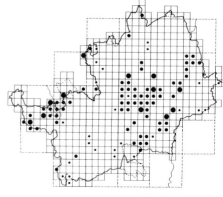

30 Woodcock
Scolopax rusticola

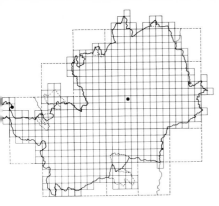

31 Curlew
Numenius arquata

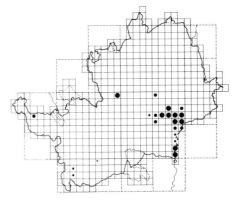

32 Redshank
Tringa totanus

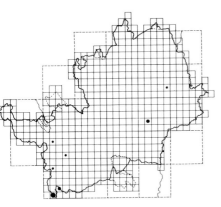

33 Common Sandpiper
Actitis hypoleucos

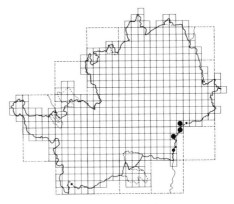

34 Common Tern
Sterna hirundo

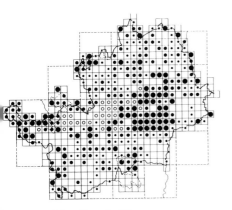

35 Stock Dove
Columba oenas

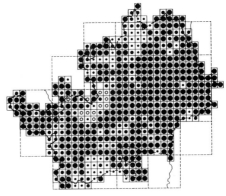

36 Woodpigeon
Columba palumbus

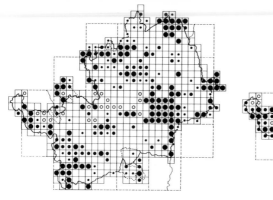

37 Collared Dove
Streptopelia decaocto

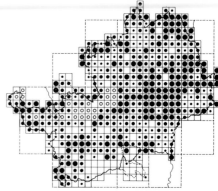

38 Turtle Dove
Streptopelia turtur

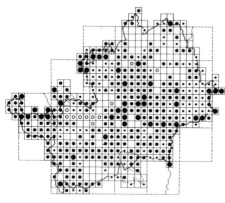

39 Cuckoo
Cuculus canorus

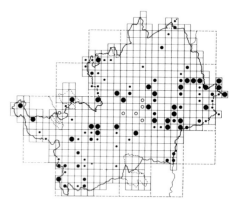

40 Barn Owl
Tyto alba

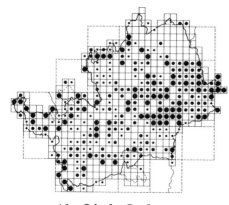

41 Little Owl
Athene noctua

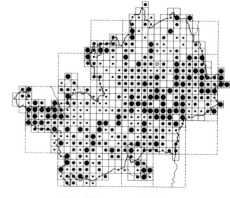

42 Tawny Owl
Strix aluco

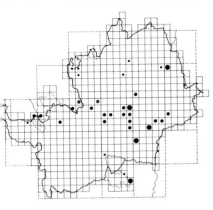

43 Long-eared Owl
Asio otus

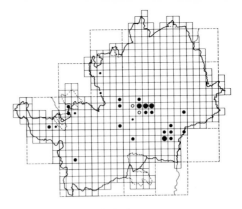

44 Nightjar
Caprimulgus europaeus

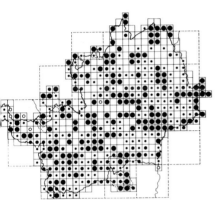

45 Swift
Apus apus

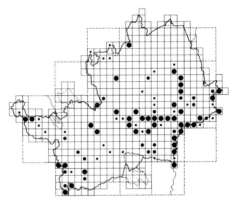

46 Kingfisher
Alcedo atthis

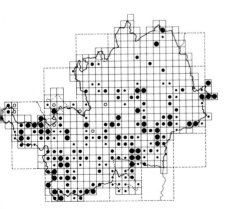

47 Green Woodpecker
Picus viridis

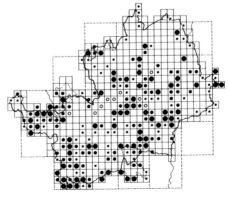

48 Great Spotted Woodpecker
Dendrocopos major

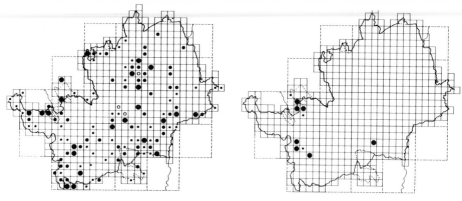

49 Lesser Spotted Woodpecker
Dendrocopos minor

50 Woodlark
Lullula arborea

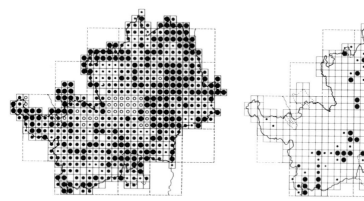

51 Skylark
Alauda arvensis

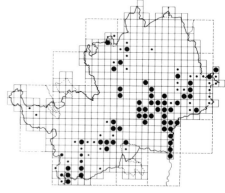

52 Sand Martin
Riparia riparia

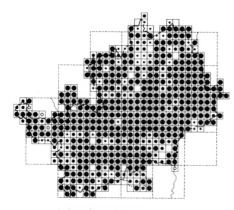

53 Swallow
Hirundo rustica

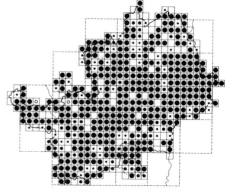

54 House Martin
Delichon urbica

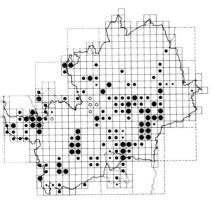

55 Tree Pipit
Anthus trivialis

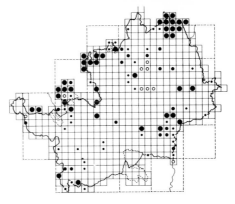

56 Meadow Pipit
Anthus pratensis

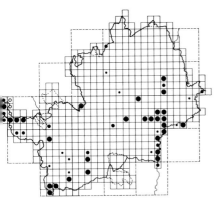

57 Yellow Wagtail
Motacilla flava

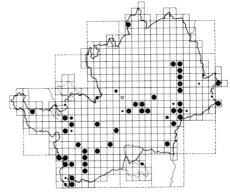

58 Grey Wagtail
Motacilla cinerea

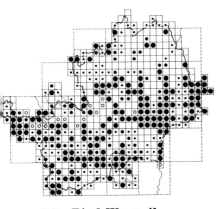

59 Pied Wagtail
Motacilla alba

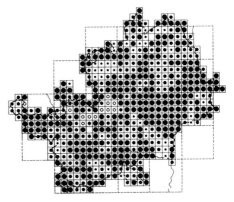

60 Wren
Troglodytes troglodytes

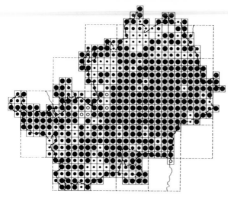

61 Dunnock
Prunella modularis

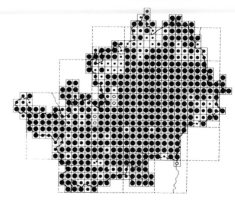

62 Robin
Erithacus rubecula

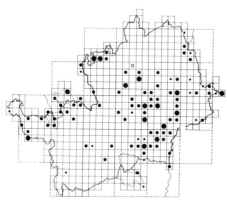

63 Nightingale
Luscinia megarhynchos

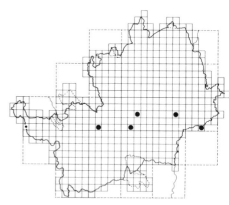

64 Black Redstart
Phoenicurus ochruros

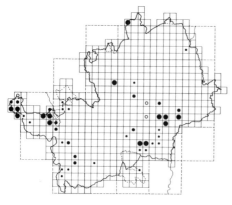

65 Redstart
Phoenicurus phoenicurus

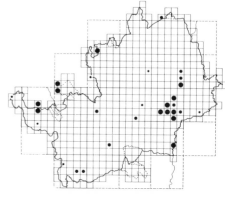

66 Whinchat
Saxicola rubetra

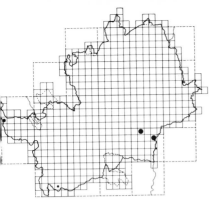

67 Stonechat
Saxicola torquata

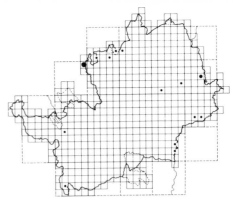

68 Wheatear
Oenanthe oenanthe

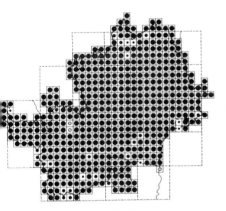

69 Blackbird
Turdus merula

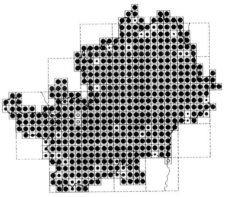

70 Song Thrush
Turdus philomelos

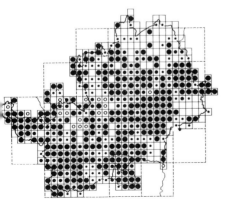

71 Mistle Thrush
Turdus viscivorus

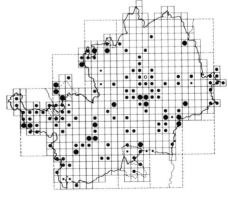

72 Grasshopper Warbler
Locustella naevia

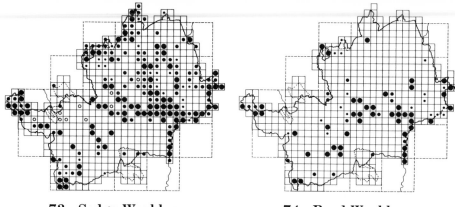

73 Sedge Warbler
Acrocephalus schoenobaenus

74 Reed Warbler
Acrocephalus scirpaceus

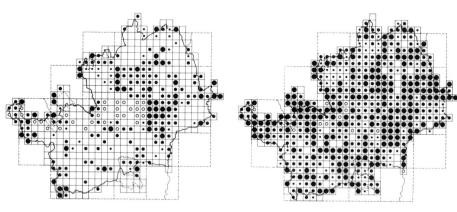

75 Lesser Whitethroat
Sylvia curruca

76 Whitethroat
Sylvia communis

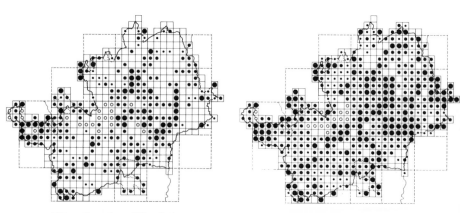

77 Garden Warbler
Sylvia borin

78 Blackcap
Sylvia atricapilla

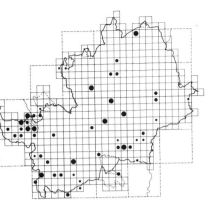

79 Wood Warbler
Phylloscopus sibilatrix

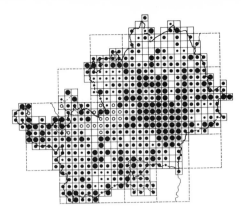

80 Chiffchaff
Phylloscopus collybita

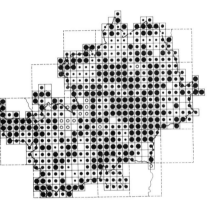

81 Willow Warbler
Phylloscopus trochilus

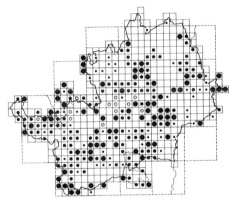

82 Goldcrest
Regulus regulus

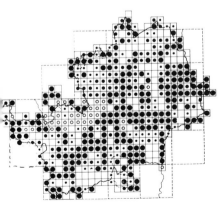

83 Spotted Flycatcher
Muscicapa striata

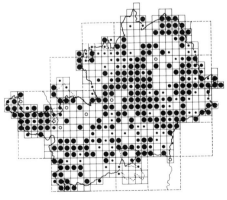

84 Long-tailed Tit
Aegithalos caudatus

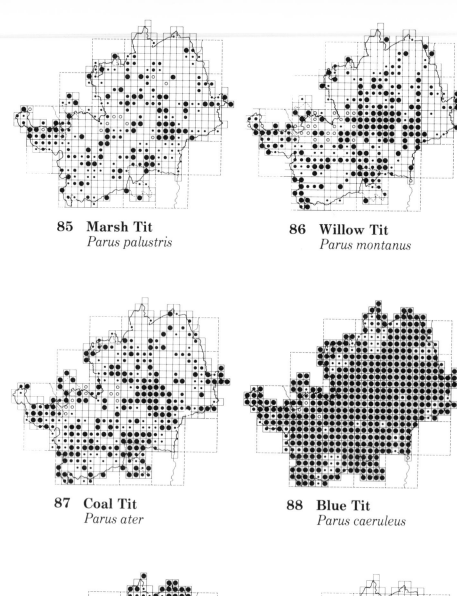

85 Marsh Tit
Parus palustris

86 Willow Tit
Parus montanus

87 Coal Tit
Parus ater

88 Blue Tit
Parus caeruleus

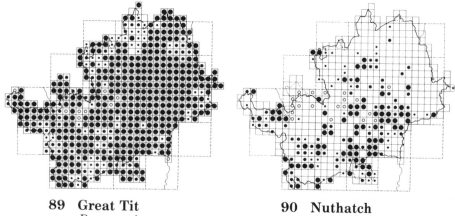

89 Great Tit
Parus major

90 Nuthatch
Sitta europaea

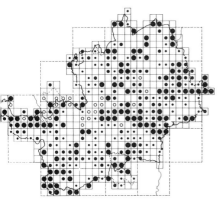

91 Treecreeper
Certhia familiaris

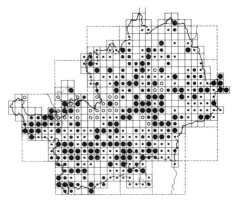

92 Jay
Garrulus glandarius

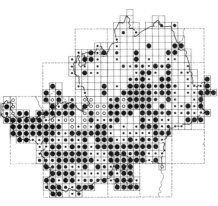

93 Magpie
Pica pica

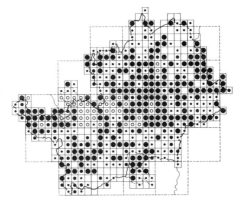

94 Jackdaw
Corvus monedula

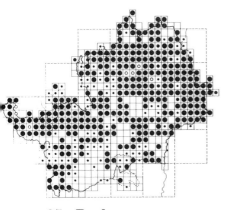

95 Rook
Corvus frugilegus

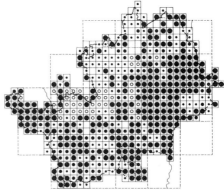

96 Carrion Crow
Corvus corone

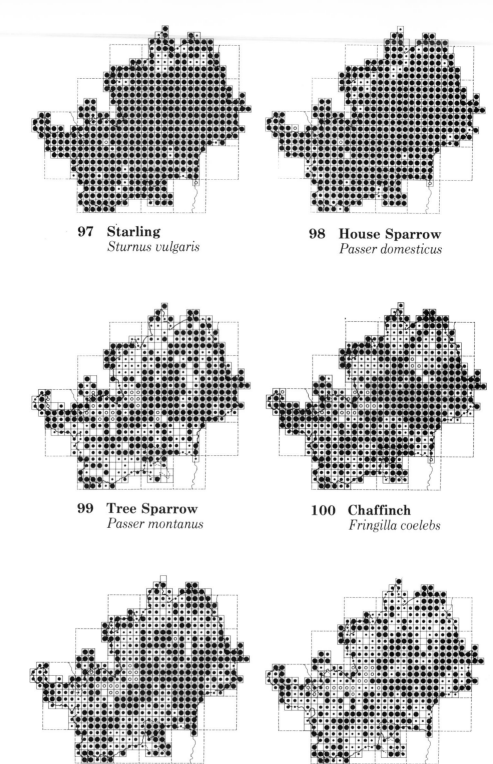

97 Starling
Sturnus vulgaris

98 House Sparrow
Passer domesticus

99 Tree Sparrow
Passer montanus

100 Chaffinch
Fringilla coelebs

101 Greenfinch
Carduelis chloris

102 Goldfinch
Carduelis carduelis

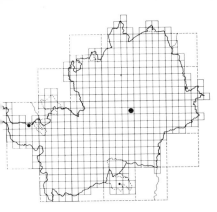

103 Siskin
Carduelis spinus

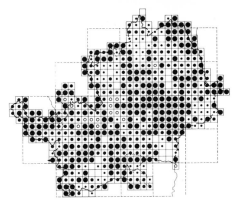

104 Linnet
Carduelis cannabina

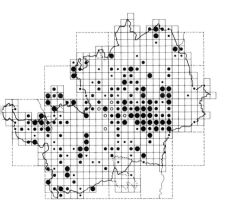

105 Lesser Redpoll
Cardeulis flammea

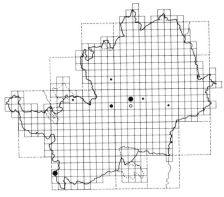

106 Common Crossbill
Loxia curvirostra

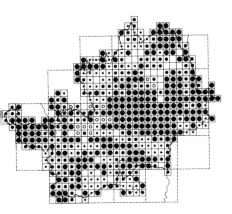

107 Bullfinch
Pyrrhula pyrrhula

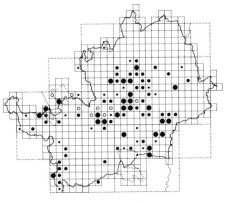

108 Hawfinch
Coccothraustes coccothraustes

309

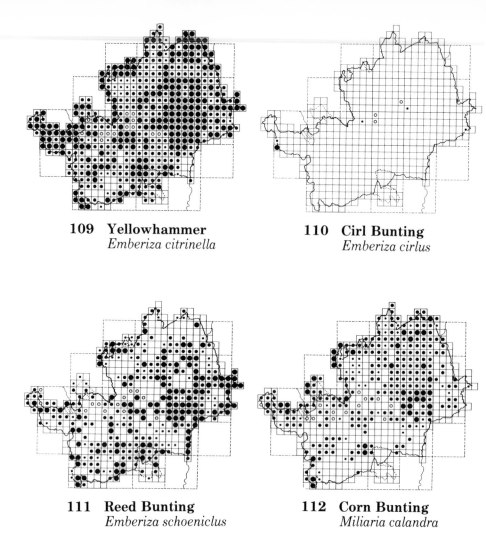

109 Yellowhammer
Emberiza citrinella

110 Cirl Bunting
Emberiza cirlus

111 Reed Bunting
Emberiza schoeniclus

112 Corn Bunting
Miliaria calandra

Appendices

Appendix   A

Winter counts of Wigeon at Tring Reservoirs 1958/59 – 1982/83

Winter	November	December	January	February	Mean
1958/59	—	4	4	12	5
1959/60	—	10	20	51	20
1960/61	—	22	6	6	8
1961/62	5	10	38	16	17
1962/63*	—	2	3	—	1
1963/64	—	26	30	6	15
1964/65	2	11	12	27	13
1965/66	7	9	15	4	9
1966/67	—	6	30	9	11
1967/68	14	34	11	8	17
1968/69	40	85	150	29	76
1969/70	5	22	16	25	17
1970/71	20	—	97	17	34
1971/72	—		88	30	31
1972/73	—	8	—	—	2
1973/74	9	16	18	5	12
1974/75	—	3	5	4	3
1975/76	5	8	—	4	4
1976/77	3	3	77	85	42
1977/78	26	14	6	9	14
1978/79	6	12	130	200	87
1979/80	1	8	41	15	16
1980/81	15	35	73	10	33
1981/82	5	60	102	30	49
1982/83	10	64	46	195	79

*Reservoirs frozen in January and February

Appendix B

Winter counts of Wigeon at Hilfield Reservoir 1958/59 – 1977/78

Winter	November	December	January	February	Mean
1958/59	50	60	68	72	63
1959/60	22	58	57	75	53
1960/61	31	40	60	60	48
1961/62	30	118	36	38	56
1962/63*	25	50	—	—	19
1963/64	8	24	22	22	19
1964/65	8	50	48	42	33
1965/66	15	20	28	24	22
1966/67	16	18	32	36	26
1967/68	18	16	25	28	21
1968/69	20	36	52	52	40
1969/70	28	18	26	28	25
1970/71	10	18	45	36	27
1971/72	10	15	18	22	16
1972/73	14	8	10	10	11
1973/74	25	24	22	—	18
1974/75	14	18	60	16	27
1975/76	20	18	27	62	32
1976/77	2	8	20	26	14
1977/78	—	6	6	12	6

*Reservoir extensively frozen in January and February

Appendix C

Winter populations of Shoveler at Tring Reservoirs 1958–82

	Jan.	Feb.	Mar.	Sept.	Oct.	Nov.	Dec.
1958	22	8	8	—	—	16	8
1959	3	—	22	8	1	18	4
1960	4	3	10	nc	42	17	6
1961	40	—	16	27	23	50	40
1962	3	10	17	—	13	15	3
1963	—*	—*	2	50	38	21	20
1964	—	—	12	18	—	16	—
1965	8	6	10	6	35	16	35
1966	4	3	3	67	111	9	21
1967	26	27	26	65	20	18	23
1968	49	53	57	80	59	47	102
1969	50	66	74	54	77	75	71
1970	94	90	70	35	94	57	26
1971	22	14	55	30	70	95	100
1972	25	38	40	70	101	60	72
1973	51	75	43	202	160	93	115
1974	90	104	73	140	130	140	108
1975	87	96	86	68	170	136	93
1976	77	190	162	114	99	40	80
1977	40	118	53	103	177	167	20
1978	68	90	150	50	150	97	60
1979	70	40	69	50	35	41	33
1980	57	59	12	58	93	83	150
1981	108	120	107	56	82	143	180
1982	52	74	84	73	113	58	71

NOTE: nc = no count available. * = reservoirs extensively frozen

Appendix   D

Breeding season surveys of the Coot in Hertfordshire in 1965 and 1973

	Number of pairs	
	1965	*1973*
Reservoirs		
Aldenham	6	3
Hilfield Park	2	4
Tring	25	3
Totals:	*33*	*10*
Colne valley		
Old Parkbury GP	?	1
Frogmore GP	0	1
Hamper Mill	6	2
Rickmansworth GPs	45	58
Totals:	*51*	*62*
Lea valley		
Brocket Park	6	7
Hatfield Park	1	14
River Lea		
(Woolmer Park–Horns Mill)	3+	7
River Lea		
(Hertford Lock–Ware Lock)	0	4
Hertford Meads	0	2
Stanstead Abbots GP	0	11
Rye Meads	20	30
Broxbourne GPs	15	19
Cheshunt GPs	29	34
River Lea		
(Aqueduct Lock–ERDE)	?	2
Totals:	*74+*	*130*
Beane valley		
Frogmore (on river)	0	1
Woodhall Park	1	4
River Beane at Hertford North	4	0
Totals:	*5*	*5*
Gade valley		
Water End	0	3
Ver valley		
Shafford Mill	0	1
Verulamium	4	14
Totals:	*4*	*15*
Mimram valley		
Digswell Lake	3	4
Tewinwater	2	2
Tewinbury	0	1
Archers Green (on river)	1	1
Panshanger	1	2
Totals:	*7*	*10*
Miscellaneous sites		
Aldenham Park	1	1
Ardeleybury	?	1

(continued overleaf)

	Number of pairs	
	1965	*1973*
Bonningtons (Hunsdon)	0	5
Bourne End	4	3
Brookmans Park golf course	?	2
Dyrham Park	?	2
Gilston Park	3	3
Gobions Lake, Brookmans Park	?	3
Great Lake, Cuffley	1	1
Greenhill Park, Barnet	1	?
Hadley Wood Lake	1	?
Kings Langley GP	4	7
Knebworth Park	3	2
New England Lake, Nuthampstead	?	1
The Node, Codicote	1	4
Nyn Park, Northaw	2	2
Radwell Mill	4	5
Smallford GPs	?	1
Stagenhoe Park	?	1
Weston Park	2	0
Wrotham Park	?	1
Totals:	27	45
GRAND TOTALS:	**201**	**280**

Appendix   E

Some examples of winter movements of Lapwing in Hertfordshire

Year	*Location*	*Narrative*
1964	Kings Langley	A marked W. to NW. passage at the end of the year, with the main movement on 27 December when 2500 passed westwards in two periods of two hours duration.
1965	Rye Meads	A steady westerly movement began on 23 November at a rate of *c.* 400 per hour in the morning, falling to *c.* 100 per hour by the evening.
1967	Tring Reservoirs	2000+ passed to the SW. on 8 January.
	Kings Langley	A westerly movement began during the last two-and-a-half hours of daylight on 7 January at a rate of *c.* 1000 per hour, continuing all day on 8 January at a rate of 250 per hour.
	Tring Reservoirs	On 9 December *c.* 4500 passed over to the SW. between 12.50 and 13.40 hours.
	Cheshunt	1000 passed to the SW. at noon on 9 December.
1968	Chiltern Hills	A large movement to the SW. in late December. On the 21st a flock of 3000+ extending for 2.4 kilometres was seen at Tring.

(continued on next page)

Year	Location	Narrative
1969	Tewinbury	On 22 February a northerly movement of *c.* 2000 per hour was noted, continuing on the 23rd at a rate of 1000 per hour.
1970	Maple Cross	1850 flew westwards on 26 December.
1976	Rye Meads	1163 passed to the SW. in eight hours on 25 January.
1978	Baldock	500 passed to the SW. in 20 minutes on 31 December.
	Rickmansworth	1000+ passed to the SW. on 31 December.
	Stanstead Abbots	A big movement on 30/31 December with 1000+ passing to the south on the 31st.
1979	Tring Reservoirs	Throughout most of the 22 February *c.* 3000 per hour passed northwards.
1980	Amwell GP	780 passed over to the WSW. on 29 November.
1981	Rye Meads	500 passed over to the NW. on 8 December.
1982	Knebworth	1400)
	Letchworth	2000)
	Norton	1000) Returned to these areas by mid-February following a cold weather exodus in January.
	Pirton	1500)
	Redbourn	2000)
	West Hyde	1100)

Appendix   F

Winter flocks of Lapwing containing 500 or more birds

Year	Location	Number	Date
1963	Rye Meads	1000	1 December
1965	West Hyde GP	1000+	5 December
	Water End (River Gade)	500+	27 December
1966	Shenley	500	18 December
	Rye Meads	1000	18 December
	Symondshyde	500+	27 December
1969	Coopers Green/Symondshyde	880	23 December
1970	Tring Reservoirs	600	5 December
1972	Marsworth Reservoir area	1600	23 January
	Maple Cross	800	23 December
1974	Therfield	800–1000	1 December
	Gorhambury	500	24 December
1975	Stanborough	600+	30 December
1976	Stanborough/Simondshyde	1500–2000	10 January
	Ashwell area	1000	5 December
1977	Wilbury Hills	500+	27 November
	Ashwell area	500	27 December
	Pirton area	1000	during winter

(continued overleaf)

Year	Location	Number	Date
1978	Ashwell area	1400	1 January
	Willian	600–700	1 January
	Graveley	1000+	30 November
	Pirton area	500+	9 December
	Ashwell area	1000+	17 December
1979	Amwell GP	1200	1 January
	Stanstead Abbots GP	1000+	1 January
	Pirton area	2000	November
	Cadwell	500	8 December
1980	Maple Cross	800	10 February
	Pirton area	600	February
	Charlton/Offley	750	27 February
	Ashwell area	500	7 December
	West Hyde	786	14 December
	Kings Langley	2000	21 December
	Langley area	800	21 December
	Ickleford	700+	23 December
	Amwell GP	900	25 December
	Marsworth village	1100	25 December
1981	Lemsford/Stanborough	800	25 January
	Cadwell	700	26 January
	Codicote (Nup End)	800	7 February
	Puttenham	3000+	15 November
	Gilston Park	600–700	17 November
	Symondsyde	870	21 November
	Long Marston	1500	22 November
	Wallington area	700	22 November
	Aldeham	500	26 November
	Amwell GP	1500	9 December
	Radlett (Park Street)	600	10 December
	Cheshunt GP	500	13 December
1982*	Baldock	1000	3 December
	Hunsdon	1000	11 December

NOTE: *See also Appendix E for mid-February flocks at six locations in 1982

Appendix G

Mid-winter counts of Gulls roosting at Hilfield Park Reservoir, 1956–83

Species	23 Jan. 1956	12 Jan. 1957	11 Jan. 1958	14 Dec. 1963	14 Dec. 1968	11 Jan. 1969	27 Jan. 1973	11 Jan. 1975	7 Jan. 1980	23 Jan. 1983
Black-headed Gull	5100	6000	9000	16 000	10 000	13 000	14 000	nc	17 400	25 000
Common Gull	150	300	1850	2000	2300	3000	800	2000	900	2750
Lesser Black-backed Gull	–	–	–	30	10	50	1000	1000	1300	106
Herring Gull	2870	3000	4000	5000	5570	7250	1800	nc	2200	98
Great Black-backed Gull	22	25	150	2500	2120	2750	105	400+	200	90

NOTES: *nc* = not counted
Hilfield Park Reservoir was filled in the spring and summer of 1955

Appendix H

Mid-winter counts of Gulls roosting at Tring Reservoirs, 1953–83

Species	Jan. 1953	Dec. 1963	Jan. 1973	Jan. 1978	Jan. 1980	Jan. 1983
Black-headed Gull	5000	4000	15 000	10 000	12 096	15 167
Common Gull	20	50	360	50	1201	124
Lesser Black-backed Gull	–	–	50	4	7	8
Herring Gull	–	10	40	16	28	2
Great Black-backed Gull	–	1	–	–	–	–

Appendix I Monthly counts of Gulls roosting at Hilfield Park Reservoir, 1982/83

Species	9 Aug. 1982	21 Sept. 1982	17 Oct. 1982	21 Nov. 1982	19 Dec. 1982	23 Jan. 1983	13 Feb. 1983	13 Mar. 1983	13 Apr. 1983
Black-headed Gull	4750	8019	19000	19000	21000	25037	12247	14088	606
Common Gull	—	—	104	1657	1850	2753	2300	130*	891
Lesser Black-backed Gull	960	2244	2200	650	142	106	23	12	11
Herring Gull	2	1	120	460	206	98	11	5	—
Great Black-backed Gull	—	1	33	87	84	90	43	3	—

NOTE: *On 11 March 1983 there were 3000 Common Gulls present most of which departed, as can be seen, in two days

Appendix J Numbers of Black-headed, Lesser Black-backed and Herring Gulls at Cole Green and Foxholes Household Waste Tips from 27 June to 27 October 1982

	June	July					August					September					October			
	27	8	9	16	23	30	6	10	13	20	27	3	9	15	22	30	6	13	23	27
Foxholes																				
Black-headed Gull	—	41	468	636	546	718	36	—	—	—	—	—	4	4	14	116	322	711	900	1050
Lesser Black-backed Gull	—	8	15	33	62	86	22	4	7	2	170	190	281	206	223	444	672	395	688	431
Herring Gull	—	—	1	1	—	1	—	—	1	—	—	—	1	—	1	43	145	25	216	205
Cole Green																				
Black-headed Gull	1	19	397	291	921	1060	293	159	122	21	3	11	4	7	26	382	677	1750	2350	2400
Lesser Black-backed Gull	14	6	20	16	189	235	82	76	83	255	467	425	582	942	1081	806	568	1135	1333	1280
Herring Gull	—	—	1	1	3	2	1	1	1	1	1	1	5	3	5	70	165	740	450	540
Totals																				
Black-headed Gull	1	60	865	927	1467	1778	329	159	122	21	3	11	8	11	40	498	999	2461	3250	3450
Lesser Black-backed Gull	14	14	35	49	251	321	104	80	90	257	637	615	863	1148	1304	1250	1240	1530	2021	1711
Herring Gull	—	—	2	2	3	3	1	1	2	1	1	1	6	3	6	113	310	765	666	745

NOTE: Common Gulls were seen on ten dates, max. 27 on 23 October, and 49 on 27 October; otherwise numbers never exceeded 13. Three Great Black-backed Gulls were seen on 13 October

Appendix K

Species which breed or have bred in Hertfordshire

Little Grebe
Great Crested Grebe
Black-necked Grebe
Bittern
Grey Heron
Mute Swan
Canada Goose (1965)*
Greylag Goose (1963)*
Mandarin (1961)*
Gadwall
Teal
Garganey (1928, 1931, 1959)
Shoveler
Mallard
Pochard
Tufted Duck
Ruddy Duck (1965)*
Red Kite (pre-1900)
Montagu's Harrier (1809 [1944?])
Sparrowhawk
Buzzard
Hobby
Kestrel
Red-legged Partridge
Grey Partridge
Quail
Pheasant
Water Rail
Spotted Crake (1967)*
Corncrake
Moorhen
Coot
Great Bustard (pre-1900)
Little Ringed Plover
Ringed Plover
Stone Curlew
Lapwing
Snipe
Woodcock
Redshank
Common Sandpiper
Black-headed Gull (1950)*
Common Tern (1963)*

Feral Rock Dove*
Stock Dove
Wood Pigeon
Collared Dove (1958)*
Turtle Dove
Cuckoo
Barn Owl
Little Owl
Tawny Owl
Long-eared Owl
Nightjar
Swift
Kingfisher
Wryneck
Green Woodpecker
Great Spotted Woodpecker
Lesser Spotted Woodpecker
Woodlark
Skylark
Sand Martin
Swallow
House Martin
Tree Pipit
Meadow Pipit
Yellow Wagtail
Grey Wagtail
Pied Wagtail
Dipper (pre-1914)
Wren
Dunnock
Robin
Nightingale
Black Redstart (1963)*
Redstart
Whinchat
Stonechat
Wheatear
Ring Ouzel (1864)
Blackbird
Song Thrush
Mistle Thrush
Cetti's Warbler (1978)*
Grasshopper Warbler
Sedge Warbler

Reed Warbler
Lesser Whitethroat
Whitethroat
Garden Warbler
Blackcap
Wood Warbler
Chiffchaff
Willow Warbler
Goldcrest
Spotted Flycatcher
Bearded Tit (1966)*
Long-tailed Tit
Marsh Tit
Willow Tit
Coal Tit
Blue Tit
Great Tit
Nuthatch
Tree Creeper
Golden Oriole (1881)
Red-backed Shrike
Jay
Magpie
Jackdaw
Rook
Carrion Crow
Raven (pre-1900)
Starling
House Sparrow
Tree Sparrow
Chaffinch
Greenfinch
Goldfinch
Siskin (1982)*
Linnet
Redpoll
Common Crossbill
Bullfinch
Hawfinch
Yellowhammer
Cirl Bunting
Reed Bunting
Corn Bunting

Total: 130 species

*Indicates a species added after the publication of Sage (1959)

Appendix L

Gazetteer of Principal Sites

This appendix comprises a list of the principal sites referred to in the text. In general the name of each site is followed by the name of the nearest town or village, and the Ordnance Survey National Grid Reference of the site.

In the case of established nature reserves the initials of the organisation owning or managing the site is given in brackets immediately after the site name.

Some sites are known by two names which have variously appeared in ornithological reports and other publications. The names used by the original observers and authors have been preserved in the text and the proper or alternative names indicated in this appendix where appropriate.

Abbreviations used are:

DLS	Digswell Lake Society
FC	Forestry Commission
GC	Golf Course
GP	Gravel Pit
HCC	Hertfordshire County Council
HMTNC	Hertfordshire & Middlesex Trust for Nature Conservation Ltd
HWT	Household Waste Tip — used to indicate sites where putrescible, i.e. bird edible, waste is tipped.
LNR	Local Nature Reserve
NNR	National Nature Reserve
NR	Nature Reserve
NT	National Trust
RSPB	Royal Society for the Protection of Birds
SF	Sewage Farm
WNHS	Welwyn Natural History Society
WT	Woodland Trust

ALDBURY COMMON (NT), Aldbury, Berkhamsted. SP972125

ALDENHAM RESERVOIR (HCC), Aldenham. Part of Aldenham Country Park. TQ170955

ALLEN'S GREEN, High Wych. TL455168

ALMSHOEBURY, Hitchin. TL206254

AMWELL QUARRY, Amwell. Sometimes referred to as Amwell GP. TL378130

ARBURY BANKS, Ashwell. TL260387

ARCHERS GREEN, Tewin. TL274136

ARDELEYBURY, Walkern. TL300270

ASHRIDGE (NT), Ringshall, Berkhamsted. Includes Aldbury Common, part of Berkhamsted Common, Pitstone Common, and Ashridge Park. SP985125

BALLS WOOD (HMTNC), Hertford Heath. TL344105

BATCH WOOD, St. Albans. TL140093

BATCHWORTH LAKE, Rickmansworth. TQ057940

BATLERS GREEN, Radlett. TQ155987

BAYFORDBURY, Hertford. TL315105

BENTLEY HEATH, Potters Bar TQ248996

BERKHAMSTED COMMON (NT), Berkhamsted. SP990115

BIRCHALL WOOD, Cole Green. TL272125

BLACKFAN WOOD, Bayford. TL313075

BLOODHOUNDS WOOD, Bishops Stortford. TL467225

BONNINGTONS LAKE, Hunsdon. TL410132

BOWER HEATH, Harpenden. TL144167

BOWYER'S WATER, Cheshunt. Part of Cheshunt GPs. Sometimes known as BOWYER'S LAKE. TL367015

BOX WOOD, Hoddesdon. TL355095

BOX WOOD, Walkern. TL270263

BOXMOOR COMMON, Hemel Hempstead. TL045061

BRAMFIELD FOREST (FC), Bramfield. A collective name for woodlands around Bramfield including Barber's Close, Basil's Park, Beals Wood, Bramfield Park Wood, Bramfield Woods, TL285167

Brickground Wood,
Bright's Hill, Hazeldell
Wood, Lower Blackbuck
Wood, Nicholson's Wood,
Open Bailey, Priest Wood,
Row Wood, Seven Acre
Wood, Symond's Wood,
Upper Blackbuck Wood,
and Wrens Wood.

BRAMFIELD PARK WOOD,   TL283155
Bramfield.

BRAUGHING MEADS,   TL388245
Braughing.

BRICKET WOOD COMMON,   TL130010
Bricket Wood.

BROAD RIDING WOOD,   TL340075
Hoddesdon. Part of
Broxbourne Woods.

BROCKET PARK, Lemsford.   TL213128
Includes Brocket Park
Lake and Crackendell
Wood.

BROOKFIELD LANE   TL353036
RESERVOIR, Cheshunt.

BROXBOURNE GPs,   TL378075
Hoddesdon.

BROXBOURNE SF,   TL371060
Broxbourne. Now defunct.

BROXBOURNE WOODS,   TL340080
Hoddesdon. A collective
term for the continuous
belt of woodland between
Brickendon and
Hoddesdon which
includes Bourne Wood,
Bramble's Wood, Broad
Riding Wood, Broxbourne
Wood, Claypits Wood,
Cowheath Wood,
Danemead Wood,
Hedgerows Wood,
Highfield Wood and
Hoddesdonpark Wood.
The majority are
managed for forestry
by the Salisbury Estates.

BULBOURNE, Tring.   SP933137

BURLEIGH MEADOWS,   TL222221
Knebworth.

BURLOES HALL, Royston.   TL405370

BURY LAKE, Rickmansworth.   TQ053938

BUSHEY HEATH, Watford.   TQ152945

CADWELL, Ickleford.   TL188325

CASSIOBURY PARK, Watford.   TQ090970

CHESHUNT GPs, Cheshunt.   TL370030
Collective name for
Seventy Acres, North Met

and Police GPs, and
Bowyers Water.

CHURCHEND COMMON,   TL280272
Stevenage.

CODICOTE BOTTOM, Codicote.   TL207179

COLE GREEN HWT,   TL272110
Cole Green.

COLNE VALLEY GPs,   TQ050935
Rickmansworth. A
collective name for the
flooded gravel pits in the
Colne valley between
Oxhey and West Hyde,
(see Appendix M).

COLNEY HEATH,   TL202058
Colney Heath.

COMMONWOOD COMMON,   TL045000
Chipperfield.

CRACKENDELL WOOD,   TL215137
Ayot St. Peter.

CROMER HYDE, Lemsford.   TL203123

CROXLEY COMMON MOOR,   TQ080947
Sometimes known as
Croxley Moor.

CROXLEY HALL GP,   TQ070943
Rickmansworth.

DERRY'S WOOD, Wormley.   TL315055
Part of Wormley Wood.

DIGSWELL LAKE (DLS),   TL243148
Digswell.

DOWDELLS WOOD,   TL207153
Ayot St. Peter.

DROP LANE GP, Colney   TL149025
Street.

DUNKIRKS FARM, Hertford.   TL238115

DYRHAM PARK, Potters Bar.   TL225987

EASNEYE, Ware.   TL380135

EASTWICK MEADS, Harlow.   TL425113

FAIRLANDS VALLEY,   TL250235
Stevenage.

FOXHOLES HWT, Hertford.   TL340123

FRITHSDEN BEECHES (NT),   SP998100
Berkhamsted. Part of
Berkhamsted Common.

FROGMORE GP, Radlett.   TL150033

FROGMORE GP, Watton-at-   TL290205
Stone.

GILSTON PARK, Harlow.   TL455127

GOBIONS LAKE, Brookmans   TL252037
Park.

GOLDINGS WOOD, Hertford   TL360115
Heath.

GOLDINGS, Waterford.   TL312140

GORHAMBURY, St. Albans.   TL115078

GOOSE GREEN, Hoddesdon.   TL353095

GOSMOREBURY, Hitchin. TL188270
GUSTARDWOOD, TL175160
 Wheathampstead.

HALL WOOD, Kimpton. TL174168
HAMEL'S PARK, Puckeridge. TL375245
HAMPER MILL GP, TQ093944
 Watford. Also known as
 Hamper Mill Lake.
HARMERGREEN WOOD, TL254170
 Welwyn.
HARPENDEN COMMON, TL136130
 Harpenden.
HARTSBOURNE GC, Bushey TQ140935
 Heath.
HASTOE, Tring. SP920098
HATFIELD PARK, Hatfield. TL245095
HELICON GP, West Hyde. TQ038909
HERTFORD HEATH LNR TL350107
 (HMTNC), Hertford and
 Heath. The site is in two TL354111
 parts the first of which is
 known as The Roundings
 and the other
 Goldingtons.
HERTFORD MEADS, Hertford. TL340135
 Properly known as KING'S
 MEADS.
HEXTON PARK, Hexton. TL110305
 Properly known as HEXTON
 MANOR.
HIGH LEIGH, Hoddesdon. TL364087
HIGHFIELD WOOD, TL344085
 Hoddesdon.
HIGHLEY HILL, Ashwell. TL285380
HILFIELD PARK RESERVOIR TQ156960
 LNR, Aldenham.
HITCH WOOD, St. Paul's TL195235
 Walden
HOG WOOD, Kimpton. TL192187
HOLLINGSON MEADS, TL457123
 Pye Corner.
HOLLYCROSS LAKE, Great TL377132
 Amwell. Part of Amwell
 Quarry.
HOLWELL GP, Hitchin. TL167316
HOLWELL HYDE, Welwyn TL265115
 Garden City.
HOLYFIELD MARSH, Cheshunt. TL373039
 Mostly in Essex.
HOME WOOD, Cuffley. TL296038
HOO WOOD, Little Gaddesden. SP993145
HOOK'S MARSH, Cheshunt. TL376024
 Entirely in Essex.
HOW WOOD, Bricket Wood TL138035
HOW WOOD, Graveley. TL246293
HUDNALL COMMON, Little TL010130
 Gaddesden.

ICKLEFORD COMMON, TL186333
 Ickleford, Hitchin.

KIMPTON HOO, Kimpton. TL192198
KINGS LANGLEY GP, Kings TL073036
 Langley. Also known as
 KINGS LANGLEY LAKE.
KING'S MEADS, Hertford. TL340135
 Sometimes referred to as
 HERTFORD MEADS.
KINGS WEIR GP, Wormley. TL374048
 Partly in Essex.
KNEBWORTH PARK, TL230210
 Knebworth.

LEA VALLEY GPs,
 A collective name for the
 flooded gravel pits in the
 Lea valley south from
 Great Amwell to the
 county boundary at
 Waltham Cross (see
 Appendix N).
LEATHERFIELD COMMON, TL300220
 Bennington.
LEMSFORD SPRINGS NR TL222120
 (HMTNC), Lemsford.
LIGHT'S WOOD, Brickendon. TL331094
LITTLE TRING RESERVOIR SP918133
 (NNR), Tring. Now known
 as TRINGFORD RESERVOIR
 and part of Tring Reservoirs
 NNR.
LODGE HOLLOW, Hoddesdon. TL358082

MAPLE LODGE NR, Maple TQ036125
 Cross, Rickmansworth.
 Formerly Maple Cross SF.
MARDEN HILL, Tewin. TL280140
MARDLEY HEATH, Welwyn. TL245182
MARDLEYBURY POND, TL260185
 Woolmer Green,
 Knebworth.
MARSHCROFT FARM, Tring. SP942132
 Formerly known as
 Parkhill Farm.
MARSWORTH RESERVOIR NNR, SP922137
 Tring. Part of Tring
 Reservoirs NNR.
MILL GREEN, Hatfield. TL245098
MIMMS WOODS, North TL215035
 Mymms. A collective
 name for the woodlands in
 and around North Mymms
 Park including Cangsley
 Grove, Cobs Ash,
 Frederick's Wood,
 Hawkshead Wood,

Redwell Wood and
Walsingham Wood.

MONKS GREEN, Brickendon.   TL335085

MOOR MILL, Colney Street,   TL151024
Radlett.

MUNDEN PARK, Watford.   TL135002

NEW ENGLAND LAKE,   TL420358
Nuthampstead.

NEW MILL END, Tring.   SP926127

NEWTON WOOD, Knebworth.   TL230220

NOMANSLAND COMMON,   TL170125
Sandridge/Wheathampstead

NORTH MYMMS PARK,   TL215045
Hatfield.

NORTHAW GREAT WOOD,   TL285045
Cuffley.

NORTHCHURCH COMMON (NT),   SP975105
Berkhamsted.

NORTON COMMON,   TL220335
Letchworth.

NYN PARK, Northaw.   TL275028

OAKLANDS, Welwyn.   TL290130

OLD PARKBURY GP, Radlett.   TL163023

OUGHTONHEAD (HMTNC),   TL165305
Hitchin. Includes
Oughtonhead Common,
and Oughtonhead NR
(HMTNC).

PANSHANGER PARK,   TL290130
Hertingfordbury. Should
be distinguished from
Panshanger Airfield and
Panshanger District of
Welwyn Garden City.

PATMORE HEATH, Albury.   TL446258

PEGSDON HILLS, Shillington.   TL130305
These hills lie along the
county boundary but are
almost wholly in
Bedfordshire. Birds seen
there, particularly
raptors, are sometimes
observed passing into
Hertfordshire.

PHILIPSHILL WOOD,   TQ010945
Chorleywood. On the
county boundary but
entirely in
Buckinghamshire.

PIGHTLE DELL, Kimpton.   TL188189

PITSTONE HILL, Pitstone.   SP952142
Not in Hertfordshire.

POLE HILL MARSH, Pye   TL454126
Corner, High Wych.

POPLARS GREEN, Tewin.   TL280133

PRAE WOOD, St. Albans.   TL120068
Part of Gorhambury.

PRIORY PARK, Hitchin.   TL184285

PURWELL MEADOW, Hitchin.   TL201296

PURWELL NINESPRINGS,   TL206292
(HMTNC), Hitchin.

PUTTOCKHILL WOOD, Welwyn.   TL243168

PYNESFIELD GP, West Hyde,   TQ035910
Rickmansworth.

QUICKSWOOD, Clothall.   TL280330

RABLEY HEATH, Welwyn.   TL237190

RADWELL MILL, Radwell.   TL230359

RICKMANSWORTH GPs,
Rickmansworth. A
collective name for the
flooded gravel pits in the
Colne valley between
Batchworth and Maple Cross.

ROTHAMSTED PARK,   TL125130
Harpenden.

ROUGHDOWN COMMON, Felden,   TL045057
Hemel Hempstead.

ROXFORD, Hertford.   TL303105
Includes Roxford Copse.

ROYAL OAK GP, Maple   TQ033918
Cross, Rickmansworth.

RYE HOUSE MARSH (RSPB),   TL386100
Hoddesdon.

RYE MEADS, Hoddesdon.   TL390100
Includes Rye Meads
Sewage Purification Works.

SACOMBE PARK, Sacombe,   TL335188
Watton-at-Stone.

ST. JOHN'S WOOD, Walkern.   TL310258

SAWBRIDGEWORTH MARSH   TL492160
(HMTNC).
Sawbridgeworth.

SCALES PARK (FC),   TL415335
Nuthampstead.

SCRATCH WOOD, Flamstead.   TL067135
Not to be confused with
Scratch Wood, North
London.

SEVENTY ACRES GP,   TL375030
Cheshunt. Sometimes
known as WAVERLY GP.

SHAFFORD MILL, St. Albans.   TL126093

SHEETHANGER COMMON,   TL035050
Hemel Hempstead.

SHERRARDS PARK WOOD,   TL230138
Welwyn Garden City.

SMALLFORD GP, Hatfield.   TL198071

SPRINGWELL GP,   TQ041930
Rickmansworth. Not in
Hertfordshire.

STAGENHOE PARK, St. Paul's Walden. TL185225

STAGS END, Great Gaddesden. TL069120

STANBOROUGH LAKES, Welwyn Garden City. TL230108

STANBOROUGH REEDMARSH (HMTNC), Welwyn Garden City. TL231105

STANDON LORDSHIP, Standon. TL392215

STANSTEAD ABBOTS, GP, Stanstead Abbotts. TL388111

STARTOP'S END RESERVOIR, Tring. Part of Tring Reservoirs NNR. SP919138

STOCKERS LAKE NR (HMTNC), Rickmansworth. TQ046935

SYMONDSHYDE GREAT WOOD, Sandridge, St. Albans. TL195110

TEDNAMBURY MARSH, Sawbridgeworth. TL495168

TELEGRAPH HILL, Lilley. TL120285

TEWIN HILL, Tewin. TL273156

TEWINBURY (WNHS), Tewin. TL264140

TEWINWATER, Tewin. TL259142

THE NODE, Codicote. TL214199

THE ROUNDINGS (HMTNC), Hertford Heath. Part of Hertford Heath LNR. TL350107

THEOBALDS PARK, Cheshunt. TL345005

THERFIELD HEATH LNR Therfield, Royston. TL400340

THUNDERFIELD GROVE, Cheshunt. TL348053

TILEHOUSE GP, Maple Cross. TQ039895

TINGLEY WOOD, Pirton. TL137304

TOLPITS LAKE, Rickmansworth. TQ085943

TRING PARK, Tring. SP930105

TRING RESERVOIRS NNR, Tring. Comprises Marsworth, Startop's End, Tringford (formerly Little Tring), and Wilstone Reservoirs. SP920135

TRINGFORD RESERVOIR, Tring. Part of Tring Reservoirs NNR and formerly known as Little Tring Reservoir. SP918132

TROY MILL GP, Maple Cross. TQ038905

TURNFORD GP, Cheshunt. Formerly known as North Met GP TL370043

WAIN WOOD, Preston. TL180255

WALLINGTONBURY, Wallington. TL295334

WALSWORTH COMMON, Hitchin. TL195303

WARREN WOOD, Ayot St. Peter. TL208148

WATER END, Great Gaddesden. TL008105

WATEREND, Wheathamstead. TL203138

WATER HALL, Little Berkhamsted. TL297098

WATERINGPLACE GREEN, Ardeley. TL332267

WATERY GROVE, Knebworth. TL231229

WAVERLEY GP, Cheshunt. Properly known as SEVENTY ACRES GP. TL375030

WELL WOOD, Northaw. Part of Nyn Park. TL275035

WEST HYDE GP, West Hyde, Rickmansworth. TQ038916

WEST MILL, Hitchin. Part of Oughtonhead. TL171308

WESTMILL FARM, Ware. TL340160

WESTON HILLS, Baldock. TL253323

WESTON PARK, Weston. TL265295

WHIPPENDELL WOODS, Watford. TQ075977

WILSTONE RESERVOIR, Tring. Part of Tring Reservoirs NNR. SP905130

WOODHALL PARK, Watton-at-Stone. TL315185

WORMLEY WOOD (WT), Brickendon/Wormley West End. TL320060

WROTHAM PARK, Potters Bar. TQ250990

Appendix M

Map showing names and location of Gravel Pits in the Colne valley

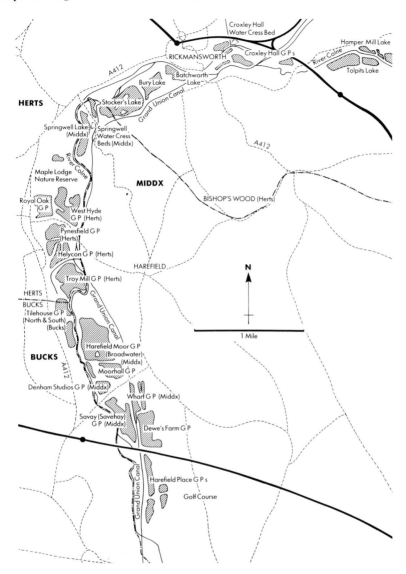

Appendix   N

Map showing names and location of Gravel Pits in the Lea valley

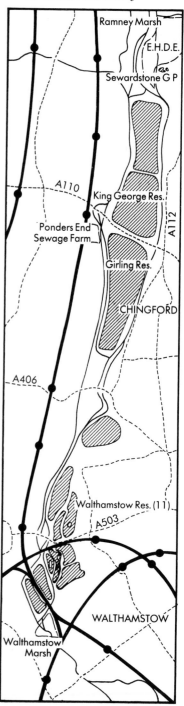

Appendix O

Selected Records for 1983 and 1984

1983

Great Crested Grebe — Hilfield Park Reservoir, 150 on 31 October and 186 on 19 November.

Manx Shearwater — One at Tilehouse GP, Rickmansworth, on 7 June.

Leach's Petrel — One at Hillfield Park Reservoir on 3 September.

Mute Swan — A breeding-season survey located a total of 64 pairs and 121+ non-breeding birds. Localities covered in both the 1978 and 1983 surveys showed a decrease from 64 to 51 territorial pairs respectively, a decline of 20.31 per cent, (Smith 1985).

Canada Goose — A breeding-season survey located 74 pairs with a total of 227 young, and 295 non-breeding birds. The major breeding concentrations were in the Colne and Lea valleys (Smith 1985). There were c. 300 at Rye Meads on 10 September, and 435 at West Hyde in the Colne valley on 11 December.

Shelduck — Bred in the county for the first time, a pair with young being seen at Rye Meads on 12 June.

Mandarin — A pair at St. Albans from 12–18 December.

Gadwall — One pair bred at Stockers Lake and another pair at Maple Cross.

Garganey — A pair may have bred at London Colney.

Ferruginous Duck — A drake at Cheshunt GPs from 17 September to 30 October.

Ruddy Duck — One pair bred at Tring Reservoirs.

Red Kite — One at Croxley Hall on 8 January, and one at Plashes Wood, Standon, on 13 November.

Avocet — A flock of 22 at Amwell GP on 25 April is the largest so far recorded in the county.

Ringed Plover — One pair bred at Cole Green.

Black-tailed Godwit — A flock of seven at Tring Reservoirs on 1 September.

Bar-tailed Godwit — A flock of 27 at Tring Reservoirs on 1 May.

Great Skua — One at Tring Reservoirs on 3 September is the third record for the county.

Mediterranean Gull — A first winter bird at Rye Meads on 27 November is the second record for the county.

Common Tern — A total of 42 pairs produced 77 young at Rye Meads.

Little Auk — Single birds found at Hitchin on 11 February; Fairlands Valley, Stevenage, on 13 February; and South Mimms in the second week of February. These are the first records since 1967.

Puffin — One found alive at Shenley on 12 February is the tenth record for the county since 1900.

Ring-necked Parakeet — Single birds at Standalone Farm, Letchworth, in early October, and at Rye Meads on 2 and 30 October.

Nightjar — The only records were from Broxbourne Woods where there was a male on 29 May and two on 18 June.

Bluethroat — A male of the white-spotted form was ringed at Rye Meads on 4 April. This is the sixth Bluethroat to be recorded in the county and the second of the white-spotted form.

Rock Thrush — A male at Chesfield Church, Graveley, on 8 May is only the second record for the county (*British Birds* 77:550).

Jay — In the autumn many birds arrived and passed through the county during the invasion which occurred throughout southern Britain. Many birds were no doubt of continental origin, and two reports of birds definitely showing characteristics of the continental race *G. g. glandarius* were received from Foxley Grove, Digswell, on 16 October and Long Marston on 13, 15 and 16 November. These are the first records of this form in the county (*Trans. Herts. Nat. Hist. Soc.* 29:162-163).

1984

Manx Shearwater — One picked up alive at Hemel Hempstead on 5 September was later released on the coast. The 14th recorded occurrence in Hertfordshire.

Leach's Petrel — One at Cheshunt GP's on 25 November. The 16th recorded occurrence in Hertfordshire.

Brent Goose — One with Canada Geese at Tolpits Lake, near Watford, on 3 November was later seen flying west along the Colne valley. The 11th recorded occurrence in Hertfordshire.

Gadwall — A pair bred and reared nine young at Tring SF. Two summered at Stockers Lake and up to ten were present at Maple Cross in June; both sites where breeding occurred in 1983.

Blue-winged Teal — A female at Stockers Lake from 20 to 27 April (*British Birds* 78:537) was the third to be recorded in Hertfordshire.

Black-winged Stilt — Two at Chandler's Cross, near Watford, on 7 May are presumed to be the same birds that were present at Perry Oaks sewage works, Surrey, on 8 and 9 May (*British Birds* 78:542). The first recorded occurrence in Hertfordshire.

Avocet — Singles at Rye Meads and Startops End Reservoir, Tring, on 24 March and 12 at Wilstone Reservoir, Tring, on 2 December.

Ringed Plover — A pair bred at Cole Green.

Dotterel — Two near Barley on 11 May.

Marsh Sandpiper — One at Broxbourne on 28 April had been seen at Fishers Green (Essex) on the same day (*British Birds* 78:550). The second recorded occurrence in Hertfordshire, the last being in 1887.

Solitary Sandpiper — A juvenile at Tring Reservoirs from 5 to at least 12 October (*British Birds* 78:551). The second recorded occurrence in Hertfordshire, the last being 1967.

Glaucous Gull — An adult at Stockers Lake on 20 February and one at Broxbourne GP on 15 March. The 16th and 17th recorded occurrences in Hertfordshire.

Little Auk — One picked up alive at Hunsdon on 6th November died the next day. The 7th recorded occurrence in Hertfordshire.

Woodlark — One at Troy Mill on 8 and 9 March. The first to be recorded in the county since 1977.

House Martin — A juvenile ringed at Rye Meads on 10 September 1983 was found at Ikwo, Nigeria, on 26 February 1984. The first recovery of a British House Martin south of the Sahara.

Golden Oriole — A male at Hilfield Park Reservoir on 2 May.

Red-backed Shrike — A female at Cheshunt GP on 15 and 16 September. Only the sixth to be recorded in the county since 1974.

Bibliography

ABERDEIN, A. F. (1982) Stanstead Abbots Gravel Pit – a review of its history, future and birdlife. *Birds in the Lee Valley* 1981: 35–43.

BARNES, J. A. G. (1961) The winter status of the Lesser Black-backed Gull, 1959-1960. *Bird Study* Vol. 8: 127–147.

BARRATT, M. J. (1981) Notes on the roost of Pied Wagtails in the Boiler House of Rye House Power Station. *Birds in the Lee Valley* 1980: 37–40.

BARRETT, W. E. (1982) Barn Owls in Hertfordshire 1978. *Trans. Herts. Nat. Hist. Soc.* 28. Pt.6: 57–58.

BATTEN, L. A. (1973) The colonisation of England by the Firecrest. *British Birds* 66: 159–166.

BIBBY, C. (1973) The Red-backed Shrike: a vanishing British species. *Bird Study.* Vol. 20: 103–110.

BISHOPS STORTFORD NATURAL HISTORY SOCIETY. Reports on Birds, 1974–1976 and 1977–1980.

BOSWALL, J. (1966) Pied Wagtails roosting inside greenhouses. *British Birds* 59: 100–106.

BOWLEY, A. (1979) Identification of important woodland sites in Hertfordshire. Nature Conservancy Council Internal Report.

BRACKENRIDGE, R. and HOGG, A. (1982) Water Pipits and Scandinavian Rock Pipits in Ayrshire, *Ayrshire Bird Report* 1981: 4–7.

BRITISH NATURALISTS ASSOCIATION (1958–1982). Newsletters and Reports of the Hertfordshire and North Middlesex Branch.

CAMPBELL, B. (1960) The Mute Swan census in England and Wales 1955–1956. *Bird Study* Vol. 7: 208–223.

CHANDLER, R. J. (1980) Pied Wagtail roosts and numbers in the London Area in winter. *London Bird Report* 44: 85–90.

CHANDLER, R. J. (1981) Influxes into Britain and Ireland of Red-necked Grebes and other waterbirds during winter 1978/79. *British Birds* 74: 55–81.

CHANDLER, R. J. and OSBORNE, K. C. (1977) Scarce Migrants in the London Area, 1955–74. *London Bird Report* 41: 73–99.

CHESTERMAN, D. K. (1978) Bird life of the Stocker's Lake gravel pits 1970–77. *London Bird Report* 42: 71–84.

CORNWALLIS, R. K. and TOWNSEND, A. D. (1968) Waxwings in Britain and Europe during 1965/66. *British Birds* 61: 97–118.

CRAMP, S. (1963) The Census of Mute Swans, 1961. *London Bird Report* 26: 100–103.

CRUDASS, J. and DEVLIN, T. R. E. (1965) Variability in Reed Warblers. *Rye Meads Ringing Group Third Report:* 13–21.

CRUDASS, J. and NAU, B. S. (1965) Immigrant Blackbirds at Rye Meads, *Rye Meads Ringing Group Third Report:* 41–44.

DAVENPORT, D. L. (1982) Influxes into Britain of Hen Harriers, Long-eared Owls and Short-eared Owls in winter 1978/79. *British Birds* 75: 309–316.

DAVIS, F. (1874) *A History of Luton.*

DAVIS, P. G. (1982) Nightingales in Britain in 1980. *Bird Study.* Vol. 29: 73–79.

DEVLIN, T. R E., JENKINS, A. R. and LLOYD-EVANS, L. (1962) Sociable Plover in Hertfordshire. *British Birds* 55: 236.

DEVLIN, T. R. E. and LLOYD-EVANS, L. (1967) Mammals at Rye Meads and Analysis of Barn Owl Pellets. *Rye Meads Ringing Group Fourth Report:* 22–26.

ELTRINGHAM, S. K. (1963) The British population of the Mute Swan in 1961. *Bird Study* Vol 10: 10–28.

FITTER, R. S. R. (1971) Black Redstarts breeding in Britain in 1964–68. *British Birds* 64: 117–124.

FORDHAM, W. H. (1965) Notes on the Weather at Harpenden and Odsey for the years 1950 to 1964. *Trans. Herts. Nat. Hist. Soc.* 26: 88–93.

FOSTER, A. H. (1914) *The Birds of North Herts.*

FOSTER, A. H. (1917) A list of the Birds which have occurred in North Herts., with Notes on each Species. *Trans. Herts. Nat. Hist. Soc.* 16: 189–220.

GAMMONS, I. *Gilston Park Bird Reports,* 1978 and 1979.

GASKELL, R. W. (1950) Red-rumped Swallow in Hertfordshire *British Birds* 43: 121.

GIBBS, A. (1963) The Bird Population of Rubbish Dumps. *London Bird Report* 26: 104–110

GIBBS, A. and WALLACE, D. I. M. (1961) Four Million Birds? *London Bird Report* 25: 61–68.

GLADWIN, T. W. (1962) The Birds of the King's Meads, Hertford. *Trans. Herts. Nat. Hist. Soc.* 27: 355–360.

GLADWIN, T. W. (1963a) Increases in the Weights of *Acrocephali. Bird Migration* 2: 319–324.

GLADWIN, T. W. (1963b) A Short Account of Rye Meads, Herts, and its Ornithology. *London Bird Report* 26: 88–99.

GLADWIN, T. W. (1969) Post-nuptial wing moult in the Garden Warbler. *Bird Study* Vol. 16: 131–132.

GLADWIN, T. W. (1970) Report on Birds Observed in Hertfordshire in 1969. *Trans. Herts. Nat. Hist. Soc.* 27: 65–66.

GLADWIN, T. W. (1976) Bearded Tits in Hertfordshire since 1959. *Trans. Herts. Nat. Hist. Soc.* 27: 355–360.

GLADWIN, T. W. (1983) Major changes in Central Hertfordshire and its Breeding Bird Populations. *Trans. Herts. Nat. Hist. Soc.* 29: 57–67.

GLADWIN, T. W. (1985) Skylarks and Yellowhammers roosting under snow. *British Birds* 78: 109–110.

GLADWIN, T.W. and NAU, B. S. (1964) A study of Swift weights. *British Birds* 57: 344–356.

GLADWIN, T. W. and SAGE, B. L. (1975) *A Revised Check List of Birds Observed in Hertfordshire.* Herts. Nat. Hist. Soc., Watford.

GRIBBLE, F. C. (1983) Nightingales in Britain & Ireland in 1981. *Bird Study* Vol. 30: 165–176.

GUBBINS, N. L. R. (1982) Wildlife at Maple Cross. Dissertation for Degree of M.Sc. in Conservation. University College, London.

HAILEYBURY NATURAL SCIENCE SOCIETY (1926) *The Fauna and Flora of Haileybury.*

HAILEYBURY and IMPERIAL SERVICE COLLEGE NAT. HIST. SOC. (1961) *Ornithological Report,* 1952–60.

HARRIS, A. and REYNOLDS, A. (1977) Breeding Studies 1974/76. *Rye Meads Ringing Group Eighth Report*: 19–21.

HARTERT, E. and JOURDAIN, F. C. R. (1920) The Birds of Buckinghamshire and the Tring Reservoirs. *Novitates Zoologicae* 28: 171–259.

HAYWARD, H. H. S. (1947) "Birds" in a List of the Vertebrates of Hertfordshire. *Trans. Nat. Hist. Soc.* 22: 173–226.

HAYWARD, H. H. S. (1968) The Coot (*Fulica atra*) at Tring Reservoirs, Hertfordshire. *Trans. Herts. Nat. Hist. Soc.* 26: 256–259.

HICKLING, R. A. O. (1967) The inland wintering of gulls in England, 1963. *Bird Study* Vol. 14: 104–113.

HICKLING, R. A. O. (1977) Inland wintering of gulls in England & Wales, 1973. *Bird Study* Vol.24: 79–88.

HINE, R. L. Ed. (1934) *The Natural History of the Hitchin Region.*

HINTON, R. F. Ed. (1980) *A Survey of Ancient, Semi-Natural Woodland in Hertfordshire, 1978.* The Hertfordshire and Middlesex Trust for Nature Conservation, St. Albans.

HODSON, N. L. (1965) The road deaths enquiry, 1960–61. *Bird Study* Vol.12: 90–99.

HOLDSWORTH, M. (1974a) Wrens at Maple Cross. *Maple Cross Ringing Group Special Bulletin,* Rickmansworth.

HOLDSWORTH, M. (1974b) Long-tailed Tits at Maple Cross. *Maple Cross Ringing Group Special Bulletin,* Rickmansworth.

HOLDSWORTH, M. *et al.* (1978) *The Birds of Tring Reservoirs.* Herts. Nat. Hist. Soc., Berkhamsted.

HOLLOM, P. A. D. (1959) The Great Crested Grebe sample census, 1946–1955. *Bird Study* Vol.6: 1–7.

HOLYOAK, D. (1974) Territorial and feeding behaviour of the Magpie. *Bird Study* Vol. 21: 117–128.

HOMES, R. C., SAGE, B. L. and SPENCER, R. (1960) Breeding Population of Lapwings, Coot and Meadow Pipits. *London Bird Report* 23: 54–61.

HUDSON, R. (1976) Ruddy Ducks in Britain. *British Birds* 69: 132–143.

HUDSON, R. (1979) Nightingales in Britain in 1976. *Bird Study* Vol.26: 204–212.

HUGHES, S. W. M., BACON, P. and FLEGG, J. J. M. (1979) The 1975 census of the Great Crested Grebe in Britain. *Bird Study* Vol.26: 213–226.

JAMES, T. J. (1981) The Distribution and Ecology of the Wood Warbler in Hertfordshire. *Trans. Herts. Nat. Hist. Soc.* 28(5): 24–29.

JAMES, T. J. and SAWFORD, B. R. (1979) Rarer British Birds in the collections of North Hertfordshire Museums Service and other local museums. *Trans. Herts. Nat. Hist. Soc.* 28(2): 29–44.

JENKINS, A. R. (1958) *The Birds of the Letchworth Region.* Letchworth Naturalists' Society.

JOHNSON, I. G. (1966) Water Pipits wintering on watercress beds. *British Birds* 59: 522–524.

JOHNSON, I. G. (1970) The Water Pipit as a winter visitor to the British Isles. *Bird Study* Vol.17: 297–319.

KNIGHTSBRIDGE, R. W. S. (1984) The Distribution of the Woodcock in Hertfordshire: results and analysis of the 1981 survey. *Trans. Herts. Nat. Hist. Soc.* 29: 37–42.

KONING, F. J. (1982) Over fenologie en biometrie va Oever-en Water pieper *Anthus spinetta. Limosa* 55: 115–120.

LACK, D. (1958) Weather movements of Swifts 1955–1957. *Bird Study* Vol.5: 128–142.

LEACH, I. H. (1981) Wintering Blackcaps in Britain & Ireland. *Bird Study* Vol.28: 3–14.

LEE VALLEY PROJECT GROUP Birds in the Lee Valley. *Annual Reports* for 1974 to 1982.

LETCHWORTH NATURALISTS' SOCIETY (1963) *In and Around Letchworth; an introduction to the natural history of the First Garden City.*

LILFORD, Lord (1883) Rustic Bunting near London. *Zoologist* 1883: 194–195.

LINSELL, S. E. (1953) Report on Birds Observed in Hertfordshire within a Six-mile Radius of Bishops Stortford. *Trans. Herts. Nat. Hist. Soc.* 24: 23–30.

LLOYD-EVANS, L. and NAU, B. S. (1965) A Ringing Study of Greenfinch Weights. *Rye Meads Ringing Group Third Report:* 23–39.

LONDON NATURAL HISTORY SOCIETY (1958–1982) *London Bird Reports* Nos. 23–47.

LONDON NATURAL HISTORY SOCIETY (Revised Edition 1964) *The Birds of the London Area.*

MACDONALD, J. W. (1962) Mortality in wild birds with some observations on weights. *Bird Study* Vol.9: 147–167.

MACDONALD, J. W. (1963) Mortality in wild birds. *Bird Study* Vol.10: 91–108.

MACDONALD, J. W. (1965) Mortality in wild birds. *Bird Study* Vol.12: 181–195.

MAGEE, J. D. (1972) Birds of Cassiobury Park, the West Hertfordshire Golf Course and Whippendell Woods, Watford. *London Bird Report* 36: 66–74.

MAPLE CROSS RINGING STATION, Bulletins Nos.1–56 (1971–1982).

MAPLE CROSS RINGING STATION, Systematic Lists (1972–1982).

MAPLE LODGE NEWSLETTERS Nos.1–7 (1983–1984).

McCULLOCH, G. K. (1943) Glaucous Gull in Hertfordshire. *British Birds* 36:204.

MEAD, C. J. and HARRISON, J. D. (1979) Sand Martin movements within Britain and Ireland. *Bird Study* Vol.26: 73–86.

MEAD, C. and SMITH, K. (1982) *Hertfordshire Breeding Bird Atlas,* Tring.

MEADOWS, B. S. (1970) Breeding distribution and feeding ecology of the Black Redstart in London. *London Bird Report* 34: 72–79.

MEADOWS, B. S. (1972) The recovery of the Kingfisher in London after the 1962/63 hard winter. *London Bird Report* 36: 60–65.

MELLING, J. (1970) Monthly Weight Variation of Post Juvenile Song Thrushes at Rye Meads. *Rye Meads Ringing Group Fifth Report:* 25–26.

MELLING, J. (1973) Retrap Records and Survival Estimates for Passerines at Rye Meads. *Rye Meads Ringing Group Sixth Report:* 28–32.

MELLING, J. (1974) The seasonal abundance of *sylvia* and *phylloscopus* warblers at Rye Meads. *Rye Meads Ringing Group Sixth Report:* 17–27.

MELLING, J. (1974) The Monitoring of Warbler Populations by Mist Netting. *Rye Meads Ringing Group Seventh Report:* 35–37.

MONTIER, D. J. Ed. (1977) *Atlas of Breeding Birds of the London Area,* London Natural History Society.

MORE, A. G. (1865) On the Distribution of Birds in Great Britain during the Nesting Season. *Ibis* 1–27, 119–142, 452–458.

MORGAN, R. A. and GLUE, D. E. (1981) Breeding survey of Black Redstarts in Britain, 1977. *Bird Study* Vol.28: 163–168.

NAU, B. S. (1960) Late nest-building of the Rook. *Bird Study* Vol.7: 185–188.

NAU, B. S. (1961) Sand Martin Colonies in the London Area. *London Bird Report* 25: 69–81.

NAU, B. S. (1965) Dunnock Wing Formulae. *Rye Meads Ringing Group Third Report:* 44–46.

NAU, B. S. (1967) Co-operative Bird-Ringing. *Bird Study* Vol.14: 1–9.

NAU, B. S. (1967) Further Studies of the Greenfinch (*Chloris chloris*) at Rye Meads. *Rye Meads Ringing Group Fourth Report:* 26–34.

NORRIS, C. A. (1960) The breeding distribution of thirty bird species in 1952. *Bird Study* Vol.7: 129–184.

NUNN, J. P. (1898) Notes on the Birds of North Herts. *Trans. Herts. Nat. Hist. Soc.* 9: 163–166.

OGILVIE, M. A. (1981) The Mute Swan in Britain, 1978. *Bird Study.* Vol.28: 87–106.

OLIVER, P. J. (1977) Great Crested Grebe Census, 1975. *London Bird Report* 40: 74–77.

OSBORNE, K. C. (1971) Water Pipits in the London Area. *London Bird Report* 35: 68–73.

OSBORNE, K. C. (1980) Checklist of the Birds of the London Area, 1901–77. *London Bird Report* 43: 71–84.

PALMER, K. H. (1983) The Breeding Season Status of the Grey Wagtail in the London Area, 1979–81. *London Bird Report* 47: 106–122.

PARRINDER, E. R. (1964) Little Ringed Plovers in Britain during 1960–62. *British Birds* 57: 191–198.

PARRINDER, E. R. and E. D. (1969) Little Ringed Plovers in Britain 1963–67. *British Birds* 62: 219–223.

PARRINDER, E. R. and E. D. (1975) Little Ringed Plovers in Britain in 1968–73. *British Birds* 68: 359–368.

PEAKALL, D. B. (1962) The past and present status of the Red-backed Shrike in Great Britain. *Bird Study* Vol.9: 198–216.

PEAL, R. E. F. (1968) The distribution of the Wryneck in the British Isles 1964–1966. *Bird Study* Vol.15: 111–126.

PETERKEN, G. F. (1977) *Woodland Survey for Nature Conservation,* Nature Conservancy Council.

PRATER, A. (1970) The Variation of the Weights and Wing Lengths of Blackbirds at Rye Meads. *Rye Meads Ringing Group Fifth Report:* 16–24.

PRESTT, I. and BELL, A. A. (1966) An objective method of recording the breeding distribution of common birds of prey in Britain. *Bird Study* Vol.13: 277–283.

PRESTT, I. and JEFFERIES, D. J. (1969) Winter numbers, breeding success, and organochlorine residues in the Great Crested Grebe in Britain. *Bird Study* Vol.16: 168–185.

PRESTT, I. and MILLS, D. H. (1966) A census of the Great Crested Grebe in Britain 1965. *Bird Study* Vol.13: 163–203.

REYNOLDS, A. (1974) A Review of the Recoveries and Controls at Rye Meads Reported up to the end of 1973. *Rye Meads Ringing Group Seventh Report:* 38–43.

REYNOLDS, A. (1975) Kingfishers at Rye Meads. *Ringing and Migration* 1: 48–51.

RIDDIFORD, N. (1983) Recent declines of Grasshopper Warblers *Locustella naevia* at British bird observatories. *Bird Study* Vol.30: 143–148.

RIDPATH, M. G. (1942) Red-spotted Bluethroat seen in Hertfordshire. *British Birds* 35: 273.

RIVERS, H. S. (1893) Supposed occurrence of *Loxia leucoptera* in Herts. *Zoologist* 1893: 27–28.

ROGERS, M. J. (1982) Ruddy Shelducks in Britain in 1965–79. *British Birds* 75: 446–455.

ROWAN, W. (1916) Dipper in Hertfordshire. *British Birds* 10: 43.

ROYAL SOCIETY FOR THE PROTECTION OF BIRDS, Newsletters and Bulletins of Hertfordshire Local Groups.

RYE MEADS RINGING GROUP (1964) *The Natural History of Rye Meads.*

RYE MEADS RINGING GROUP, Reports 1–9 (1961–1983).

RYE MEADS RINGING GROUP, Ringing Bulletins (1960–1983).

SAGE, B. L. (1954) Ortolan Bunting in Hertfordshire. *British Birds* 47: 446–447.

SAGE, B. L. (1958) A New Gull Roost in the London Area. *London Bird Report* 22: 50–51.

SAGE, B. L. (1959) *A History of the Birds of Hertfordshire,* Barrie and Rockliff, London.

SAGE, B. L. (1960) The Spring Migration of the Common Gull through the London Area. *London Bird Report* 23: 69–74.

SAGE, B. L. (1962) A History of the Birds of Hertfordshire: Some Supplementary Data. *Trans. Herts. Nat. Hist. Soc.* 25: 188–92.

SAGE, B. L. (1963) The Breeding Distribution of the Tree Sparrow. *London Bird Report* 27: 56–65.

SAGE, B. L. (1964) The Gull Roosts of the London Area. *London Bird Report* 28: 63–68.

SAGE, B. L. (1966) Report on Birds Observed in Hertfordshire in 1965. *Trans. Herts. Nat. Hist. Soc.* 26: 107–139.

SAGE, B. L. Ed. (1966) *Northaw Great Wood,* Hertfordshire County Council, Hertford.

SAGE, B. L. (1969) Breeding biology of the Coot. *British Birds* 62: 134–143.

SAGE, B. L. (1970) The Winter Population of Gulls in the London Area. *London Bird Report* 33: 67–80.

SAGE, B. L. (1972) The decline of the Rook population in Hertfordshire. *Trans. Herts Nat. Hist. Soc.* 27: 1–17.

SAGE, B. L. (1973) A breeding season census of the Coot and Great Crested Grebe in Hertfordshire, 1973. *Trans. Herts. Nat. Hist. Soc.* 27: 240–244.

SAGE, B. L. (1976) The national survey of rookeries, 1975: Hertfordshire Rookeries. *Trans. Herts. Nat. Hist. Soc.* 27: 361–364.

SAGE, B. L. (1980) The species of birds recorded in Hertfordshire. *Trans. Herts. Nat. Hist. Soc.* 28: 45–56.

SAGE, B. L. and CORNELIUS, L. W. (1977) Rook population of the London Area. *London Bird Report* 40: 66–73.

SAGE, B. L. and JENKINS, A. R. (1956) White-winged Lark in Hertfordshire. *British Birds* 49: 41–42.

SAGE, B. L. and NAU, B. S. (1963) The population ecology of the Rook in Hertfordshire. *Trans. Herts. Nat. Hist. Soc.* 25: 226–244.

SAGE, B. L. and VERNON, J. D. R. (1978) The 1975 national survey of rookeries. *Bird Study* Vol.25: 64–86.

SAWFORD, B. R. (1981) 1980 Nightingale Survey: Hertfordshire Results. *Trans. Herts. Nat. Hist. Soc.* 28. Pt.5: 30–32.

SIVA-JOTHY, M. (1982) Some observations on the arrival patterns of gulls at a winter roost. Third Year Student Project. University College, London.

SMITH, K. (1983) The Status of the Nightjar in Hertfordshire. *Trans. Herts. Nat. Hist. Soc.* 29. Pt.1: 68–70.

SMITH, K. (1984) Breeding Waders in Hertfordshire. *Trans. Herts. Nat. Hist. Soc.* 29. Pt.2: 33–36.

SNOW, D. W. (1965) The relationship between census results and the breeding population of birds on farmland. *Bird Study* Vol.12: 287–304.

SPENCER, R. and HUDSON, R. (1978) Report on Bird Ringing for 1977. *Ringing and Migration* 2: 90.

STAFFORD, J. (1958) The Census of Heronries 1957. *Bird Study* Vol.5: 121–125.

STAFFORD, J. (1959) The Census of Heronries 1958. *Bird Study* Vol.6: 175–179.

STAFFORD, J. (1961) The Census of Heronries 1959. *Bird Study* Vol.8: 38–42.

STAFFORD, J. (1962) Nightjar Enquiry, 1957–58. *Bird Study* Vol.9: 104–115.

STAFFORD, J. (1963) The Census of Heronries 1960–61, *Bird Study* Vol.10: 29–33.

STAFFORD, J. (1969) The Census of Heronries 1962–63. *Bird Study* Vol.16: 83–88.

STAFFORD, J. (1979) The national census of heronries in England & Wales in 1964. *Bird Study* Vol.26: 3–6.

STEVENAGE ORNITHOLOGICAL SOCIETY, Annual Bird Reports 1965 to 1981.

STONE, N. K. (1932) Roller in Hertfordshire. *British Birds* 25: 335.

TERRY, J. (1980) Lesser Black-backed Gull movements into Hilfield Park LNR 1979–80.

TUCK, E. J. (1856) Occurrence of the Rose-Coloured Pastor and Woodchat Shrike in Herts. *Zoologist* 1856: 5203–4.

VERNON, J. D. R. (1969) Spring migration of the Common Gull in Britain and Ireland. *Bird Study* Vol.16: 101–107.

VOOUS, K. H. (1977) List of Recent Holarctic Bird Species. *Ibis* 115: 612–638 and 119: 223–250.

WEBB, R. (1981) A note on Water Rails in the Hitchin area during the 1979/80 winter. *Trans. Herts. Nat. Hist. Soc.* 28. Pt.5: 23.

WHITE, G. J. (1982) A note on the food of Short-eared Owl *Asio flammeus* in the Lee Valley. *Birds in the Lee Valley* 1981: 33–34.

WHITE, G. J. (1984) A look at the last ten years. *Birds in the Lee Valley* 1982: 26–31.

WHITEMAN, R. (1936) *Hexton — A Parish Survey.*

WILLIAMSON, K. (1965) Moult and its relation to taxonomy in Rock and Water Pipits. *British Birds* 58: 493–504.

WILLIAMSON, K. (1968) Buntings on a barley farm. *Bird Study* Vol.15: 34–37.

WILLIAMSON, K. (1969) Habitat preferences of the Wren on English Farmland. *Bird Study* Vol.16: 53–59.

WILLIAMSON, K. (1975) The breeding bird community of chalk grassland in the Chiltern Hills. *Bird Study* Vol.22: 59–70.

Index of Bird Names

English vernacular names are indexed under the last word and are printed in Roman type. Scientific names are indexed under the genus and appear in italic type. The page numbers of the main species accounts are in bold type and of the *Breeding Bird Atlas* maps in italics. Commonly used English names of sub-species are also included.